AN AMERICAN DOCTOR'S
ODYSSEY

DOCTOR VICTOR HEISER

An
American Doctor's
Odyssey

Adventures in Forty-five Countries

by VICTOR HEISER, M.D.

NEW YORK

W·W·NORTON & COMPANY·Inc
PUBLISHERS

ACKNOWLEDGMENT

When I began to write this book I found there were literally huge boxes of memoranda, notes, diaries, and other manuscripts to be sifted and read. Mrs. Rackham Holt, ably assisted by Mr. Walter Hayward, has been of invaluable help in organizing this vast amount of material and in preparing it for publication. I am deeply grateful to them both.

I am also most grateful to Miss Grace Carpenter who as my secretary for twenty years worked so indefatigably over this long period to prepare the daily notes which made this volume possible.

CONTENTS

I.	Just Short of Eternity	3
II.	The Lame and the Halt	8
III.	The Promised Land	20
IV.	And Bid the Sickness Cease	36
V.	Little Brown Brother	40
VI.	Washing Up the Orient	59
VII.	The Black Death	79
VIII.	Eat, Drink, and Be Merry	100
IX.	Water, Water, Everywhere	121
X.	Not with Beat of Drum	133
XI.	For Their Own Good	151
XII.	The Heavenly Flower	176
XIII.	Alas and a Lack	192
XIV.	The House of Pain	211
XV.	Prisoners of Hope	235
XVI.	Dividends from Philanthropy	265
XVII.	A Drummer of Ideas	291
XVIII.	Much Have I Traveled	308
XIX.	Snakes in Eden	327
XX.	The White Man's Last Refuge	344
XXI.	Parasites Lost and Parasites Regained	358

CONTENTS

XXII.	Fish Stories	386
XXIII.	A Great Little People	395
XXIV.	Picking Up Broken Threads	417
XXV.	An Ounce of Prevention	437
XXVI.	And Make Persuasion Do the Work of Fear	461
XXVII.	Hustling the East	480
XXVIII.	Pearl of Great Price	503
XXIX.	Pilgrim's Progress	519
XXX.	Grant but Memory	532
Index		537

AN AMERICAN DOCTOR'S
ODYSSEY

CHAPTER 1.   JUST SHORT OF ETERNITY

ALL during the latter part of May, 1889, a chill rain had been descending in torrents upon the Conemaugh Valley. The small city of Johnstown, walled in by precipitous Pennsylvania hills, was invaded by high water which stood knee deep in front of my father's house on Washington Street.

Nobody seemed particularly concerned at the time over the dam which rich Pittsburghers had maintained high up on the South Fork to provide water for their fishing streams. When the earthen dam had first been constructed, there had been some apprehension. There was a ninety foot head of water behind the embankment, and only a small spillway had been provided. But the dam had never burst and, with the passage of time, the townspeople, like those who live in the shadow of Vesuvius, grew calloused to the possibility of danger. "Some time," they thought, "that dam will give way, but it won't ever happen to us."

During the afternoon of the thirty-first the overflow from the river crept steadily higher, inch by inch, through the streets of the town. Although it had not yet reached the stable, which stood on higher ground than the house, my father became concerned over the safety of his fine pair of horses which were tied in their stalls, and suggested that I make a dash for the stable and unfasten them. The rain was falling so hard that I was almost drenched as I plowed my laborious way through the two feet of water.

I had loosed the horses and was about to leave the shelter of the doorway when my ears were stunned by the most terrifying noise I had ever heard in my sixteen years of life. The dreadful roar was punctuated with a succession of tremendous crashes. I stood for a moment, bewildered and hesitant. I could see my mother and my father standing at an upper window in the house. My father, frantic with anxiety over my safety, was motioning me urgently toward the top of the building. Fortunately, I had made a passageway only a few days before to the red tin roof, so that some necessary repairs could be made. Thus it was only a matter of seconds before I was up on the ridge.

From my perch I could see a huge wall advancing with incredible rapidity down the diagonal street. It was not recognizable as water; it was a dark mass in which seethed houses, freight cars, trees, and animals. As this wall struck Washington Street broadside, my boyhood home was crushed like an eggshell before my eyes, and I saw it disappear.

I wanted to know how long it would take me to get to the other world, and in the split second before the stable was hit, I looked at my watch. It was exactly four-twenty.

But, instead of being shattered, the big barn was ripped from its foundations and began to roll, like a barrel, over and over. Stumbling, crawling, and racing, I somehow managed to keep on top.

In the path of the revolving stable loomed suddenly the house of our neighbor, Mrs. Fenn. To avoid being hurled off by the inevitable collision, I leaped into the air at the precise moment of impact. But just as I miraculously landed on the roof of her house, its wall began to cave in. I plunged downward with the roof, but saved myself by clambering monkey-like up the slope, and before the house gave way completely, another boiled up beside me. I caught hold of the eaves and swung dangling there, while the weight of my body drained the strength from my hands.

For years thereafter I was visited by recurring dreams in which I lived over and over again that fearful experience of hanging with my fingernails dug deep into the water softened shingles, knowing that in the end I must let go.

When my grip finally relaxed, I dropped sickeningly into space. But once again I was saved. With a great thud I hit a piece of the old familiar barn roof, and I clutched with all my remaining power at the half inch tin ridges. Lying on my belly, I bumped along on the surface of the flood, which was crushing, crumbling, and splintering everything before it. The screams of the injured were hardly to be distinguished above the awful clamor; people were being killed all about me.

In that moment of terrible danger I saw the Italian fruit dealer Mussante, with his wife and two children, racing along on what seemed to be their old barn floor. A Saratoga trunk was open beside them, and the whole family was frantically packing a pile of possessions into it. Suddenly the whole mass of wreckage heaved up and crushed them out of existence.

I was borne headlong toward a jam where the wreckage was already piling up between a stone church and a three story brick building. Into this hurly burly I was catapulted. The pressure was terrific. A tree would shoot out of the water; a huge girder would come thundering down. As these trees and girders drove booming into the jam, I jumped them desperately, one after another. Then suddenly a freight car reared up over my head; I could not leap that. But just as it plunged toward me, the brick building gave way, and my raft shot out from beneath the freight car like a bullet from a gun.

In a moment more I was in comparatively open water. Although no landmark was visible, I could identify the space as the park which had been there only a short while before. I was still being swept along, but the danger had lessened. I had opportunity to observe other human beings in equally perilous situations. I saw the stoutish Mrs. Fenn astride an unstable tar barrel which had covered her with its contents. Rolling far over to one side, then swaying back to the other, she was making a desperate but grotesque struggle to keep her head above water.

There was nothing I could do for anybody.

Dr. Lee's negro hostler, all alone and stark naked, was shivering on the roof of his master's house. In the penetrating rain his supplicating hands were raised toward the heavens. As I tore by I heard him shouting, "Lawd ha' mercy on dis pore cold nigger."

I was carried on toward the narrows below the city where the tracks of the Pennsylvania Railroad crossed both valley and river on a high embankment and bridge. When the twisted, interlaced timbers ahead of me struck the stone arches, they plugged them tight, and in the

5

powerful recoil my raft was swept back behind the hill which had saved the lower part of the town from complete destruction and left many buildings standing.

I passed close by a two and a half story brick dwelling which was still remaining on its foundations. Since my speed as I went up this second valley was about that of a subway train slowing for a stop, I was able to hop to the roof and join the small group of people already stranded there. Realizing then that I was, perhaps, not immediately destined for the other world, I pulled out my watch. It was not yet four-thirty; three thousand human beings had been wiped out in less than ten minutes.

For the remaining hours of daylight we derelicts huddled disconsolately on the roof. Now and then we were able to reach out a hand or a pole and haul in somebody drifting by, until finally we numbered nineteen. Though we were in a backwash, many of the houses had been seriously damaged below the water line. Occasionally one would melt like a lump of sugar and vanish. We did not know whether our refuge had been undermined, but there was no way for us to escape to the surrounding hills which rose invitingly above the flood, so near and yet so impossible to reach. The cold rain was still driving down, and it was growing dark. We were so miserable that we decided to open the skylight and climb under cover.

There in the attic we spent the night, starting whenever we heard the whoo-oo-sh which meant that another building had sunk. Ours was straining and groaning. From moment to moment we could not tell whether it were to suffer the same fate as its neighbors. Although exhausted we could not sleep. The waiting, in its way, was almost worse than the previous turmoil, because if our shelter collapsed it would become a trap in which we would drown miserably.

Dawn brought a transcendent sense of relief. The rain had ceased at last, and the water had receded until it reached only part way up the first story. Between us and the safe hills a half mile away was a mat of débris, broken here and there by patches of dirty water. Scrambling over the wreckage, wading through shallows, and rafting the deeper spaces, with an inexpressible feeling of relief I finally set my feet on solid ground again.

I started downstream at once, trying to find my father and mother.

Everyone I met was on the same sad errand—looking for parents, children, relatives, or friends. Bodies were already being taken out of the ruins.

As I approached the railway embankment, I saw that it had given way in the night and allowed the water to rush unimpeded toward Pittsburgh and the Mississippi. The consequent subsidence of the flood had left in front of the stone bridge several acres of wreckage in which many people were still imprisoned. This inflammable material had caught fire. I can still hear the maddened shrieks of the men, women and children, as the flames approached. I joined the rescue squads and we struggled for hours trying to release them from this funeral pyre, but our efforts were tragically hampered by the lack of axes and other tools. We could not save them all. It was horrible to watch helplessly while people, many of whom I actually knew, were being devoured in the holocaust.

At last I met one of my friends who lived outside the city and whose house had not been harmed. His family took me in, and gave me food and shelter. The people of the United States were unbelievably generous to the stricken community. The relief trains which soon were pouring in brought me clothes and money.

Day after day I searched among the ruins and viewed with a tense anxiety the hundreds of corpses constantly being carried to the morgues. Two weeks were devoted to this gruesome task, a most agonizing experience for a boy. Eventually the body of my mother was found; my father never was identified with certainty. Most of the victims were buried in the "plot of the unknown dead," but I laid my mother in our own cemetery lot.

I was alone in the world.

CHAPTER 2.   THE LAME AND THE HALT

THE Johnstown flood ended the prescribed course of my life, which until then had been carefully planned for me by my parents. My education had been forced beyond my years. All winter long I used to sit with the other children at my desk in the public school, and, in summer, when all my friends were playing baseball and fishing, I was still sitting at a desk, but this time in a private school. My evenings were spent under a study lamp learning French and German with a tutor by my side. The sole concession to leisure allowed me out of the year was one month on a farm. Although I was particularly fond of sports and hated the steady grind, I rebelled only once. Learning to play the violin was too much.

When the catastrophe came, I was ready for college, but ill-equipped for life.

By a freak of chance, a chest which had stood in the upper hall of our house was found practically intact on one of the piles of wreckage. In it were my father's Civil War uniform with a large old penny in one pocket, a miscellaneous collection of flat silver, and my mother's Bible. The sole value of these slender possessions lay in their associations.

Since everything else belonging to my father had been swept away in the flood, I had to find immediately some way of earning a living. I hired out as a plumber's assistant, and rapidly learned to cut and fit pipe, and even to "wipe" a lead joint, which is generally regarded as one of the most difficult accomplishments in the plumbing trade. But

I also discovered there was a good deal of truth in the jingle about the plumber who, after the manner of the Assyrian, came down like a wolf on the fold, and

> "For nine hours and a half he talked to the cook,
> And sixty-five dollars was charged on the book."

My next job was with a carpenter. Framing a house was more difficult than wiping a joint but, to my own satisfaction at least, I soon considered I had mastered carpentry. I aspired also to cabinet making but, fascinating as this was, it too failed to offer sufficient inducement as a life work.

I then decided to become a mechanical engineer. By this time some of my father's real estate had been sold, and with the money thus salvaged I went to an engineering school in Chicago.

Although I did fairly well in my studies, met many people, and gained much worldly experience, I could not be entirely happy. For a youth of seventeen, particularly one who had led so well-ordered a life, to be cast out into the cold world was not an easy experience. Other boys were able to turn to their parents, relatives, or friends, who were genuinely interested in them. I had no experienced person with whom to discuss my perplexities, and had to make my own decisions. For many years I suffered because I could not avail myself of adult counsel and advice. My first lesson in the realities of life was that nobody wanted to be bothered with the problems of others; I had to learn to keep my troubles to myself.

I do not know definitely what turned me toward medicine, but, after my first year at engineering school, I concluded that I wanted to be a doctor. Nevertheless, I have never considered the time wasted which I spent in learning to do things with my hands. The practical knowledge thus acquired has been of incalculable service to me all over the world in the career which I ultimately chose.

I did not have the necessary academic credits for admittance to a medical school of top rating, but I determined to acquire them, and set to work at my books once more. In addition I haunted the public libraries and enrolled in courses offered in such subjects as mechanical drawing and engineering design. To test my progress, I regularly took the examinations of the University of the State of New York, until I had attained enough credits to give me the equivalent of an A.B. degree.

I then entered medical school in Philadelphia, worked hard, and finished a four-year course in three years. Upon graduation from Jefferson Medical College, I was fortunate enough to be accepted for my internship at Lankenau Hospital. There I not only had ward experience, but was given the special opportunity of attending private patients. From both the uncomplaining and the exacting I learned much about human nature and ways of dealing with it.

The spur which drove me was sharp. I was involuntarily following the forcing process of education on which I had been reared. I took on added duties, read books not on any prescribed list, and dashed indefatigably from public ward to private pavilion and to clinics in other hospitals.

The customary routine after finishing at the hospital was to go immediately into private practice. But the more I saw of the latter, the more I came to consider it a retail effort. If I were to make a place for myself in the medical world I must necessarily learn first to be a good doctor, but before I had spent many months as an interne I knew I was not going to be either a general practitioner or a specialist. The prevention of disease on a wholesale basis appealed to me far more.

At the end of my first hospital year, I considered I had earned a vacation, and went to Washington to see the sights, with no plan in mind except diversion. But before I could get well under way with this project, I chanced upon a notice that an examination for entrance into the Marine Hospital Service was about to be held. I had already considered attempting to enter this branch of the Service because of my great admiration for the officer in charge of the Marine Ward at Lankenau. I knew these examinations were extremely difficult, but I thought this was a good opportunity to find out the exact requirements.

In answer to my question, the officer in charge said, "Since you're here, why don't you take the examination?"

"I'm not prepared. I could never pass."

"Well, suppose you didn't, what then? You could come up again next year. If you took it now, you'd have the actual experience, which would be far more helpful than anything I could tell you."

He convinced me there could be no harm in trying. I telegraphed immediately for letters of introduction and credentials to be sent special delivery, and these arrived in time for me to be admitted to the examination at nine the next morning. I was somewhat startled to find I was one of forty-two candidates for only three vacancies, and not encouraged by the remark of one of my classmates who greeted me with, "Why in God's name are you going into this examination? You haven't had any special preparation."

"I'll stay as long as I can," I assured him with an appearance of confidence I did not feel.

The preliminary physical examination was so rigid that twelve aspirants were promptly ruled out. Thirty began the week's ordeal of writing. Each day's paper contained only four questions, and, since eighty was the minimum passing mark, whoever failed in a single one was automatically eliminated. The Board read the papers at night, and just before nine o'clock of the second day the announcement was made, "The following gentlemen will be excused," and five disappointed young men filed out.

I decided there was at least a chance for me to get through. I remembered my classmate's taunt, and my resolve to stick it out stiffened. I wired for my Practice of Medicine, Surgery, Therapeutics, and other text books and, as soon as they arrived, I organized each twenty-four hours. The examinations lasted from nine to twelve and two to five; evenings I devoted to study.

It was July in Washington. I would sit in my room with no clothes on, and, even though the windows and transom were open, the perspiration would run off me in streams. At three o'clock I would tumble into bed and reluctantly out at eight in time for bath and breakfast before the torture began again.

I grew more and more excited as our numbers dwindled. However, I still did not see how I could face the humiliation of walking out. I observed each morning the precaution of placing my hat within easy reaching distance, so that, at the sound of my name, I could make my exit as speedily and inconspicuously as possible.

Happily I was spared, and found myself among the ten who finished the written part of the examination. But the pre-medicals were still to come. We were to be orally examined in history, philosophy, economics, literature, and kindred subjects which I had not studied for four years. I knew I could never get through these on the basis of exact information. I should have to devise some method.

One by one we went up before a Board of three. As soon as a candidate would emerge, damp and perspiring, the rest of us would rush to cross-examine him. We were thus able to get a general idea of the field of inquiry, even though the actual questions might never be duplicated.

My turn finally came. Each examiner interrogated for a half hour; obviously the more delays I could introduce, the fewer would be the questions. If I knew the answer well I would make false starts and hesitate until one of the Board would exclaim in irritation, "Come now, we must get on. Do you know this or don't you?" Just before his patience was exhausted, I would give my answer clearly and briefly.

On the other hand, if I were unable to answer concisely, I would ramble on and on, and try to involve the whole Board in a discussion.

After the pre-medicals, each of the survivors was taken to a hospital and requested to examine and diagnose six patients. Although they had been told to mislead us if possible, the clinical signs were theoretically so obvious that we should be able to make correct diagnoses. The same technique was followed in the laboratory, where we were required to analyze specimens and identify bacteria and parasites under the microscope; many of these slides had been specially prepared to confuse us.

At the end of a grueling two weeks, eight were left from whom the lucky three were to be chosen. I resumed my interrupted vacation, dismissed the examination from my mind, and started off with my bicycle, leaving my cares in the wild Pennsylvania hills. Pedaling vigorously on level stretches, coasting down the long slopes, wandering around the little towns, I soon regained my spirits and was rapidly recovering the twenty pounds I had lost.

The morning of my arrival in Pittsburgh, I saw an announcement in the *Post* that Fricks, White, and Heiser had passed the examination for the Marine Hospital Service. Naturally, I was jubilant over this triumph, but doubtful over the wisdom of accepting the commission, because I was only half through my interneship at Lankenau. In the belief that another year's intensive work and study would make me far better equipped I wrote the Surgeon-General a long explanatory letter, hoping he would agree with my conclusions and, furthermore, appreciate the sacrifice I was willing to make in giving up a year's salary for the sake of further training.

The only reply was a peremptory telegram that I should report at once to Boston. I was now in the Service. Since I could not question orders, I necessarily complied.

The reason for official disregard of my proposals was evident. The year was 1898, and many soldiers, desperately ill, were returning from Cuba and Puerto Rico. The facilities of the Boston hospitals were overtaxed by this unprecedented influx, and an appeal had been made to the Marine Hospital Service for help. I was assigned to this task.

Any Federal officer, regardless of his deserts, has much prestige. Therefore, in spite of my inexperience, I was able to advise several hospitals how to deal with the situation.

But when this organizing work was over, hospital routine seemed uninteresting. I explained this to my commanding officer, who said, "Very well, I'll assign you to the medical examination of immigrants. You'll find enough there to keep you busy."

For years the flood of imported cheap labor had poured unchecked through the wide-open gateways of Boston, New York, Philadelphia, San Francisco, and other large ports, bringing with it the lame, halt, and blind. Even lunatics and idiots had not been barred until 1882. Nine more years passed before public sentiment, slowly rising against the foreign labor invasion, forced Congressional action. At that time, not only were the Chinese excluded, but the Marine Hospital Service was charged with the duty of recommending for rejection immigrants afflicted with loathsome or contagious diseases, or those who were likely, for any physical reasons, to become public charges.

The invaders were arriving in such numbers that individual physical examination with our meagre staff was out of the question. A snap diagnosis which stood a reasonable chance of proving correct had to be made in the space of a few seconds. I read everything on the subject that I could find, supplementing my own ideas with the experiences of others, and, after much trial and error, developed a system.

In Boston the medical examinations were always held by daylight on the pier where the ship docked. The stage had to be carefully set so that the immigrants would not be aware that they were being observed. I had it so arranged that they would walk down a lane, in single file, ten feet apart, unencumbered by baggage, and then make a right turn in front of an examining officer. From his apparently casual station at the angle, he could obtain a front, side, and rear view of each passer-by. The path had to be level, so that the immigrant would not have to watch his feet, and also lead away from the water, so that there would be no glare to cause squinting.

Some afflictions were easily picked out. A deaf man in almost every case held his head slightly to one side. Valvular diseases of the heart were often detectable by the ridged nails and peculiar pallor of face and neck, suggesting faulty nutrition. Less simple were cases of favus, a contagious filth disease of the scalp or nails. We would have to be on the alert for the fine, wire-like hair and the betraying bald patches symptomatic of the disease, because a ship's physician would often dissolve off the scales to make the head reasonably clean for our inspection.

I found that a man's walk was often characteristic of his physical and mental state. Hernia, for example, caused a distinctive though indescribable gait, and faulty vision was betrayed by hesitation on reaching the corner. Trachoma, a contagious inflammation of the eyelids, had always to be watched for with special care. It was estimated fifteen percent of the blindness in United States institutions at that time was due to this disease. Clinics in our large cities were overrun with cases which proved stubborn to treat and often impossible to cure. The typical thickening of the lids or roughened condition of the cornea could be caught as the immigrant turned, because the light then struck his eyes at changing angles of incidence.

Though the work was exciting and interesting, it had many distressing aspects. Heartbreaking incidents were constantly occurring when rejections had to be made. A Scandinavian farmer might spend years in Minnesota earning enough money to pay the passage for his wife and their five children. When they would finally arrive, and the long separated family would be reunited, ours would be the painful duty of singling out one of the children, and of saying, "She has trachoma. She cannot enter." The mother and the rest of the children would often have to return to Europe with the diseased one, and, until the boat sailed, the father, wretched and unhappy, would haunt the detention quarters, while his family kept up a constant wailing and crying. But the law was on the statute books and we had to enforce it, regarding the child as a potential focus of infection rather than as a figure of tragedy.

In order to reduce the hardships as much as possible, government hospitals were established in which curable cases might be treated. But inevitably many hard decisions had to be made. Young women with illegitimate pregnancies, whose family or friends frequently had sent them to this country in the hope of covering up their disgrace, were particularly pathetic. The regulations forbade the entrance of these unfortunates, because of the likelihood that they and their children would become public charges.

A detailed examination was impossible, but I had observed that on the left side of any immigrant woman's head was a strand of hair which, under normal conditions, was more or less lustrous. If it hung dull and lifeless over her ear, it marked her at once as possibly pregnant. Other medical men may ridicule the observation, and I cannot explain it myself scientifically, but time and again suspicion turned out to be fact.

The distinguishing differences between a healthy and a diseased person were often subtle, but practice made us reasonably proficient. The system of diagnosis worked so well in Boston that I was promoted to the chief center of immigration at New York, where a new system was to be developed for the inspection of first and second class passengers. Up to this time no examination had been required for these classes, and many immigrants who had been rejected when they had come steerage, were adopting the dodge of traveling cabin. Other defectives, forewarned, were doing likewise. Over the loud protests of the steamship officials, who were fearful of offending their best paying clientele, the regulations had been extended to first and second class passengers.

The government realized it was treading on delicate ground and that such inspections would have to be handled with great finesse. A health officer needed more than technical training to succeed at such a task. In fact, it appeared that diplomacy should constitute a major part of his equipment.

It was vital, first of all, to make sure that no American citizen should be mistakenly included in the examination. Before we had really formulated an efficient working method, one of my subordinates made a serious error. One day he called exultantly, "I've a fine case of acne rosacea."

"Let's have a look at him."

To my horror I recognized the elder Pierpont Morgan. My assistant had been led by his professional enthusiasm to forget the routine question as to citizenship. I have rarely seen such an angry man. At first he would accept no apology, but I explained to him that my assistant was very young, and we really ought to be easy on him because everybody makes mistakes. Perhaps Mr. Morgan, observing my own youth, was amused at these solemn platitudes; he finally began to laugh and said he would forget the incident.

My task was complicated by the intense rivalry which at that time existed between State and Federal authorities over the administration of a quarantine law designed to protect the country against such diseases as plague, cholera, smallpox, leprosy, typhus, and yellow fever. Although Federal laws and regulations applied to quarantine, the local port authorities interpreted them as they saw fit. A ship might dock at Boston under one set of regulations, but, if Baltimore were to be its first port of call, preparations would have to be made for a different set. Because of the resultant confusion, the business interests of the country had added their mite of pressure toward unification, and the Federal government was now trying to arrange for taking over all quarantine services still being administered by State officials. For reasons not always creditable, the latter, pleading their constitutional right to exercise "police powers," resented what they considered Federal interference with their affairs.

The Marine Hospital Service in New York was concerned only with the diseases and physical handicaps of the immigrant, and had nothing to do with the State administration of quarantine laws. The Immigration launch used to go down the Bay at about five-thirty in the morning to meet any incoming vessel, although we were not allowed to board her until she had been released from quarantine by the State officers. We would then employ the hour's passage up the Bay in examining the cabin passengers so that American citizens and foreigners with clean bills of health could be free to leave the moment the ship docked.

One dreary, drizzly March dawn, so thick with fog that visibility was almost zero, our launch approached a French boat which we believed had cleared quarantine. I clambered up the high side and jumped to the deck. To my surprise, Dr. Jenkins, the State quarantine officer, was still there. The sight of my Federal uniform was as a red rag to a bull. He bristled. "Doctor, you're under arrest. This ship's in quarantine for smallpox."

I saw I was in for it. I shouted warningly over the rail to my companions who were already starting up the ladder after me. "Don't come up. Smallpox on board."

The launch pushed off again. As I turned back to Dr. Jenkins, he said with satisfaction, "You'll have to stay in quarantine fourteen days, Doctor."

For a Federal officer to be arrested by a State officer because of assumed ignorance of the law would have made a wonderful newspaper story. In my mind's eye I could already see the headlines. I sat down on one of the damp hatches and, with my head in my hands, gazed up into space, and cerebrated hard.

When Dr. Jenkins had finished his work, he strolled over to me. "We're ready to go. You'll have to spend the next two weeks on Hoffman's Island, Doctor," he rubbed it in.

"I'm not going with you," I said.

"I hope you won't compel me to use force."

"Oh, no, that won't be necessary," I retorted. "But still I'm not going with you."

"Why not?" he demanded.

"Because there's a law in this State that every ship must fly the yellow flag at her masthead while she's in quarantine. If you'll show me any such flag on this boat," I answered, peering up through the fog, "I'll go with you. Otherwise, I'm afraid I must say goodby."

The little man could do no more than stamp his foot helplessly and utter a fervent damn. I hailed a nearby government launch and was taken ashore.

I found the office in a turmoil. When my detention had been dolefully reported, there had been tremendous excitement over the inevitable ridicule. The wires to Washington had been set humming, and only my appearance had forestalled the issue of a writ of habeas corpus.

Shortly after this occurrence I received a summons to Washington, where Surgeon General Walter Wyman congratulated me on my success in having extricated myself from an awkward predicament, and informed me I was to undertake a delicate mission to Europe.

After the International Cholera Convention of 1893, officers of the Marine Hospital Service had been stationed at the main sources of emigration from Europe to attempt to guard against the introduction of cholera into the United States. Later they had extended their activities to making preliminary examinations of emigrants, and to advising the steamship companies which ones were likely to be rejected at American ports of entry on account of physical disqualification under our immigration law. The steamship companies had been glad to cooperate because the rejected emigrants had to be returned to their ports of departure at the expense of the line which had brought them over. But the governments concerned had resented the presence of these inspectors and had insisted on their recall. This action not only had increased the burden on the Service over here, but also had worked hardship and disappointment on those who had to be rejected. Since Naples was the port of departure for the majority of emigrants, it was believed that if Italy could be induced to receive our officials again, other governments would follow suit.

Surgeon General Wyman outlined my job as one of convincing all concerned that cooperation and allowing our officers to be reinstated would be to their interest as well as ours. At the end of the interview he instructed me never to send in any reports in my own handwriting, explaining that its illegibility had cost me first place in the entrance examinations.

"We're presenting you with a new typewriter," he said jocularly. "And we want you to use it."

Since I would have to deal with ambassadors, ministers, consular officers, and other officials, I would have to learn the rudiments of international law and of procedure expected of consular and diplomatic officials, such as matters of precedence and formal calls. Consequently arrangements had been made for me to take a primary course in diplomacy at the State Department.

After a month of learning the things I must do and the things I must not do in ambassadorial halls, and a post-graduate drill in the Immigration Laws, I was ready for Europe.

CHAPTER 3. THE PROMISED LAND

A FIRST ocean crossing holds more glamour than a hundred succeeding ones. This voyage, old to the seasoned traveler, is one of exploration to the neophyte. I had watched thousands of passengers stream down the gangplanks of the giant ocean liners. I knew the interior of the one on which I was sailing almost blindfold, but never before had I felt the throb of the engines on a ship outward bound beyond Ambrose Light.

To become familiar with the problems I should have to solve in my new assignment, I journeyed from one capital of Europe to another. The mellow grime of London, the feverish boulevards of Paris, the goose-stepping orderliness of Berlin, and the grey ruins of Rome, each in turn captured my imagination, each was new and strange, no matter how familiar its external characteristics from books and pictures.

At last I arrived at Naples, melodious with sound and glowing with color, where I secured reluctant consent from Italian officialdom to act as temporary medical officer.

Living at a hotel branded me at once as a forestiero, and all foreigners were fair game for cabmen. When I would hand out the proper fare the cochiero would invariably break out in violent remonstrance, and my Ellis Island Italian was in no way adequate to cope with him. To protect myself, I evolved a little strategem, which I used with great success. After a number of cochiere had insisted they were underpaid, I tried the experiment of hailing a well-dressed Italian walking along the street, told him I was a stranger, and showed him the fare and tip I had offered to pay. "Will you please explain this to the cab driver?" I asked.

The two immediately fell into a violent altercation. I left them on the sidewalk, went into the hotel, took a hot bath, dressed for dinner, and came down to find them in the same place, still indefatigably arguing about the inadequacy of my fare.

The discovery that any stranger to whom I appealed would support my contention I put to good advantage frequently. I once boarded a tram bound for the center of Naples. I gave the conductor my destination, paid him the specified sum, and received in return a pink slip in the true Mark Twain tradition. When we reached the end of the zone, the conductor tapped me on the shoulder and asked, "Are you going further?"

I looked up from my paper in surprise. "Certainly," I said.

"Then you'll have to pay more fare."

"But I told you where I was going," I protested. "It's your fault if you didn't charge me enough." I then turned to the man next me. "Didn't I tell him?" I demanded.

"Yes, yes, of course you did," he chimed in eagerly.

Somebody else stood up and cried loudly, "No, he didn't!"

In no time all the passengers had taken sides and, with shouts and gesticulations, had risen to their feet. The motorman stopped the car and himself joined in. The tumult grew fiercer and fiercer.

Since the matter was now out of my hands, I settled back in my seat and resumed my reading. Time passed. Presently an inspector appeared. "What's going on here?" he called to the conductor. "You're tying up the whole line!"

I looked back; there were literally dozens of trams behind us.

The same psychology could be invoked against the arm of the law. A ship was waiting for its clearance papers one day, and I had only a few moments in which to reach it. I directed the cochiero, therefore, to drive as fast as he could to the pier. The street along the waterfront was fenced off into two parts, one for heavy traffic, and one for carriages. The latter was blocked solid; the former was deserted. I signaled to the cochiero to take the free lane, but no sooner had we started than a policeman waved and shouted, "Get back! You're on the wrong side of the street!"

I expostulated that I was in a hurry, but the policeman did not appear at all impressed. I beckoned to a passer-by, and explained the difficulty. In a second he became my ardent champion, and plunged into the usual argument with the policeman which went on and on. I, also, went on to the ship, signed the papers, and drove leisurely back on the proper side of the enclosure. Through the grating I could see them still engaged in verbal combat over the ethics of my procedure.

I did not long bear the stigma of forestiero. Naturally I was anxious to live as the Neapolitans did, and I welcomed, therefore, the invitation of a young Netherlander, van Berlo, to share with him a beautiful villa on the Corso Vittorio Emmanuele. We used to dine on a veranda, surrounded by roses, geraniums, and oleanders, and look across the deep blue bay to distant Vesuvius. Johnstown, Pennsylvania, was farther away then, perhaps, than ever before or since.

Van Berlo wanted to learn English and I, too, was anxious to improve my languages. We made a bargain that whether it were a question of passing the salt or international politics, we would confine our conversation exclusively to one language a week, using English, French, German, and Italian in turn. At first I sat with a dictionary in my hand nearly all the time, looking up words he used or I wanted to use. We resolutely observed the rules, and by the end of a year were almost unconscious of what language we were using. Each of us, month and month about, ran the house, ordered the meals, and saw that the routine was carried out by the servants, and this gave me much valuable practice in Italian idioms.

But before my tongue was in any way able to keep pace with my thoughts, I was appointed official delegate for the United States to the International Congress on Tuberculosis which was being held in Naples. This added another thrill to the excitement and variety of life. I met the leading specialists from Europe, among them Rudolf Virchow of Berlin, the mightiest lion of them all, the first great pathologist and political opponent of Bismarck. At evening functions I gazed with awe at his coat, which was one blazing mass of decorations and medals; he had been honored by virtually all the royalties of Europe.

King Humbert invited all the delegates to a great reception in the old palace of the Bourbons. According to the rules of precedence, I was at the end of the long line which passed before him as he stood on a dais, speaking a few formal words of greeting to each in turn. In translating my reply, the interpreter hesitated for the correct word and, before I realized what I was doing, I had supplied it in Italian.

I was overcome with confusion, but the King's official attitude at once relaxed. He smiled. "Oh, you know Italian," he said, and, waving the interpreter aside, put his arm through mine, and led me to a window seat.

My knees literally shook. I had been studying Italian only a few weeks, and I knew the King spoke no English.

"I've been wanting to talk directly to an American for a long time, and get some first hand information," Humbert continued.

The King's pronunciation was so clear that I could follow his question about the Spanish-American War. Thinking to myself, "This will end in one second," I replied stumblingly. The situation was saved by the appearance of Queen Margharita, to whose beautiful German I could make answer with a fair degree of fluency. The Crown Prince and Princess also joined us, and they were all so pleasantly friendly that I was soon at my ease.

It was an excessively hot evening. The Crown Princess, fatigued at having stood so long in the reception line, fainted and was carried into an ante-room. Because I happened to be talking with the royal family at that moment, I was asked to attend her. During the hour or so in which she was recovering, I continued my discussion with the Crown Prince, now King Victor Emmanuel III, but somewhat more volubly because of his excellent command of English.

Understanding King Humbert's classic Italian was quite another matter from comprehending the multifarious Italian dialects. But these also I had to learn if I were to dispense with interpreters in dealing with emigrants. The dialects were vastly different. The Genoese would have no idea what the Neapolitans, with their innumerable slang expressions and clipped words, were talking about. The soft Sicilian speech differed from the Calabrese. It was surprising, nevertheless, how quickly the essential words of each could be picked up.

Considerable organization was required to examine expeditiously and properly the three thousand emigrants who would sometimes sail from Naples in one day. Since they were unfamiliar with any folk-customs save their own, they could not understand, for example, why they had to produce their belongings a few days in advance of sailing. Loud complaints usually rose as clothing and bedding disappeared into the disinfecting plant. Not only the procedure but the necessity for it bewildered them.

Practically all the emigrants were inveterate smugglers, with a particular predilection for cheese, on which they thought there was a high duty in the United States. This they would hide in the most impossible places, even sewing it in the lining of their clothes. They would protest violently that they had no cheese, although we explained to them again and again we were not customs officers and had no interest in their cheese beyond preventing damage to their possessions. When the doors of the ten-foot cylinder were locked and the steam was turned on, the effect of the heat was often disastrous. On one occasion when we opened the chamber, a great stream of hot, sizzling, liquid cheese came running out.

Shoes also were favorite objects of concealment. The owner's eyes would start with amazement when a pair which he had tucked away in his mattress roll would emerge from the cylinder shrunk to the size of two watch charms. Only the metal eyelets and the nails would keep their shape, and in the tiny shoes these appeared enormous.

In line with the attitude of cooperation which I was trying to bring about, I had, from the very beginning, asked the Italian doctors to help me in making inspections. But as time went on and nothing untoward happened, they left me to do the work after my own fashion.

My most serious trouble came from an entirely different quarter. I had been in Naples a little more than a month when I encountered the Camorra, at that time a powerful secret organization which, like the modern racket, levied a toll on many civic activities. It was said even the mayor could not act without its sanction.

The power of the Camorra was strikingly illustrated in the disputes which arose between the society and the agent of one of the large German steamship companies. This agent once had the temerity to inquire why the ships of his line should not dock at the government pier, and thus avoid the annoyance and the exorbitant charges of the boatmen who conveyed passengers and baggage from steamship to wharf and vice versa.

A representative of the Camorra informed him, "It will be better for your business if your ships anchor in the harbor. We can't control the boatmen; they are disagreeable people when aroused. If you land passengers on the pier, something unpleasant may happen."

The agent, however, relying on the close relationship between his country and Italy, considered his company was in a peculiarly strong position, and began having the liners brought to the pier.

Nothing happened at first. The society waited until a day when the single pier was already occupied and three ships of this one line were in port. The ubiquitous Camorra had in its ranks people who spoke all languages, and had attired a number of them in Company uniforms. In the confusion attendant upon sailing, nobody noticed the many unfamiliar faces.

As a passenger came down the wharf, he would be asked, "Where are you going?"

"America."

The boatman would reply, "I'll look after your baggage."

The passenger would be put on the right tender and the right ship, but his baggage would be placed on a vessel going to South Africa, and that of a passenger embarking for South Africa would be sent to China.

Almost immediately the offices of the line everywhere were bombarded with the protests of the righteously indignant, and the officials, becoming seriously alarmed over the bad name they were acquiring, threw up their hands and said, "We surrender."

Thus simply did the Camorra deal with such situations.

My own run-in with the society came over the inspection of baggage. One day I was waited upon by a courtly gentleman who remarked that it must be an arduous and difficult task to examine the belongings of so many people. I agreed that it was not easy.

"You might be having a good time out in the country," he suggested. "Not far from Naples are some delightful amusement places, scenic outdoor restaurants, and pleasant feminine companionship. I'd like to relieve you of your burden. I'll give you a thousand lire for each ship, and see that the baggage is properly disinfected. All you have to do is to leave me your official seal, and I'll stamp everything for you."

I assumed the plan of the Camorra was to charge a fee to each emigrant which, in the aggregate, would have brought in a tidy income. "Your suggestion sounds very pleasant," I temporized, "but I'd better think it over before I decide. Suppose you come back in a few days."

Shortly, another gentleman, even more polished than the first, put in an appearance. "I'm sorry," I told him, "but I can't accept your proposition."

He then pointed out other aspects of the matter. "You know yourself a number of people are stabbed here in Naples every night. Few questions are asked. A British engineer was knifed just last week. The British government is a powerful one, but no action was taken. A thousand lire is a fair offer and, if you accept, you'll be protected."

Obviously, the possibility of being killed altered the situation. The only reply I could make at the moment was, "I'll have to think this over again."

"You give it serious thought," he admonished me.

In the absence of the American Ambassador, I consulted Iddings, the Chargé d'Affaires at Rome, who assured me that, if I stood my ground, I should receive the full protection of the American government.

I was not surprised when, in the course of time, still a third gentleman, even more suave than his predecessors, called to see me. Neither he nor they ever admitted any connection with the society, yet he made it apparent that an immediate answer was required.

This time I was able to be definite. "I'm very sorry, but I can't accept your offer. Furthermore, I don't really believe that anything will happen to me."

"What do you mean? There are ways of dealing with this," he warned.

I answered this threat directly. "I'm not afraid. You must surely realize that, if you kill me, another officer will come in my place. You might even kill him. But there are one hundred and fifty officers in my Service, and they would keep coming. By the time you had disposed of several of us, the United States would take action, and the clamor would be world-wide. The American public already has a grievance against your country over the payments we had to make after the New Orleans Mafia riot. The Roman government may be weak in Naples, but my government is strong, and would bring such pressure to bear that the Camorra might be wiped out. You go back to your people and tell them that I'm going to continue running the baggage inspection myself."

This was my first and last difficulty with the Camorra. They held no rancor over the fact they had failed, and eventually many became my friends and more than once rendered me valuable aid.

In the course of the day's work my assistant, Dr. Norman Barnesby, was once obliged to advise against a Neapolitan named Giuseppi. A storm of abuse in which the word "kill" frequently recurred followed the adverse verdict. We paid no attention; such occurrences were common. A few nights later, just after Barnesby had left my house, he was attacked. Because he was a good boxer and extremely agile, he was able to dodge so that the man's knife went through his sleeve, wounding him only slightly.

Barnesby believed his assailant was Giuseppi, although it had been too dark to make absolutely sure. He reported the incident to the police who, with characteristic Latin shrugs, replied, "If we question the man, he will only deny it. You have no witness. We can do nothing."

Barnesby's bride was frantic with anxiety. I, too, was concerned and went for aid to one of the steamship companies. These were my chief supporters. Because it cost so much money to bring back rejected immigrants, my word was invariably accepted as to physical condition; they would refuse to sell tickets to anyone named on my list. After explaining the circumstances to a sympathetic official, I suggested, "If you're willing to take a chance on this fellow, he could sail."

"Suppose we try," he replied.

But when Giuseppi was rejected at New York, he was so anxious to remain in the United States that he escaped from Ellis Island and swam to the mainland before he was recaptured and shipped back to Naples. The morning after his return I found him sitting on the curb across the street from my house. As I walked toward the tram

I could hear his stealthy footfalls behind me. I half turned my head so that he could not come upon me unobserved. On the tram I prudently stood on the rear platform; had I taken a seat a knife might have lodged between my ribs.

All day long Giuseppi sat on a bench in a small park opposite the office, waiting patiently and watching the door like a cat at a mousehole. When I went out to lunch, his pursuing steps followed me. There was no mistaking his intentions; he had transferred his animus to me, convinced I was to blame for his rejection.

Thereafter this dark shadow never left me. Each morning when I arose he was already on guard. The first few days of this I endured with a fair degree of patience. But after a while my nerves were so on edge that I complained to the authorities. They said they could do nothing until Giuseppi committed some overt act; threats and even attacks were not actionable in Naples. I must wait until I was killed, or at least wounded, before steps could be taken.

This espionage went on for so many months that finally I took it for granted. One evening after the opera I forgot my pursuer completely and, without thinking, took a short cut home through a narrow dimly-lighted viculo winding between tall, dark houses. Just as I turned a corner, Giuseppi jumped out at me with a knife in his upraised hand. His shortness of stature gave me the advantage. I knocked him down with an uppercut to the jaw. I did not hurry the rest of the way home; but neither did I dawdle. The next morning Giuseppi was not there but, to my intense disgust, the following day he was back again.

A week later I had lunch on board one of the steamships where I had been making an examination, and told the assemblage about my disagreeable experiences.

It could be assumed that wherever one went in Naples the Camorra would be represented. One of the guests said immediately, "Why didn't you mention this before? The matter could easily have been arranged. But I assure you that there will be no further trouble."

I never saw Giuseppi again.

I had worked almost a year in Naples and was beginning to make progress in winning the confidence of Italian government officials when I received an urgent message from Washington saying one hundred thousand bales of rags had entered the United States unaccounted for. Many of them were readily identifiable as Egyptian robes, some of which might have come from the bodies of bubonic plague victims. I was ordered to Egypt to solve the mystery.

The American public was becoming alarmed over the steady march of plague around the world. Crawling insidiously from Hongkong into the Red Sea ports, it had fastened upon Egypt. Coming slowly West, reaching out to India, it had filtered into Spain and subsequently Italy, England, and France. Its progress could be followed on the map also as it crept around the other way. In 1899 it leaped to Hawaii, and in relatively few months bridged the final gap to our own Pacific Coast.

In 1900 the method by which plague was transmitted, in spite of unremitting research, still remained a riddle. But it was suspected that these dirty, filthy, cotton rags of Egypt, most of which ultimately found their way to the paper mills of the United States, might be sources of infection. I was to determine how these rags were getting into the country, when every port was blocked against them, and also to apply myself to research on the disease.

In Alexandria the plague was endemic; sometimes epidemic. A case would break out in one section of town. It would be isolated at once by the English and German doctors in the employ of the Egyptian government. We would set to work to investigate all the circumstances. Just then another case would be reported from an entirely different section. Since we were certain contact between the two must have taken place, we would follow every clue in the effort to establish some possible connection. Discouragingly seldom were we able to find any. The difficulty of the work was increased because we could not make these Orientals realize the importance of giving straight answers.

The fleas must have been laughing at our ineffectual efforts.

After considerable detective work I traced the Egyptian cotton rags to Liverpool, and found they were thence being reexported to Canada. A final manifest made them appear as Canadian rags, in which guise they could enter the United States freely. I suggested simple legislation requiring shippers to declare the place of origin of the rags. When passed by Congress this bill effectively put an end to the abuse.

The Egyptian rag shippers professed a willingness to comply with our regulations. During the winter I supervised the construction of fumigating sheds and saw that the rags were exposed for three hours to sulphur fumes. After being baled, they were sealed by an American consular officer and shipped directly to the United States.

The cooperation of the rag shippers was forced because they had no true conception of our aims. Although they were actually being saved the trouble and expense of their former surreptitious methods, they thought they were being bothered for nothing. This was my first experience with Oriental guile. I found that nothing irritated the Oriental more than to have to comply with the regulations which sprang from Occidental ideas of sanitation.

One of the favorite subterfuges of the Egyptians was to falsify the time during which the rags had been in the fumigating sheds. Another was to place rags only on the forward part of the trucks, so that when the doors of the shed were opened, the cars would appear to be filled. I would have to prowl about constantly in the alleys between the sheds where women were sorting rags into heaps of colors, whites, and woolens. I would often discover huge piles about to be baled which had never been inside the sheds. The dealers were constantly surprised and disgruntled when I would demand that the untreated rags be fumigated.

I found a sympathetic and responsive listener to the amusing occurrences of the day in Joseph H. Choate, our Ambassador to Great Britain, who was then vacationing in Egypt. My conversations with this profound student of human nature, famous the world over for his wit and his legal pronouncements, proved an inspiration. On many occasions to come, when my duties included drawing up and securing passage of legislation, my recollections of the latter were of great assistance.

As soon as the exportation of rags from Egypt was under control, I went back to finish my work at Naples. The United States immigration officers were gradually being permitted to return, first to Italy, where the government this time welcomed them, and later to the other countries which were sending us their excess population. I had scarcely returned, however, before the Surgeon-General delegated me to stop another leak in the health dam. Back across the water I came.

Immigration laws had been growing more and more effective in our own ports. But their success was largely nullified because the rejected aliens soon learned a method of circumventing them. No matter how incapacitating or contagious the disease might be for which they had been barred, they were finding free entry from Canada.

Canadian steamship agencies in Europe were advertising how easy it was to avoid inspection by traveling to the States through Canada. One circular was printed and distributed which announced:

"For sickly or defective passengers who want to avoid to land in the United States ports, I recommend my new Canadian line to St. John, where passengers are freely landed, without any examination. From St. John passengers can get within a few hours ride by rail to any place in the United States."

It was impracticable to guard three thousand miles of border, but our government had obtained permission to open stations at Quebec in the summer and at Halifax and St. John in the winter, where a Commission could examine every immigrant who applied for entry into the United States. This measure, however, was of only slight assistance, because proportionately few of the defectives announced their intentions beforehand.

In Canada, as in Egypt, I had a dual assignment. Although I was technically medical officer for this Commission, my real function was to persuade reluctant Canada to pass an immigration law similar to ours. Because of their widespread resentment over the high protective tariff of the United States which interfered with their trade, Canadians were not likely to lend a willing ear. They might go as far as to like an individual American here and there, but if the United States wanted any certain thing, they definitely did not want it.

During the year I spent in Canada, I became familiar with the entire border, and knew almost every stream and town along it. Wherever I went, I talked about immigration laws. Ultimately I

31

decided to do the obvious thing and enlist the aid of the railroads, which were then a power in Canadian politics. The Canadian Pacific Railroad had always been on the side of the government, whether Liberal or Conservative, and any government was embarrassed without its support. The road was willing to cooperate with us because it did not want its passengers further inconvenienced by the ever more stringent regulations we found it necessary to impose.

The Premier of Canada, Sir Wilfred Laurier, on whom final action depended, was reluctant to take any steps toward keeping immigrants out of the country, which was large and needed filling. He had first to be persuaded that his policy of settling would be helped and not hindered by barring the same types of aliens we had found undesirable. But, once convinced, he acted immediately. An Order in Council was promulgated which embodied the important provisions of our immigration laws, and later a bill was enacted by the Canadian Parliament which turned the Order in Council into law, and thus largely plugged the immigration leak.

A certain amount of running of aliens across the border still continued. Once when I was staying at Lake Memphremagog, Vermont, some of my friends in the Immigration Service had received word to be at the border the following midnight and, thinking I might be interested, they invited me to go with them. We had not long to wait before a covered undertaker's wagon loomed out of the dark.

"Halt! Everybody out!" called one of the officers.

The driver, in a shocked tone, exclaimed, "You can't interfere with us. I'm taking these sisters of charity to a funeral."

"Let's see 'em," ordered the officer peremptorily.

From the wagon descended first one sister, then another, and another, their white coifs gleaming in the faint light. But when the lantern was lifted to the eight faces, parchment yellow skins and flat eyes were revealed. The officer sardonically requested the pseudo-sisters to disrobe, and underneath the voluminous trailing black garments appeared Chinese cotton trousers and jackets.

The men were all deported under the Chinese Exclusion Act.

Often applicants for entry had to be barred because of some irregularity. Usually these poor people, amid strange surroundings, were almost overwhelmed by their misfortunes. In response to a call to act as interpreter, I arrived late one evening at another Vermont border town, and found in detention an unmarried Swedish couple. Even before I saw the woman, I could hear her loud sobs; the man stood aside resentfully. It seemed hard to send her back just because she was pregnant. I explained to them in my none-too-good Swedish that she would be allowed to enter if they would first get married. They could not comprehend why the American government should concern itself with their private relationship. They were going to get jobs, they said. The man impassively explained that he intended to marry her as soon as he had enough money. I reiterated that, under the law, she could not enter unless they were first married.

After I had talked with them most of the night, the man reluctantly consented. In the early morning I found a minister who was willing to marry them and accept my services as interpreter, though I had many qualms myself as to whether I should be able to translate questions and responses correctly. The service was a sketchy one, but the minister said it was legal, and the bride and groom, not looking particularly happy, departed into the promised land.

After Canada had passed her immigration law, the main reason for my having been sent there was concluded. Four years of study of the immigration problem at Boston, New York, and Naples, as well as Canada, had convinced me that more constructive legislation was needed. During the long winter evenings in Canada I had studied law, which helped me to gather together in legal form the data I considered vital for this purpose. I submitted these to Washington, and they formed the nucleus of the Immigration Act of 1907.

This bill was passed with the active support of labor. During its preparation I frequently met Terence V. Powderly, the former head of the powerful Knights of Labor, who had been appointed to the Bureau of Labor as a concession to those who claimed that the hordes of Europe were being brought in for the use of American capital.

Powderly gave me a valuable piece of advice which has often stood me in good stead. "You probably will have to deal with newspapers a good deal, young man. Here's a little rule for you. If you've

33

anything you don't want published, just give the reporters the whole story and then tell them how much of it is off the record. They'll never go back on you."

I have always followed this precept and have never in any country had a reporter abuse my confidence in a personal interview.

But long before the Immigration Law had been passed, my activities had been completely shifted. I received the appointment of Chief Quarantine Officer for the Philippine Islands on the other side of the world.

At the end of the Spanish-American War the United States was confronted with large responsibilities in the field of tropical sanitation. Suddenly we found on our hands an unsought duty. In the Philippines the Army Board of Health was presented with a medical situation of unparalleled gravity; an entire nation had to be rehabilitated.

The British, the French, and the Dutch had had years of dealing with administration and health in the Orient and the tropics, but, broadly speaking, American medical officers were inexperienced. Almost the only exception—and that a recent one—was the dramatic and successful fight waged in Cuba against yellow fever, which had caused such a high mortality there, and often invaded our own shores. To prevent this danger was one of the principal reasons for our going to war with Spain. Public attention had been focused upon this yellow fever battle conducted by Military Governor Leonard Wood, the Walter Reed Commission, and Major William C. Gorgas of the United States Army Medical Corps.

Discussion and argument over our making another tropical venture had simmered for years and was now coming to a boil. The French effort to build a canal at Panama had broken down because of their failure to conquer yellow fever and malaria, and we were about to make our attempt to cut the Isthmus. Success in this endeavor must rest upon sanitation, and Gorgas was the logical person to supervise it.

The government concluded that, before taking up our posts, both Gorgas and I should be fortified with information as to what was being done in the Orient in the field of tropical medicine, and, therefore, sent us in 1902 to the International Congress on Medicine at Cairo.

Medical officers from most of the tropical countries were present.

34

As is true of all such association gatherings, I learned far more in conversation on the famous veranda of Shepheard's Hotel than I did from hearing papers read at the meetings. I was particularly impressed with the Germans who, at that time, stood at the top of the world in scientific research, and were attacking the problems of tropical medicine with their usual thoroughness.

We spent several weeks in the Egyptian capital, and I found Gorgas a most delightful colleague. We were both reluctant to make public addresses but, since he was my senior, it became his duty to serve as spokesman, and he accepted this obligation manfully. He, who had so reluctantly adopted the mosquito theory of yellow fever, with all the zeal of the convert was anxious to have this Congress formally recognize his yellow fever work in Cuba, and have it on record that the medical profession was convinced the stegomyia mosquito was the sole conveyor of the disease. I argued with him privately as to the desirability of making such an all-inclusive statement, but the Congress, swayed by his magnetic personality, passed the resolution in the form he had written it. A recent expedition into Brazil sent by the Rockefeller Foundation once more raises the question and throws a cloud of doubt over the theory.

After the Congress was concluded, Gorgas returned to await developments on the Isthmus, and I went on my Eastward passage through the hot countries India, Ceylon, Malaya—alluring names for carefree travelers, but each a tocsin for the health officer from the New World, anxious to redress the balance in the Old.

All along the way I heard the same arguments: the Oriental could not be sanitated; he always had lived in filth and squalor; to persuade him to live in any other way was hopeless; he was happy in his present mode of existence and it would be a shame to disturb him; all efforts, therefore, should be concentrated on making living conditions safe for the European who was obliged to sojourn in his midst.

I listened patiently, but I knew the American people would never sanction such an attitude toward our "little brown brother."

CHAPTER 4.   AND BID THE
SICKNESS CEASE

"WHICH of you, intending to build a tower, sitteth not down first and counteth the cost, whether he have sufficient to finish it."

From the time the slow *Rohilla Maru* left the roadstead at Hongkong there was no peace from the frothing, churning turbulence of the China Sea until, some sixty hours later, she steamed through the Boca Chico, between Mariveles and the Island of Corregidor, into the calm of Manila Bay. There, in panorama, was spread out the teeming water life of the Orient's largest harbor. Little inter-island steamers chugged busily up and down. Praos with lateen sails and crews balanced on outriggers sailed in from remote places. Fishermen's bancas bobbed up and down in the shallows. Scores of bamboo fences jutting from the water enclosed the fish weirs, which looked like fields of rippling grain, marked out in orderly array.

At intervals along the twenty-five miles to Manila the embracing arms were dotted with clusters of little nipa huts, sprouting from the water's edge like four-legged mushrooms. Among them Cavite, the American naval base, gleamed with fresh American paint, and the white ships of the White Fleet rode at anchor.

Toward the end of the day the hot sun, beating on the water, piled up a huge feather bed of fluffy clouds. A faint steam arose, and through the haze glowed sunsets unequaled the world around. I had seen the sun sink behind Capri in gaudy glory, the vivid radiance of the Golden Gate, the torrid blaze of the African desert, and the

36

delicate pastel pinks of New York, but nowhere else, before or afterwards, did I ever see sunsets of such grandeur or so varied in their swift changing colors, ranging over the spectrum even to delicate green.

From far out in the Bay Manila appeared in the distance, with its red roofs gleaming amid the dense green of the cocoanut fronds. Above the royal palms along the Malecon Drive stood out the crosses of the church buildings. Water once lapped about the foundations of these structures, but now the Americans, to make way for new and important commerce, have dredged the harbor, filled in the foreshore, and pushed the tidal flats away from their doors. Great ships, which formerly had anchored perforce in the roadstead, are now escorted to the new piers, and the smoke from their funnels drifts like incense through the naves of the ancient stone churches.

All the long way out to the Philippines I had considered the nature of the task before me. As Chief Quarantine Officer, I was to work with the Health Board so that when the time came to release the Army officers who largely controlled it, I should be ready to add to my duties those of Commissioner of Health. My future was in my own hands.

I had already formulated my answer to the constant reiteration of the British, the French, and the Dutch that it was waste of time and money to sanitate Orientals, who wanted to be left to their ancient unsavory habits. My answer was, "You cannot let people suffer if you have the means to relieve them."

In addition, I had not overlooked the fact, repeatedly impressed upon me in my immigration training, that disease never stays at home in its natural breeding places of filth, but is ever and again breaking into the precincts of its more cleanly neighbors. As long as the Oriental was allowed to remain disease-ridden, he was a constant threat to the Occidental who clung to the idea that he could keep himself healthy in a small disease-ringed circle.

It should also have been evident to employers of colonial labor that human life had a direct monetary value, even though it might be difficult to estimate and might vary greatly with age and race; the Orientals had too long held a position near the bottom of the scale.

I believed that health should be regarded from the economic as

37

well as from the humanitarian viewpoint. To be without it was to be without earning power. A people once relieved of unnecessary burdens caused by sickness and death, could compete on equal terms with races not so handicapped. Cholera, malaria, and smallpox had made any successful commercial development of the Philippines impossible under the Spanish. Again and again they had failed in their efforts to cultivate sugar on a large scale.

In 1903 throughout the Islands death was the one event in a harried life that brought tranquillity and peace to its victims. The population for years had been at a standstill, or even on the decline, as the inevitable result of war and unobstructed devastating disease. Farmers had discarded the plow for the bolo and the gun, and as a consequence the haciendas were idle and the gardens overgrown with weeds. Long years of insurrection, discontent, and discouragement had wrought disaster in every department of government, and in every business interest. The money of the Treasury had to be spent in protecting the loyal people from the bullets of insurrectos rather than from disease.

Whatever the relative importance of the medical man in other parts of the world, he, and the profession he represented, stood first in the Philippines. The health of the people was the vital question. To transform the Filipinos from the weak and feeble race they were into the strong, healthy, and enduring people that they might become was to lay the foundations for the future on a sound basis.

Across the street from my office was smallpox, to the right was plague, and to the left cholera.

We had first to extinguish the conflagration of disease, started long before the American occupation. Plague was creeping through the alleys of Manila. The morgue was piled high with the bodies of cholera dead. Forty thousand unvaccinated were uselessly slaughtered each year by smallpox. Tuberculosis, unconsidered and unfeared, was responsible for fifty thousand deaths annually. The beriberi victims were numbered in the tens of thousands. Every other child died before its first birthday; the Philippines had the unenviable distinction of having the highest infant mortality rate in the world.

More than ten thousand men, women, and children, blighted by the scourge of leprosy, wandered, sad and lonely, among the uncontaminated. Only a few hundred were cared for by the Church. The insane were chained like dogs underneath the houses. Imitation quinine pills were sold at fabulous prices to the wan and shaking sufferers from malaria. Medical relief had never been extended to the three hundred thousand wild peoples of the mountains. Even as simple a thing as a fracture caused severe suffering, lifelong deformity and handicap which could so easily have been avoided by proper setting of the broken bones.

Sections of Manila were so closely crowded that no room for streets or even alleys was left, and the wretched people who lived there had to creep through human excrement under one another's houses to reach their own. Six to eight human beings packed themselves to sleep into a room hardly large enough for one.

With the exception of an antiquated and polluted Spanish water system in the Capital, there was not a reservoir, not a pipe line, and not an artesian well in the Islands. Without let or hindrance the vilest class of food products was shipped into the country. Perishable provisions were sold from the ground, so that dust and dirt were soon intimately mixed with them. No proper inspection of animals was made before slaughter, and diseased cattle were constantly marketed to the public.

In general the people of the Philippines were strongly imbued with superstitions and traditions. They were apparently contented in their ignorance and poverty, and resigned to their many ailments.

I set myself the goal of trying to save fifty thousand lives a year.

CHAPTER 5.   LITTLE BROWN BROTHER

MANILA, like all Oriental ports, had a water life separate and apart. The boat people did not mingle with the shore people, except when they went to the markets or to the cockpits to try their luck with their fighting roosters. They lived all their lives in their boat homes on the waters of the Bay, the Pasig River, and the esteros, or canals. They died there and would have had water burial had not a strict and seemingly unkind government forbidden it.

In those days Manila looked as though it might sink into the water. A heavy rain and an inshore wind would invariably flood the low-lying barrios. The storm waters could not be carried off by the time-worn esteros, which served as natural but ineffective drains. The tide was too languid to cope with the accumulated human filth, and a miasma of nauseating odors followed the passage of every boat.

A huge moat stretched around the Intramuros, the old Walled City, holding it python-like in indolent grip. Four sewers emptied into these twenty-five acres of swamp and morass—stagnant, noisome, and crawling with huge snakes. Beyond affording the lazy carabao, the water buffalo, an unequaled opportunity to wallow, and the mosquitoes an unsurpassed breeding place, this slough served no useful purpose. The fussy Americans filled it with good ground, converting the poisonous algae green to the fresh green of grassy parks.

The mighty walls, forty feet thick where the crenelated towers rose above the battlements, had stood siege more than once. It was true they barred entrance to the invader, but they also slowed the plodding traffic stream and excluded light and air. In disregard of the hurt feelings of antiquarians and historians, we admitted Twentieth Century vehicles, and ventilated the quarter by punching holes through the walls. In our holy zeal for sanitation, we might have razed them completely. But fortunately the anguished lamentations of American historical societies were potent enough to stay the execution. Before this happened, however, the river wall was entirely removed, and the quarter made thoroughly accessible.

The old Spanish houses which lined the narrow streets of the Intramuros leaned lovingly toward each other. These heavy masses of stone, weathered and grey, for centuries had withstood the triple threat of fire, earthquake, and invasion. Their cautious owners had locked the doors securely against thieves, but had locked within the damp, insanitary interiors the deadly germs of tuberculosis, dysentery, and cholera, and had invited plague rats to dine with them.

By far the majority of Manila's population of two hundred and fifty thousand lived outside the walled city in more modern houses. The first story often was of sandstone, soft when sawed from the quarries, but hardening when exposed to the air. Above was a projecting wooden superstructure around which was a passage way, forming a double wall and providing air space to keep the interior cool.

The first thing a Filipino did when he rose in the social scale was to build one of these hard material houses with a decorative hardwood floor made of the polished yellow molave, more beautiful than mahogany. If more esthetically-minded, he might alternate the molave with the colorful reddish ipil.

The airy baskets on stilts in which the fishermen and the toilers on land lived were fashioned after the old Malay villages built always on tidal flats or along river banks. Roofs and sides of these huts were of nipa palm, frames and floors of ant-proof bamboo, the whole bound together with withes of vegetable fibres—there was not a nail in the peasant Filipino house. The poles for the floor were split and placed flat side downward, thus making a smooth and resilient surface on which were spread their *petates*, or sleeping mats. Other furniture they had none except, perhaps, the ever-present Singer Sewing Machine. To catch vagrant currents of air, door and window flaps were propped open with sticks. Underneath the houses were the foul puddles formed by refuse dripping through the floors.

The nipa palm, rooted in salt water, grows luxuriantly in the Philippines, but does not occur again until far away Sumatra. The Filipino takes it for granted, but without it his life would be vastly more difficult. It provides him with the roof for his home and with internal warmth. Because it has no insect enemies the crop is unfailing, and until the ocean dries up it can suffer no drought. With little effort, the boats of the harvesters wind their way through narrow water ways, cutting the protecting fans, tapping the slender stalks, and emptying the little cups of their sweet sap. Out of this are distilled alcoholic imitations of beverages ranging from chartreuse to cognac— imitations so closely resembling the originals that only the most delicate palate can distinguish the difference.

The nipa hut, frail as it is, can withstand one enemy to which wood rapidly succumbs. One oppressive November day I went to a Thanksgiving party in Manila, and when, after the home fashion, a huge turkey was brought to the table, instead of bearing the weight cheerfully, the festive board literally groaned and collapsed at our feet. Everybody was startled, but nobody was surprised. Termites had bored up through the legs, leaving only a shell of varnish.

These white ants were the great destroyers in the tropics. At the Mariveles Quarantine Station where, during the first years, I spent much of my time, four carpenters were kept busy as the busy ants themselves, replacing their depredations. If the queen ant could be located and destroyed, the colony would die off, but she was usually hidden so carefully that it was well nigh impossible to find her. Each ant colony was built underground, tier on tier like a huge upside-down skyscraper. Somewhere in the middle of the structure was the boudoir, bed chamber, and lying in room of the fat and bulbous queen, who passed her life there in purdah, because her jealous subjects had designed the exit and entrance tunnels far too small for her passage.

I remember spending almost an entire Sunday afternoon watching these blind workers solve a complex engineering problem, apparently requiring a high degree of reasoning power. Up the side of the bathroom wall they had constructed their tunnel of mud and sand, cemented with a glue-like secretion which, when dry, was hard and fairly waterproof. Opposite the wooden flush tank, their objective, some six inches from the wall, they stopped to consider the question. First they vainly endeavored to bridge the gap with their ordinary tunnel structure by projecting it into the intervening space. When this did not work, they carried out one of the most ingenious operations I have ever witnessed. Against the side of the wall opposite the tank they extended the tunnel horizontally, forming an L, and then waited for it to dry. While a few of them wet it at the joint, the majority took hold of the vertical section and slowly turned it until the horizontal section bridged the gap. Without instruments and without sight they had constructed the connection the exact six inches necessary. Two ants cautiously ran across and fastened it; in a few moments it was ready for use.

Skilled artisans though they were, the habits of these ants were notoriously bad. In the vaults of the Treasury the great silver cartwheel pesos were stored in canvas sacks. The rude and pushing insects entered the cracks of the vault and devoured the sacks. When, for all their nibbling, the silver remained intact, their low and revengeful natures came to the fore. They covered the coins with a thick and horrible deposit which no soap, no water, and no solvents could remove. Small boys earned large sums scrubbing away with stiff wire brushes at the pesos, trying to get them clean.

Many of the hot dusty streets of old Manila presented a grey monotone until the Americans, with tremendous enthusiasm, began planting trees. Growth in the tropics is so rapid that much of the city was soon sheltered. In April and November, when the leaves of the fire tree dropped and the blossoms emerged, the town was aglow with incandescent flame.

Travel on the thoroughfares of Manila was not without its hazards. Ordinary asphalt paving was tried but the continuous heat melted it; similarly, the tar filling around wooden blocks ran away. Until recently there remained only the large cobblestones, heritage of Spanish rule, over which vehicles rattled with careless abandon and deafening noise. In the Escolta and Calle Rosario, ambulances, even when carrying emergency cases, had to proceed at a walk; the violent jolting might easily have caused further injury.

No street scene in Manila would have been complete without the springless, two-wheeled little carts with long shafts and flat platforms. Each was drawn by a carabao, strong as any two horses, moving sedately a mile an hour and hauling behind him a heavy, precariously-balanced load. This stolid animal would not be hurried or pushed aside, and his great wide horns, swinging ponderously, were a constant source of danger to the innocent bystander.

For more select transportation, the quilez, with seats along the side and steps that came down in the back, was preferred by the Filipinos. The driver sat outside in the front and directed a small trotting ox, which clattered merrily along at eight miles an hour.

The common horse-drawn vehicle was the two-wheeled, solid-topped carromata, shaped much like the old-fashioned hansom, except that the driver was perched low between the shafts. As soon as the carromata stopped and the occupant alighted, the driver would leap into the passenger's seat, seize the reins with his toes, and sink into profound slumber. He was able to sleep under all circumstances and for an indeterminate period of time.

The slender, slant-eyed, brown people of the Islands are of many kinds and speak many tongues. Forty-three ethnographic groups have been distinguished and eighty-seven dialects, most of them differing so widely that those who speak one cannot make themselves understood to a neighboring group. The Spanish had never imposed their tongue on the people; only the upper classes acquired it in the course of being educated. With the coming of the Americans, the use of English was gradually extended throughout the length and breadth of the Archipelago, but when I first went there interpreters were frequently necessary. Now the younger men in the Legislature do not even speak Spanish, because they were educated in American schools; English is to be the language of the new Commonwealth.

Though Malay in origin the Filipinos are Christian in their religion and Occidental in their form of government. Largest in numbers and gentlest of the racial groups are the Visayans of Southern Luzon and the central islands—Panay, Cebu, Leyte and the rest. Most civilized when Miguel Lopez de Legaspi established Spanish rule in 1565, they later yielded the leadership to the more aggressive Tagalogs of Manila and Central Luzon, who have been head and front of the independence movement since the old days of the Katipunan, the revolutionary secret society led by José Rizal and Emilio Aguinaldo. To the Northwest are the hard-working Ilocanos, true sons of Martha, who, in their thatched-roof carts, follow the harvests around Luzon.

In the central hills are the five wild tribes, animistic in their religion; and here and there in Luzon, tucked away in the recesses of the Mariveles hills and the East Coast, are the Negritos. Far to the South in the Islands of the Sulu Sea—Mindanao, Jolo, Tawi-tawi—are the fierce Moros, last of the Malay invaders and the only Mohammedans in the Archipelago.

Fortunately, the race question has never proved a stumbling block between whites and Filipinos. Perhaps three hundred years of Christian influence have given the latter an attitude toward Western races not shared by other Orientals. Of *mestizos* there are many, mostly a mixture of Filipino with Spanish or Chinese, and from these are generally drawn the leaders of the people, including Manuel Quezon, a Spanish-Tagalog, and Sergio Osmeña, a Chinese-Visayan, both exceptionally able men.

The Filipinos, with the exception of the wild tribes and the Moros, were devout Catholics. But their grievances against the Church were so bitter that the Revolution had been directed as much against it as against Spain. Many of the Independistas wanted religious as well as political freedom, so that a Filipino might become a priest or a Filipina a sister. In Father Aglipay, who had been Aguinaldo's chaplain and one of the brains of the Revolution, they found a leader.

The schismatics took possession of the Catholic churches in the districts where they were strongest. The question of ownership was taken to the Supreme Court of the United States where the adherents of Aglipay contended that the churches had been built by the people of the community, and therefore belonged to them; the Roman Catholics, on the other hand, claimed that a church once built belonged to the Holy See forever. The Supreme Court decided for the orthodox religion, and the Aglipaists had to give up the churches. They, however, were not to be checked so easily. They erected churches of their own, first of bamboo and wood to serve until, as their numbers swelled to a million and a half and funds increased, they could afford better ones.

The bulk of the population of the Philippine Islands was agricultural. The tao, or peasant farmer, was a friendly creature, simple and uncomplaining. In the old days, half the village might be dead of cholera, but the survivors would be cheerful. Or if his house burned down the tao, with no caviling at fate, would set to work the next day to build it up again.

All the Americans felt sympathy and affection for the tao and wanted to protect him. But this was difficult because of the cacique system, so strongly entrenched that neither Spaniards nor Americans had been able to root it out. The cacique was the rich man of the town, who owned all the property and received a percentage on all the produce. Through his system of usury he kept the tao in a state of serfdom.

In the health service we had to recognize the power of the cacique; usually an intelligent person, his opposition could have nullified our efforts. But as soon as he realized he could get no graft from us, and that, on the contrary, we might bring him added income by making his subject taos more productive, he ranged himself on our side. The tao, who was as unprogressive as he was gentle, often offered passive resistance to Westernizing, but at a threatening word from his cacique he would prove amenable.

It is always easy to condemn a whole people by calling them this or that when, as a matter of fact, the adjective may only be true in part. The Filipinos have been termed lazy, but the tao, the submerged nine-tenths, is anything but lazy. With his carabao he works his plot of ground day in and day out. The class above the tao, on the other hand, is frequently disinclined to physical exercise—carpentering, gardening, or even walking. But even they could not be called mentally lazy.

All Filipinos have the siesta habit, although it was abruptly broken into by bustling American office routine. Americans found it difficult to appreciate the leisureliness of the Filipinos, who, for example, measured distance by the time it took to smoke two cigarettes, or five, or whatever the number might be. The Filipinos, on the other hand, failed utterly to comprehend the importance of time as viewed by Westerners. To an American, an appointment at ten o'clock meant ten o'clock, but to the Filipino it meant the time at which he left his house; he might arrive at the meeting place at eleven.

The net result of centuries of subjection was a tendency to evasion, a characteristic of people who have long lived in a state of dependency. This indirection was carried over into daily conversation. I soon learned that I must never say "no" to an Oriental, because nothing gave greater offense than the direct negative. If a Filipino asked me for the loan of an umbrella, I must not say, "I'm sorry, but I have no umbrella," but rather, "I don't think it's going to rain." He would understand and not be affronted.

Though the Filipino seldom smiled, he was by no means dour. Kindliness was one of his most charming traits. Family life was invariably amicable and friendly. Harsh or scolding voices were seldom heard. Even the little children were polite to each other. No child was rude to strangers or failed to obey. He seldom whined or cried.

Equally endearing was the generosity which welled spontaneously from Filipino hearts. I was once accompanying Jacob M. Dickinson, Secretary of War, on a tour of the provinces when, due to a motor mishap, we had to stop at a village which had not been expecting us. Our party was composed of at least twenty-five, but within an hour an excellent banquet was produced, complete even to such orations as would have made a United States Senator envious. Mr. Dickinson was much impressed with the spirit of hospitality he found everywhere, and at the conclusion of his five weeks' stay among the Filipinos quoted as his valedictory the words of Charles Sumner, "Let us know each other better and we will love each other more."

Former custom had been to "civilize" native populations with the aid of a whiskey bottle, the Bible, and the Krag. The United States was determined that different methods would be employed in the Philippines. Kipling's advice to the American people was noble but unnecessary; in our hearts we had already assumed the white man's burden. President McKinley had sincerely believed, as he said, "There was nothing left for us to do but to take them all, and to educate the Filipinos, and uplift and civilize and Christianize them, and by God's grace to do the very best we could by them."

In harmony with this sentiment he selected men who would also wish to avoid the horrors which usually had accompanied the efforts of a white race to impose its civilization on one of darker color. William Howard Taft was sent to the Islands early in 1900 to head a Commission of Five, two of whom were to become governors after him—Luke E. Wright, Secretary of Commerce and Police, and Henry C. Ide, Secretary of Finance and Justice. One of the others, the dynamic Dean C. Worcester, was to serve ardently, faithfully, and long as Secretary of the Interior.

The views of all these men coincided with those of President McKinley. Their conception of their responsibilities included immediate attention to the material and physical needs of the Filipinos. With that speed and energy which we like to think of as American, one million dollars was appropriated at once for roads and three million for improving Manila harbor, a thousand American school teachers were imported, civil service by merit was installed, a native constabulary formed, a whole new system of government with its manifold ramifications designed and executed.

One of the outstanding acts of Governor Taft's administration was the peaceful settlement of the Friar Lands Controversy. The four orders of friars had obtained most of the desirable land in the Islands, and had rented it out to the Filipinos on terms which they resented. The Revolutionaries had driven the priests helter-skelter, killing or imprisoning any they could catch. Embittered public sentiment was almost unanimously against their return. Governor Taft interested himself wholeheartedly in this important question. To settle the unrest he went in person to Rome and, after consultation with Pope Leo XIII, he arranged for the purchase of these lands for seven million dollars by the Filipino government and their resale to the Filipinos at fair rates.

Economic betterment could not be successful until Filipino confidence had been secured. The Filipino had a difficult time comprehending that anybody should want to do anything for him without expecting something in return; he was always looking for a concealed motive. Service without expectation of reward, in the Anglo-Saxon sense, was outside his cosmogony, and he regarded giving for the sake of giving as absurd.

At the outset, Taft enunciated that the American goal in the Philippines was to train the Filipinos to self-government as quickly as possible. To attain this end, as well as to increase goodwill, three Filipino members were added to the Commission. They were participants, and their wishes were carefully considered, but the five Americans retained the deciding vote by reason of their numbers, although it is interesting to note that the vote seldom split along racial lines. Until the advent of the Democratic Administration in 1913, it was a consistent American policy never to delegate authority to Filipinos until they had been trained to responsibility, just as it was the policy to train them to this responsibility as quickly as possible.

Another immediate problem was due to the inevitable friction caused by a military occupation; the soldiers with whom the Filipinos had been at war were naturally still regarded by them as their enemies. Taft had to make himself popular as a necessary incident to initiating a civil government. He was so successful in this endeavor that when there was talk of President Theodore Roosevelt offering him a Supreme Court justiceship, thousands of Filipinos serenaded him with the stirring sentiment, "We want Taft!" His winning smile and his jovial good nature were maintained in the face of every obstacle. The Filipino took life seriously. The Americans were so burdened with the responsibility of their mission that they had little inclination for humor. But Taft, amid the encircling gloom, would tell his stories with such gusto as to command appreciation and delight.

Taft came down shortly with amoebic dysentery, the inevitable result of his constant attendance at banquets. He believed it his duty to partake freely of the soft drinks and the strange food until, as he himself expressed it, his "intestines harbored a first class zoological garden."

In spite of his size, and although the perspiration poured from him, he was a glutton for work. He had a most extraordinary talent for preparing laws. I have seen him dictate ex tempore to a stenographer a legal document running into several pages in which scarcely a word would have to be altered.

Taft created hundreds of laws, but the man who saw to their administration was Luke E. Wright, a former general of the Confederacy, a typical Southern officer with upright bearing and clear, cool eye. His wisdom had much to do with the success of Taft's administration, and when he succeeded as governor, he ably carried out the laws which Taft had drawn up.

Wright was followed by Henry C. Ide who held office only a short time. Then in 1906 came the picturesque James F. Smith, Colonel of California Volunteers, who had served as Customs Collector, Justice of the Supreme Court, and Vice Governor-General. He was likeable, sincere, honest, and, above all, human. It was during his term of office that the railroads of the Islands were built and the government finances stabilized. He could secure Filipino support for his measures, a gift which, as time went on, became increasingly essential.

Each administration reiterated Taft's original promise of independence when the Filipinos were prepared for it. One step toward its fulfilment came in 1907 when the first Philippine Assembly was opened by Taft, then Secretary of War in President Theodore Roosevelt's cabinet, who had made the long journey across the Pacific for this express purpose. The Commission, soon increased by the addition of a fourth Filipino member, then became the upper house of the legislature.

I have known all the governor-generals of the Philippines and, in my opinion, the one most gifted in administrative ability was W. Cameron Forbes. He laid a firm foundation for sound government which might totter in political earthquakes but would not fall. His nine years of service began in 1904 when he became a member of the Commission. As Secretary of Commerce and Police he controlled many of the basic government entities upon which the material prosperity of the Islands depended—Public Works, Coast and Geodetic Survey, Posts and Telegraph, Inter-Island Navigation, and a Constabulary of ten thousand men. He did much to create the forces which would eventually make the Islands fully rounded and self-sustaining economically. Improvement of harbor facilities and reduction or abolition of harbor dues did much to stimulate commerce. His brilliant achievements in all these fields ranked with those of Lord Cromer in Egypt.

This grandson of Ralph Waldo Emerson, the transcendental theorist, used his brains to build up the most efficient government the world has ever known. For a population of ten million he did all the things a government had to do—courts, constabulary, harbors, education, civil service—on thirty million dollars a year. He ran the Philippines as a business; politics were allowed to play no part.

Every item of expense, no matter how minute, was carefully scrutinized by his loyal lieutenant, auditor Lawshee, who would lop off here and whittle there, waging a successful war against the common human failing to pad expense accounts. I remember one occasion when Lawshee's eagle eye was skimming the expense account of one of my subordinates. When it lit upon an item charging two dinners in one day, his inexorable blue pencil ruled it out. My man explained defensively that he had been on shipboard one rough night and had lost his dinner. But shortly the sea had grown calm, and he had been able to return to the dining room and consume a second dinner. His contention was that the first had been lost in the line of duty. But the Rhadamanthine Lawshee brushed this explanation aside, saying one dinner was all that could be allowed.

Philippine revenues were small, and much money was needed to turn into reality the American dream of rehabilitating the Islands. Forbes started in to develop their material resources. But before this could be done, roads had to be constructed. The military caminos which the Spanish had built for conquest had long since fallen into decay and disrepair. Forbes built new ones, also for conquest, but this time intended to seize the treasures of Mother Earth.

According to the Forbes plan, after a road had been built, a caminero was hired to patrol each kilometer on the sound theory that a stitch in time saves nine. He would plod up and down with his little cart, his eyes scanning the surface, and then, with simple tools, a bushel of stone, and a bucket of tar, he would mend immediately each rift or hole.

Though Forbes was doing this work for the good of the Filipinos rather than for their exploitation, he, like every departmental head, had always to battle with the ghosts of past abuses; the Filipinos had vivid memories of the corvee system under which they had been conscripted for road work. Nevertheless, so persistently did Forbes bend his energies in this direction that, half jokingly, half affectionately, he was dubbed Caminero Forbes.

Wealth began to flow along the roads which he had opened. His efforts resulted in raising sugar production from fifty thousand tons to a million and a half a year and in developing the copra industry to an extent hitherto undreamed of. Wherever we went in Southern Luzon we used to see the silvery white hemp fibre hanging out to dry like washing. The staple, ten to fifteen feet long, stronger under water than any other fibre grown, has made Manila virtually synonymous with good rope throughout the world. Forbes encouraged gold mining and the Philippines are rapidly becoming one of the world's leading producers.

Forbes did much to advance the Philippine tobacco industry against the bitter antagonism of American corporations already interested in the Cuban product. As soon as Philippine tobacco, which has a smaller nicotine content than the best Havana and is unsurpassed in quality, began to win popularity on its own merit, reports were circulated that Philippine cigars were made by lepers and syphilitics. Such is the suggestibility of human nature that even the red sentinels at cigar store entries seemed to hold their right hands aloft with, "Thou shalt not enter."

The Bureau of Health, trying to combat this unfounded prejudice, certified that each box exported was manufactured under absolutely sanitary conditions. But a bad name, once given, clings as tenaciously as a lanky hound to the trail. The old stories would keep cropping up. Whenever I would try to purchase a Philippine cigar in the United States, the cigar store clerk would reply, "We don't carry 'em. They'd ruin the rest of our stock." Then he would deliver a lengthy homily on the dangers inherent in even having them in the store. He would show me Philippine cigars with tiny holes in them, and instruct me in the habits of worms, with many details as to how they would infect the good clean Havanas.

My explanation differed from his. Occasionally, as is common to any tobacco, eggs had been laid on a few of the leaves. After they had been rolled into the cigars, the eggs had hatched and the worms bored their way out. But the worms had long since gone their way and therefore could not possibly have "infected" any other cigars.

Forbes' interests were not alone material. He had a strong sociological bent, particularly directed toward penology. The great central prison of Bilibid was becoming much overcrowded. Instead of

52

adding to its great stone walls, or to its wings, radiating from the central tower where the guards unceasingly watched, Forbes established the partially self-governing community of Iwahig, consisting of twelve hundred adult criminals, on the far distant island of Palawan. As in the George Junior Republics in this country, there were no walls at all; Iwahig was designed to reform rather than to punish. Privileges were won by merit. After two years of good behavior a prisoner could send for his family, set up housekeeping, and develop a plot of land independently as though he were at home in his own village. Half of what he produced was his. If he did not care for agriculture, he could learn a trade.

Few escapes were attempted; most of the murderers, highway robbers, and burglars loyally observed the conditions of their parole. After release they were in great demand for servants because of the excellent training they had received, and the reliability they had proved. Paradoxically, released convicts found it easier to get jobs than those who had not served an apprenticeship at Iwahig.

Such was the power of Forbes' personality that it pervaded every department. The esprit de corps was raised to so high a pitch that all labored joyfully and without regard for their own interests; even the office boy was heart and soul a part of the movement and firmly convinced that if he were not there at eight o'clock in the morning the wheels would stop.

Although he worked so hard, Forbes seemed to be able to stretch the twenty-four hours farther than most people. He attended official functions faithfully, and did more than his share in furthering good fellowship between Filipino and American. He was at the height of his success and had attained world renown when in 1913 the administration changed. President Woodrow Wilson subjected him to one of the extreme cruelties so often perpetrated under a democratic form of government. Without warning he received the following curt cable from Washington:

"Washington, August 23, 1913. Harrison confirmed August 21. The President desires him to sail September 10. Will it be convenient to have your resignation accepted September 1. Harrison to accept and take office September 2. The President desires to meet your convenience. Should

Harrison take linen, silver, glass, china, and automobiles? What also would you suggest? Wife and children will accompany him. Please engage for him servants you leave."

Two days later, President Wilson, apparently realizing that something more was due, wrote as follows:

"Washington, August 25, 1913.
My Dear Governor Forbes,

I have appreciated your willingness to remain as Governor General of the Philippines until I might with deliberation select your successor. I realize the amount of excellent work which you have done in the Islands as Secretary of Commerce and Police, and as Governor General, and I desire to thank you for your faithful and careful service. It is my desire that your successor should, if possible, reach the Philippines before October 16, and I therefore accept your resignation to take effect September 1 from the service."

Forbes had performed a great work for the American government in a position which, in administrative importance, ranked next to that of the Presidency itself. Wilson's abrupt action was a poor return for one who had spent his personal fortune freely and had worked so hard, often against the opposition of the Assembly, that his health had given way a number of times.

Under Osmeña and Quezon the movement for independence had been steadily growing, although, in their desire for personal power, the leaders often talked in generalities, either without knowledge of the facts or disregarding them. Forbes had no intention of denying independence to the Filipinos but only of withholding it until he considered these novices in self-government had become experienced enough to manage their own affairs without tariff concessions and military protection from the United States.

The arrival of Francis Burton Harrison, former Congressman and the avowed champion of Filipino independence, was awaited with much speculation and curiosity. Who knew what happy hunting grounds in the various government departments might be opened to the politicos?

As a gesture of courtesy, an envoy was sent to meet Governor Harrison's ship at Nagasaki to answer any questions he might wish to ask about the country he was to administer. When he propounded the rhetorical question, "I suppose I should wear a silk hat and morning coat when I enter Manila?" the envoy, anxious to please, replied politely, "Of course."

But the moment the emissary was out of the presence he sent off warning cables to Manila that the new Governor General intended landing in silk hat and frock coat. The Filipinos were always immaculately and neatly clad but always in white, and even formal occasions called only for mess jackets. There were no more than a half dozen top hats in Manila and no time in which to procure more. They were not to be found lacking in etiquette, however. They organized the official reception in relays. Several hundred people are supposed to have defiled before Governor Harrison, exchanging the six silk hats rapidly behind a screen.

Meanwhile emergency telegrams by the hundred were being despatched to Singapore, Hongkong, and Calcutta calling for hats, but to fill this unprecedented demand the emporiums of the East were able to send hardly two of the same shape or vintage.

Governor Harrison was both amused and embarrassed at the furore he had unwittingly created. After his first appearance he had discontinued toppers, but for many months they were faithfully worn by the Filipinos to the delight of Philistine beholders. When we went on inspection tours it was the custom for the officials of each town to line up in the main street. I used to pull out my binoculars as we approached. Governor Harrison would ask anxiously, "How are they dressed?"

I would take a gleeful look and reply, "They're all out in their silk hats."

Governor Harrison would sigh and say, "I suppose I'll never be able to live that down."

In spite of Governor Harrison's personal charm, he was to create much havoc throughout the Islands. Because he said to the Filipinos, "What you want you may have," his popularity with them was immense. But he had not been in Manila twenty-four hours before he began dismissing American officials of the Philippine government who, as Civil Service incumbents, had considered their tenure permanent. They were informed, often with only a few hours' notice, that their jobs were terminated, and they were left stranded ten thousand miles from home. The blade rose and fell, and one head after another rolled into the basket. Many Filipinos were lifted into positions which they were not qualified to fill.

Two schools of thought about the Philippines existed among Americans. One was to allow the Filipinos to direct the lesser units of government and, as they showed fitness, to turn over to them the higher units. The other, to which Governor Harrison belonged, believed the only way for people to learn how to govern was to let them do the governing as they wished.

Since 1907 there had been two main parties in the Philippine Assembly—the National Independent, which wanted freedom at once, and the Democratic, which was always in the minority and favored going slowly. Additional parties kept cropping up, only to be plowed under again. One of them, the Electric Independence party, wanted independence as fast as electricity could travel.

The two leaders of the National Independent party were Sergio Osmeña and Manuel Quezon. Undoubtedly the latter was even then the chief figure in the Islands. Although our objects were often antithetical, he had such charm that it was impossible to dislike him, and our relations were always friendly. Osmeña, long Speaker of the House, and then President of the Senate, was second only to Quezon in prominence.

After Rizal, Emilio Aguinaldo was the most outstanding figure in Philippine history. He was a full-blooded Tagalog from Cavite, in whose name the Filipino insurrection had been conducted. This school teacher, exiled by Spain for political activity, in spite of his originally peaceful occupation, had shown a certain talent for military tactics. After Funston had captured him by a daring ruse, he gave his parole, and from that moment became a loyal citizen, who did his utmost to help build up the Islands. He retired from active life and concentrated on his farm in Cavite.

In and out of the course of duty I saw Aguinaldo often. He still had a great name. During presidential campaigns, politicians would come all the way from the United States to wring from him his opinion on the progress the Filipinos were making toward independence. Ammunition was always needed for pre-convention speeches.

Senator William J. Stone, a Democrat from Missouri, appeared on one of these missions. Americans in the Islands kept telling him that Aguinaldo had no influence whatsoever politically, but Stone naturally considered that these artful Republicans were trying to lead him astray, and prevent him from tracking down the truth. Stone was a guest of the Governor General at Malacañan, the former residence of the Spanish governors, and Aguinaldo was produced for him. Since no interpreter was present, I was asked to fulfill that function.

"Now, General," Stone began. "Don't you think the Filipinos would have been much better off if we hadn't occupied the Islands?"

"I really don't know," replied Aguinaldo, "but I'm trying to raise some corn in Cavite. Now I understand you come from a great corn-raising state, and I wish you'd tell me something about the essentials of seed selection."

"I haven't ever thought about it. I don't know anything about corn. But you, General, know that the Democratic party in the United States has always stood for release of the Islands. Don't you think you should have independence right away?"

"That's a debatable question, Senator, but now about fertilizers. What fertilizer do you use on your corn?"

"I don't know anything about fertilizer," asserted the Senator firmly and with signs of irritation. "But I'd like to get your opinion on what America should do right now, and whether it wouldn't be the correct policy to turn these Islands over to you. What do you think?"

"Oh, there are many people who know much more about governmental matters than I. But in Missouri—"

"To hell with Missouri," shouted the Senator, and stamped out of the room.

But if Aguinaldo were lukewarm to independence some years ago, he was in the minority, because independence was the burning issue. A school superintendent in Cebu reported that he had received from a small potential voter the following answer to his request for a description of a cow. "A cow is an animal which has a leg at each corner, it has horns and gives milk, but, as for me, give me Independence."

By the passage of the Jones Act in 1916 an elective Senate replaced the Commission, leaving the legislature in financial control. Thereafter Filipino bills were subject only to the veto of the Governor

General. With complacent Harrison failing to assert his prerogative, the Filipinos had affairs in their own hands. Unfortunately, the novitiate had not lasted long enough; the vows of government had been taken too soon. The people had not "had time to absorb and thoroughly master the powers already in their hands."

CHAPTER 6.

WASHING UP
THE ORIENT

THE Philippine Archipelago stretches along the coast of Southern
Asia for more than a thousand miles; a fast ocean liner can
pass by in no less than two full days. The only quarantine station in
this vast and scattered collection of Islands was at Mariveles. Ships
which came into any port of entry with communicable diseases sometimes had to be remanded enormous distances. In order to ease the
burdens on commerce one of my first duties was to build a quarantine
station at the populous port of Cebu, and later others at Iloilo, Zamboanga, and Jolo.

In Spanish days the quarantine department had been run on a
simple system. Whenever a ship sailed into Manila with dangerous
communicable disease aboard, its captain would take up a "collection,"
as it was called. If it were sufficient, the ship would be promptly released without being delayed in quarantine. If not ample, another
collection, and perhaps even a third, would have to be tendered. The
result was that an outbreak of plague, cholera, or smallpox in China or
Japan would usually be followed by an outbreak in the Philippines.

We applied water, soap, and disinfectant rigorously. Whenever
ships came in from Hongkong or Amoy, the crews, many of whom
had loathsome skin diseases due to filth, were scrubbed, sometimes
forcibly. After a few rounds of bathing most of these skin troubles
disappeared.

Later we had an arrangement with Hongkong so that the crews of
ships about to sail for Manila would be bathed there. The Chinese,

who objected strenuously to bathing and who were always highly skilled in evading regulations, promptly formed a guild of professional bathers. A boatload of sailors on its way from ship to quarantine station would change places midway with a boatload of the professionals, and depart to seek pleasure elsewhere. The only certain way to stop this practice was to send inspectors to see that the Chinese performed their ablutions satisfactorily.

A detail, but a bothersome one in the quarantine service, was cleaning up the Spanish-operated inter-island steamers. Everything about them was indescribably filthy. The ice boxes spread abroad a noxious odor which tainted the food. The knives and forks were dirty, and so were the table cloths. Toilets and baths were unspeakable, and drinking water was unsafe. I put every arriving boat in quarantine until it could pass an inspection for cleanliness. The captain would run up a signal when, according to his way of thinking, the ship was immaculate. We then went out and inspected. If it were still dirty, we left the crew again to their housecleaning. They did not understand the meaning of the word dirt until its presence had been actually pointed out to them. But in the end they met our exacting demands and learned how to scrub.

America was literally washing up the Orient.

The Army Board of Health had also inaugurated a general campaign on land of cleaning and sweeping, so characteristic of the American sanitarian. In the four years of its existence this Board, composed of three American surgeons as active members and two prominent Filipino physicians as honorary members, had done what it could in the face of an overwhelming problem. But its work had necessarily been confined largely to protecting the health of the troops and sanitating the city of Manila, although municipal boards of health had been organized to study the requirements of the different towns and suggest remedies.

There was never money enough for all our needs. Hence, anybody was cherished by the Commission who could reduce expenses and at the same time produce results. I bore this constantly in mind. It was astounding to find how the employment of a little ingenuity would accomplish great things economically. I have often thought our work was done more efficiently because things were not too easy. One simple method of creeping into the hearts of my superiors was to save them the annual expenditure of three hundred dollars for a launch awning. The rot in this humid climate was so great that the canvas would quickly mold away. I adopted the simple expedient of having it washed once a week with bichloride of mercury, thereby killing the mold germ and extending the life of the canvas considerably.

The financial stringency under which I worked as quarantine officer permeated all government departments, and was an ever-present and pressing problem in the Bureau of Health. We were at all times handicapped by the shortness of the Treasury purse. Whatever we accomplished had to be done within the revenues of the Islands, and, moreover, appropriations had to be secured from a reluctant and un-comprehending legislature. We had approximately fifteen cents per capita compared with the $3.65 which Gorgas could spend yearly in Panama. Moreover our territory covered a hundred thousand square miles and three hundred inhabited islands instead of the narrow strip of Canal Zone. Contrary to general belief, the Philippines never re-ceived any financial assistance except three million dollars from the United States to repair the losses of the frightful rinderpest epidemic.

Another handicap with which I struggled for a year was the limited power granted to the head of the health department. For example, under the Health Act as originally drafted, I had to secure the per-mission of the Governor General and of the Commission before mak-ing any important move. When I had to have an assistant the list of eligible appointees limited me to five ex-presidents of provincial boards of health. One had an aortic aneurism which made him a hopeless invalid, one weighed two hundred pounds and could not speak after climbing a flight of stairs, and the others had no technical training.

Governor General Ide, at my request, cabled to the United States for an assistant. When Dr. Burdette arrived, the members of the Commission, angered at what they considered derogation of their authority, refused to confirm the appointment, and offered to pay Dr. Burdette's passage back if he would take the first boat. Within a few hours, however, they had reconsidered and informed me they would confirm Dr. Burdette's appointment, but only because of the expense already incurred in bringing him out.

I earnestly wished to do my duty, but it was impossible to work under these conditions. If anything were to be accomplished it was absolutely essential that the Director of Health have almost military authority, and not be hampered either by politics or personalities. Otherwise the organization would be in such confusion that little could be accomplished. For efficiency and economy the administrative set-up of the department should be changed. I, therefore, submitted a new draft for a Directory of Health which, after much discussion, was accepted, and I was furnished dictatorial powers.

At first I had great difficulty finding medical men who were qualified and at the same time interested enough in the cause of humanity to undergo the innumerable hardships and discomforts to be encountered in the provinces. But ultimately the Bureau of Health had a staff of three thousand employees, two hundred doctors, and many sanitary inspectors. One of our great and continuing problems was to educate such a large force of men, and several million dollars a year were required to operate the complex machinery. Among other things the accounting system had to be elaborate, because we were determined never to have it said that an inspector could be bribed.

We kept ourselves informed in various ways whether the force was carrying out orders. We insisted on detailed reports; daily during epidemics, weekly otherwise. We also made surprise visits, and had inspectors to watch the inspectors. The sanitary squads had to display a big flag to show the section of the town in which they were working so that they could be located immediately if required. Since they might be called at any time, they never strayed.

I cannot now recall one case of breach of trust, although members of the force were often guilty of peccadillos. It was extremely difficult to bring them to book because the Oriental is so adept in extracting himself plausibly from the most compromising situations. I once had an idea that the doctor in charge of a nearby district was in Manila when it was vital he should be attending to his duties in the provinces. I had no definite basis for my suspicions, because his daily reports came in regularly. But, as a test, I suddenly sent an order transferring him to another province. He acknowledged this in the correct manner and telegrams began to arrive from the new headquarters.

Oddly enough, however, telegrams were being received at the same time from his previous station. I summoned him to an interview and waved the telegrams in front of him, demanding, "How could you have been in both Cavite and Laguna at the same time?"

"Oh, that's very simple," he replied disingenuously, "I knew how worried you were about the cholera epidemic, and I told my subordinate to keep on sending reports after I had left. He simply made a mistake and signed my name to them. He shouldn't have done that."

I often used to play the fascinating game of catching an Oriental squarely in a lie. The caretaker of the Manila morgue had the strictest instructions to see that rats were kept out. One day when I made my inspection, it was all too evident that, in spite of my injunctions, rats had been there.

"There are rats here," I said sternly to the caretaker.

"It's impossible," he replied stoutly.

"Oh, yes, there are," I corrected him.

"No, sir, there are no rats," he stubbornly maintained.

"What's that right under the roof?" I asked, pointing to a dark object on top of the wall.

"That's just some old rags I put up there." Rather than take the trouble to remove the cloths with which he had wiped off the tables, he had tossed them up on the rafters. But I knew that cloths could not move of themselves.

"You go get them."

"I haven't any ladder."

I had one brought in and he gingerly climbed up the rungs. The animated bundle of cloths quivered as he approached. The caretaker hesitated.

"Bring them down," I ordered sternly.

He reached over, and the rat, who could retreat no further, bit him savagely. He uttered a bloodcurdling yell.

"Are there any rats in here?" I demanded inexorably.

This was the only time I ever won the game.

My subordinates did not lie with malice but rather as children do. At first they had little comprehension of the essential purposes behind the innumerable instructions which they had to carry out. They fulfilled their duties mainly by rote. But they, being under my immediate control, could be trained to see; to move the vast inertia of the populace was far more difficult.

Nevertheless, the sanitary regeneration of the Philippines had to be brought about, not in spite of the Filipino, but with his assistance. It was natural at first that a people should resist measures which, in their inmost hearts, they believed were being enforced by the governing power for the express purpose of making them miserable, unhappy, and uncomfortable.

President McKinley had once promised that the United States would do nothing to interfere with Filipino habits and customs. But the Bureau of Health was constantly doing this very thing, and any measure proposed which the Filipinos did not like was ipso facto not one of their customs. I could sympathize with them; it was doubtless unpleasant to be ordered about by sanitary officers and nurses.

Popular hostility was naturally reflected in the press, and even the doctors joined in the hue and cry when I submitted a sanitary code for Manila. I was invading the privacy of the home. After they had delayed its passage for a year, I called them into conference and asked, "Gentlemen, what corrections would you like to make?" They submitted their proposals. I agreed they were excellent, but needed only a few slight changes here and there of a purely technical nature. I then rewrote the code, essentially as it had been before, and everybody was happy.

I used this same system often in the legislature, where hostility could be converted into active cooperation by the simple expedient of saying to the most violent objector, "Will you draft this bill for me?" His opposition would evaporate instantly, and he would eagerly accept the commission. When he brought it back, I would agree that his version was excellent, and then recast the entire bill. As the bill thereafter bore his name, the theoretical author and I would remain faithful allies forever.

We always had to bear in mind that we had to have public opinion on our side. Public opinion conceives of sanitation in terms of collecting garbage and cleaning dirty streets, removing dead animals, cutting weeds and grass on vacant lots, keeping goats out of back alleys, sweeping sidewalks, penning up pigs, and deodorizing foul smells. We had to do all the things which the public regarded as of most importance, even to seeing that their whiskey was free of impurities.

The citizens were being bitten continually by mosquitoes, and hence mosquitoes became, in their eyes, the paramount health problem. In reality the mosquitoes of Manila, though enormous in numbers, were negligible from a health point of view because they did not transmit any important disease there. Even to free the city of flies was not of vital importance but had to be done. Every householder and stable-keeper in Manila was required to have a garbage and refuse receptacle, which was emptied daily under the eyes of the Bureau of Health employees.

Epidemics of flies, however, sometimes served a good purpose. People never count their blessings until they suffer a little annoyance. If the inspectors became careless, flies would promptly breed. The press would come out with loud denunciations of the Health Bureau. I would dutifully promise, "We'll get rid of them in two weeks." When this miracle was achieved, the people were alive to the fact that they had a sanitary department. I would not have been able to carry them with me in greater things if they had not been able to say, "Manila is the cleanest city in the Orient."

But the public never realized that the real health work went far deeper than this. Water and soil pollution are the root causes of mortality in the tropics. We would have saved more lives in the end if we could have worked on these alone and disregarded the things which were merely irritations and not major health hazards.

A direct correlation is not always traceable between the amount spent for health and the death rate. People talk glibly about the pricelessness of human life, but they really do not believe this. If the cost of saving lives is too great, the money must be spent where it will do the most good. Though we could not install a permanent water system when thousands of people were dying of cholera, plague, and smallpox, I did what I could. According to a consistent governmental policy, anything I could save from my appropriation might, with the approval of the Governor General, be used where necessity demanded. It was my custom to take each peso that became available and use it to free a certain number of individuals of intestinal parasites, or employ it to help drill an artesian well, or vaccinate forty people.

In later years my great satisfaction came from walking along the streets of Manila and seeing that under a certain age nobody was pockmarked. But the public in general was bored by the ceaseless detail which had gone into achieving this result; although after a disease had been reduced, they would be prompt to applaud and cheer to the echo.

It is hard for the white man in the Philippines to work for the joy of it. He is oppressed by the humid heat and has to drive himself constantly. Perspiration begins to roll from him the moment he leaves the shelter of the cool interior, even to walk across the street. Only after sundown is it possible to be comfortable, and then only by establishing sleeping quarters on the windward side. One guest at a hotel will complain at breakfast, "I've had a frightful night," while the canny old-timer will report, "I've rarely had such a pleasant sleep." It all depended where their rooms had been located, whether on the windward or lee side.

The climate of Luzon has its vagaries, though they are well regulated. When the Northeast monsoon comes over the Pacific, it strikes the mountain range which divides the island in the middle, and drops its load of rain on the sparsely inhabited East Coast. In Manila, which is on the West Coast, the seasons are exactly the reverse. The frequent rains begin in June with the advent of the Southwest monsoon, and last until October; for hours each day it may pour in torrents.

The winds at Manila blow five months and change, and five months and change again. November and May are uncomfortable because of the calm that comes when the winds are gradually shifting. Through December until the middle of January is the season to which everybody looks forward, when the nights are cooler than the daytime, and when there is always a refreshing Northeast breeze. Thereafter, however, the country takes on a brown and dead appearance. Vegetation is burned up. Only the beautiful round mango trees, with their tremendous long tap roots seeking water at unbelievable distances in the earth, show spots of green.

In the early summer, the dreaded typhoon season begins. Father José Algue, S.J., in charge of the Manila observatory, first won fame when he made storm warnings public while Dewey's fleet was blockading Manila in the typhoon season, losing his Spanish citizenship thereby. He later invented a baro-cyclometer which invariably indicates the center of the storm. Much of our present knowledge of these disturbances is attributable to his scientific observations.

From the time the typhoons form in the Ladrones until they hit the China coast, or are lost in the China Sea, they are carefully watched and reported, so that every place in the Islands with telegraphic communication is seasonably informed. The typhoons move along certain belts, according to the time of year. The early ones go South and, as the season advances, they gradually move North until they miss the Islands entirely.

Death and destruction are left in the path of a typhoon. I have seen trans-Pacific liners come limping into Manila Bay after passing through such a storm, not only with their boats gone, but with the sturdy iron railings torn away by the force of wind and wave. In one wild blow at Leyte a large steamer was carried half a mile inland, and a huge channel, costing almost as much as the vessel was worth, had to be dug before it could regain the sea.

Since the track of the typhoon is never over fifty miles wide, and its speed is only six to ten miles an hour, any modern boat can run away from it, but most vessels remain prudently in port until the storm is over.

I remember once being caught by a typhoon in the treacherous waters off the East Coast of Luzon, when I was carrying a load of lepers in the government steamer, the *Basilan*. The trembling vessel would climb up and up a huge forty-foot wall of water, and then from the dizzy peak she would toboggan down the other side with terrific speed, and plunge her nose so deep into the trough that she seemed headed for the bottom of the sea. The whole ocean was standing in pinnacles which moment by moment broke, smothering the boat in foam. We had not dared approach the treacherous shore. Toward midnight the captain said the ship could not last more than a few hours; he must take a desperate chance, and make for the narrow, unlighted, rock-bound entrance to the harbor of the little island of Polillo.

It was dark as ink. The boat plunged, pitched, tossed, and rolled, and then suddenly steadied and grew still. The captain let the anchor go, and we waited for what might happen next. In the dim grey light of dawn we saw the rocky shore looming up all around us only a terrifyingly short distance away. This most remarkable seaman had managed to guide his craft, by what could only have been sheer luck or instinct, through the narrow passage and into the very center of the tiny harbor.

On land also the typhoon was a fearful thing. No one who has not been through it can appreciate it. The impressive thing is the way the wind increases, increases, and increases until it seems impossible that it can blow harder—and then it does. One particular typhoon I was able to watch from the reasonably safe doorway of a strong stone house. It was as though I were looking at the stage of a theatre. I alone was motionless. Huge trees would be lifted up, roots and all, and go sailing off into the atmosphere. Small houses dashed after them. In the harbor steamers of ten thousand tons, with noses pointed frantically at the open sea, with the anchors out and steaming full speed ahead, were piled stern foremost on top of the breakwater. Street cars left the tracks; down went the wires. Sheets of corrugated iron roofing soared through the air, sometimes cutting off the arms or legs of desperately hurrying pedestrians seeking shelter.

Then in the midst of the wildest confusion came the ominous dead calm, which marked the so-called center of the typhoon. But the quiet was only momentary. The other edge arrived, the wind reversed, and everything moveable went roaring back again.

Nature in the tropics tends to excesses and forces human beings to set up a wall of apathy to protect the nervous system from constant shocks. The things that happen near the Equator are dramatic and appear with cyclonic suddenness. Earthquakes occur more frequently than typhoons and the inhabitants must become accustomed to these terrifying experiences or each time they would be overwhelmed. During a quake, when I used to look out the window of my office on the narrow Calle Palacio, and observe the houses swaying toward one another, I would have the illusion that they were actually bumping heads.

Before the days of reinforced concrete, sections of Manila would be periodically demolished. I have seen a bottomless crack streak like a flash of lightning across the ground and split a big church in two. Years ago it was observed that these seismic waves came in known directions, and a Catholic priest, wise beyond his generation, instead of building his church on rocks, mounted it underground on rockers, turned in the direction of the waves. It has stood several hundred years, complacently rocking while its contemporaries crumbled to pieces beside it.

On the night of January 30, 1911, the ears of all Manila were shattered by the loudest noise in the world, audible for two hundred and fifty miles. In a few moments the streets were filled with people, gazing with awe and consternation at a titanic Fourth of July celebration. The whole sky was filled with stars, shooting toward infinity. The Taal volcano, thirty-five miles south, standing silent in the middle of a lake since 1754, had presumedly sprung a leak, generated steam, and blown up. It was celebrating its release with a gigantic eruption of lava, mud, fire, smoke, and gas.

Thousands of the inhabitants of Batangas Province lived in the vicinity. Although the full enormity of the catastrophe could not be determined until reports began to come in from the stricken towns and barrios, I set the machinery in motion to organize a relief expedition as quickly as possible. We could not travel by motor car because the old broken-down Spanish roads leading there were impassable. But the next day, with ample hospital supplies, a detachment of the sanitary corps, and a body of constabulary under Colonel William Rivers, we embarked on a government steamer and anchored in Balayan Bay. Thence we made all possible speed the seven miles inland to the scene of the disaster.

The sight was horrible. Not only had all life been wiped out on Volcano Island itself, but also for miles away from the shore of the lake. The dead could wait; our first care was for the wounded and the homeless strays who were without food, drink, and shelter. Temporary hospitals were set up; acres of gauze were used to dress the frightful burns, bruises, and fractures. Many women and animals were found to have aborted, doubtless from the terrific concussion.

The number of wounded was in remarkably small proportion to that of the dead, and the evidence showed that the majority of the fatalities had been caused by the explosion of gases. When nature runs amok, she often becomes pranksome in a ghastly way. The Filipinos are normally so modest that they are never caught with their clothes off. Even in bathing they are well covered. But among the ruins we found Filipinos stark naked, standing upright and embedded in ashes to their knees, still holding protecting umbrellas over their heads. They had apparently been attempting to get away when the ashes rained over them and the vacuum caused by the exploding gases had torn off their clothes.

Only about seven hundred and fifty bodies were recovered out of an estimated two thousand killed. Many had either been buried by the mud or ashes or washed back into the lake by the immense wave which had inundated several barrios and, in receding, carried practically every moveable thing with it.

Our work was interrupted by constantly recurring quakes which continued for several weeks. Colonel Rivers and I slept in the same tent and for the time being adopted the Filipino indifference. Our nervous systems became so adjusted to the shocks that we would sleep soundly at night, but kept a lantern burning in case we should be needed, or should have to make a quick exit. One night came a quake violent enough even to waken me. I returned to consciousness just in time to hear Colonel Rivers utter a startled "Whoo—ooo—ooo" as he sat up in bed and rubbed his eyes. A crack had dug diagonally across the ground covered by the tent, and the earth was sinking fast on his side. He made a leap toward me. I beat a hasty retreat under the side of the tent and he came tumbling after.

In the course of a day or so the quakes settled to their business with clock-like regularity. Every twelve minutes the ground shook, and the earth opened. When we amused ourselves straddling the clefts and riding the quakes we would receive an exaggerated sense of up and down motion. It was much like trying to stand with the right foot in one rowboat and the left foot in another when a light sea was running. These cracks might fall together at the next shock or remain gaping for months before they were filled with débris.

From the dressing stations we hauled the wounded to the coast on high, two-wheeled, canopied, pony carts, using the board seats as stretchers. I was taking a full load on one of these carretelas down a long hill when suddenly a tremendous quake came and a crack appeared in the road directly ahead of us. The cochero could not pull up the pony in time. The animal fell into a crevasse, but the shafts bridged the gap, and the harness held him.

We knew we had twelve minutes in which to work. Saplings were hastily procured, the pony was pried out, and the board seats were laid across the crack. We continued to the coast unharmed. The hardening process we had gone through made this only an incident in the day's work.

Newspaper reporters came from all over the East to cover this catastrophe. Among them were two Frenchmen who arrived after most of the rescue work had been accomplished, and who remarked superciliously that it had hardly been worth their while to come. In the endeavor to make it worth their while, fifty stalwart constabulary were selected, who eagerly entered into the plan. The next night we waited until the Frenchmen were asleep, and then cast a rope over the roof of the nipa shack in which they were housed. The soldiers took hold of either end, and stood poised. When the customary *tremblement de terre* came, they began to sway, pulling back and forth on the rope in accelerating tempo. The bamboo creaked and groaned under the stress as the hut lurched dangerously on its stilts from side to side. The soldiers gathered momentum, and it swung faster and farther, until the terrified Frenchmen catapulted out the window, hit the ground, like Antæus gained new strength, and sped away into the darkness.

We learned later that they had not stopped until they had reached the nearest town, many miles distant, and we read with great interest and amusement their account of the frightful earthquake at the scene of the Taal volcano.

The Filipinos who survived continued phlegmatically with their regular round of duties. I remember watching an old peasant plowing a nearby field with his ancient and resigned carabao. When he reached the lower end, suddenly there came a tremendous quake, and that side of the field sank about three feet. The carabao never stopped, but kept methodically on and around until he came up against the raw embankment which marked the scission. I saw him cock an eye quizzically as though to say, "Where did this come from? I never had to climb anything like this before." And then he wearily hoisted himself over the acclivity and monotonously continued on his way.

Whenever the heat became too great at Manila Americans would make the three day journey to the hills, sometimes by steamer and pony, sometimes by train and four-mule team. The heavy oppressiveness of the capital changed to the sparkling wine-tang of the rarefied mountain air. At night the soughing of the wind in the pines was reminiscent of home. It invited the Americans, exhausted by their labors in a heat strange and difficult for them to cope with; the sick were made well and the tired were refreshed.

The development of picturesque Baguio, a city planned in every detail by D. H. Burnham of Chicago, was, for years, the object of more criticism on the part of the Filipinos than all other American ventures. Nevertheless it created much attention throughout the East, and the French government once sent a delegate to observe and report on the possibility of building a similar paradise for Indo-China. The Governor General asked me to serve as a guide to this representative. The Frenchman showed great interest, asked pertinent questions, and was enthusiastic about what had been accomplished.

We came back on the same train as the Japanese Consul, and I introduced the two. We happened at the moment to be passing a succession of pits along the railroad line, and the Japanese, with the insatiable curiosity typical of his race, asked, "What are those?"

"I can't talk about them," I assured him.

"Why can't you tell me?" he persevered.

"I can't tell you why. I simply cannot say anything about them."

Since it was becoming more and more difficult to avoid his importunities gracefully, I retired to the smoking compartment. When I finished my cigar and was returning down the corridor, I could hear sounds of violent upheaval. On opening the door, I was dumbfounded to find the Japanese Consul on the floor and my French friend on top pounding his head up and down.

With one hand I grabbed the Frenchman by the collar, and with the other pulled the Japanese Consul to his feet. "What in the world is the matter?"

They glared at each other. Then the Frenchman, in lofty dignity, said, "I won't talk about it here."

The Japanese, who was almost inarticulate, managed to stutter, "This is perfectly outrageous!"

With my protégé, who was boiling with indignation, I repaired once more to the smoking compartment.

"Do you know what that Japanese proposed to me?" he sputtered. "He wanted to have me ask you what those holes were along the railroad. Does that scoundrel think a guest of the government would betray a secret? I wouldn't stand for such a thing. It reflected upon the honor of a Frenchman."

For a few moments it seemed probable that an international incident would follow, but with soothing words I managed to calm them down, and finally persuaded them to shake hands.

This required all my diplomacy. What I had intended as a mild joke had got out of hand. Had I explained about the pits it would have been very embarrassing to all concerned and I would have been the object of their joint wrath. The simple explanation was that the Filipinos did not like day labor and hence, when they needed filling material, the railroad engineers had found it much simpler to stake out places for the workers, and say, "When you've dug those out, you'll be paid for so many cubic yards," and the system had left borrow pits along the right of way.

Many of the attacks leveled by the Filipinos against Baguio were not so much on its own account, but because of the unexpected and appalling cost of building the Benguet Road, which was to connect it with the lowlands.

Seventy thousand dollars was appropriated for its construction. It appeared that this was hardly a start. The two hundred thousand which was confidently asserted would be ample also gave out. Half a million more had to be provided and still the road was not completed. There seemed to be a hoodoo upon it. The typhoons hit it,

73

the floods washed it out, cholera scattered the workers, and the engineering difficulties were far greater than had been foreseen. The soil had no cohesion, and landslides covered the road periodically. The building of the road became almost a scandal, but the government was committed to its completion. All the previous investment would be lost by withdrawal. Money, therefore, was poured into it continuously, until finally a million dollars was required to finish it.

But the road would not remain completed. Fresh disasters kept putting it out of commission. The work went on for years, and all this time the Filipinos were vociferating that they were not interested in a cool place, and improvising every variety of criticism which could occur to the exceedingly fertile Oriental imagination.

Although Harrison's arrival caused an upheaval in government, it was apparently pleasing to the forces of nature, because no tornado, no landslide, no flood ever again struck the Benguet Road. The evil spirit was exorcized. The magnificent road wound up and away to this vacation land in the hills.

The Democrats turned their backs upon the project which had just been finished at such great expense, and said to the Filipinos, "This is your road. Since you dislike it so much, you may abandon it if you wish."

The Filipinos, who had assailed it so bitterly, now said, "This is a beautiful road. We love it dearly."

They flocked to Baguio and added the final touches which made it into one of the most beautiful hill stations in the world.

The natives of a tropical climate, generally speaking, are not affected injuriously by the meteorological conditions of their environment any more than are the inhabitants of more temperate climates; their physiological activities are adjusted to their surroundings. But many Island residents are subject to the condition facetiously termed Philippinitis. It has recognized symptoms—mental and physical torpor, forgetfulness, irritability, lack of ambition, aversion to any form of exercise, and want of interest in passing events. It is usually blamed on the climate but, like many other ailments, it often results from direct violation of hygienic laws, especially those governing the production and dissipation of body heat. Many Europeans and Americans eat even more in the Philippines than they do at home. In Manila the daily temperature is usually ninety degrees. Since that of the body is 98.6, fewer heat units are needed than in the temperate zone. I never knew anyone to get Philippinitis who took the proper amount of balanced food, or consumed his excess heat units in regular exercise, and lived a reasonably hygienic life. Like many of the diseases of the Islands, it was self-induced.

The rays of the sun are not a danger in the Philippines. But I never succeeded in convincing the conservative British that tennis may be played the year around at Manila. They always abstained during the hot season, and consequently became so out of practice that the Americans who followed my example could usually excel them.

It was, however, necessary to guard against heat. In the course of experimentation, the army developed a felt campaign hat with a ventilated sweat band so that a current of air could pass over the head. This was much more agreeable to wear than the awkwardly shaped sola topee.

The British were horrified when I appeared in India equipped with one of these innovations. What was good enough for the Britisher's grandfather was good enough for him. My friends said, "If you persist in going out with that on your head, we won't go with you. You'll get sunstroke and we'll have all the bother of bringing you back."

However, I continued to wear this hat to my own satisfaction and comfort.

At one time it was believed all the heat troubles of the white man in the tropics could be ascribed to the ultra-violet ray and that this could be excluded by wearing orange-red underwear. The American Army was interested but skeptical. They decided to equip one thousand men with the orange-red and use another white clad thousand for controls. Five thousand suits were ordered which were intended to last a year. From the beginning the experiment met difficulties. Less than a quarter of the underwear was furnished in the 36 and 38 sizes worn by the majority of the soldiers. Therefore, the unfortunate subjects had to be chosen largely from among the smaller men. When it was discovered five suits a year were not sufficient, the number of victims had to be cut in half.

The experimentees to a man became universally color conscious and protested violently against the indignity. They continued to protest more loudly as the bright garments returned from the laundry a most peculiar and unpleasant shade of muddy yellow. They were taunted by the white controls, and wore them only under strict orders from the officers. It became a disciplinary problem. The soldiers claimed the despised articles retained the heat and the humidity, and asserted they could detect no great improvement in their health; when the year was over the ragged remains of the orange-red underwear quietly disappeared.

In spite of the failure of this great experiment, studies in acclimatization continued. Professor Aron of the Medical School determined that, whereas a Filipino had sweat glands evenly distributed all over his body, those of a person from a temperate zone climate were largely limited to forehead, armpits, back and groin. He observed, however, that after two years' residence, the sweat glands of the soldiers had increased tremendously.

In the effort to decide whether the light rays or the heat rays were responsible for sunstroke, Professor Aron found that monkeys which died when exposed to the sun were unharmed if an electric fan were blown upon them. It seems likely the heat and still air and not the light rays cause the damage.

Health in the tropics is largely a matter of observing simple hygienic rules rather than of climate. The physiological machinery of the body is so adjusted that great variations of atmospheric temperature can be supported without detriment. Indeed, it is very rare that temperature acts directly as a pathogenic factor. The white man's chances of contracting disease are actually less in the Philippines than in the United States.

In the white man and in the brown man alike, everywhere and among all peoples, the spectacular diseases are usually of specific origin, that is, they are almost always due to specific germs.

The germs of many diseases are true parasites, and, to retain their existence, they must pass from host to host. If, during this passage, the temperature of the transmitting medium be too high or too low, the germ dies or ceases to be infective. In this way may be explained the absence from the tropics of a class of infectious diseases represented by scarlet fever, measles, and diphtheria.

The transmission of some other diseases from one human being to another requires the agency of a third or entirely different animal. If this animal is found only in the tropics, the disease will, of course, be confined to the tropics, and may be accurately called a tropical disease.

Most of the more serious diseases in the tropics can be avoided by the observance of a few simple little rules. Anyone who follows these faithfully will be practically sure to remain well. Among these, the first and foremost is never to drink any water that has not been boiled or otherwise sterilized. It may be pure, but the chances are against it. Another, is never to eat raw, any low-growing garden truck, such as lettuce or cabbage, because they may, in spite of laws against it, be fertilized with human excreta. I am certain that at least a third of the people who violate these two laws sooner or later have amoebic dysentery or some other form of intestinal parasite.

The Philippines were a huge laboratory in which my collaborators and I could work out an ideal program. Often in emergencies this would have to be dropped, and months might elapse before we could return to it, but in the end, in my opinion, we had the most complete set of sanitary laws and as good enforcement as any country ever had. In the course of these years we met the chief enemies of man in the tropics, and fought and conquered many of them by simple prophylaxis. The goal of saving fifty thousand lives a year was so soon attained that I realized it should have been set at one hundred thousand.

When I returned to New York the medical profession gave me a dinner. The chairman, Dr. Abraham Jacoby, made many pleasant remarks, most of them dealing with my bravery in facing the pestilential diseases of the tropics, and congratulating me on being safely back in New York. As he portrayed the perils I had faced, I could see on the countenances of those present evidence of sincere sympathy for one who they believed had been exiled by official duty to a service of affliction and danger in a foreign, God-forsaken land.

I thanked Dr. Jacoby for his kindly words. "But in reality," I said, "I come back to the United States in fear and trembling. The diseases of the tropics which sound so terrifying here we know how to prevent. But even among you I see joints gnarled by rheumatism. I read every day of deaths from pneumonia, scarlet fever, and other diseases which practically never cast their shadows over the happy homes of the

Philippines. We know the prophylaxis for cholera and dysentery, the mode of transmitting malaria, the causes of plague and typhus, and the reasons for beriberi. We run practically no danger of contracting them. But there is no prophylaxis against pneumonia or rheumatism. Do not, therefore, condole with me. I assure you I consider you, who live among dangers that you know not how to control, the real heroes."

CHAPTER 7.   THE BLACK DEATH

"The houses were filled with dead bodies and the streets with funerals; neither age nor sex was exempt; slaves and plebeians were suddenly taken off amidst the lamentations of their wives and children, who, while they assisted the sick and mourned the dead, were seized with the disease and, perishing, were burned on the same funeral pyre. To the knights and senators the disease was less mortal though these also suffered in the common calamity."

SUCH is the account of the pestilence which struck Imperial Rome and which, during the ensuing centuries, was repeated again and again. In the Second Century A. D., according to Herodian, the Emperor retired to Laurentium because it was considered the fragrance of the laurels acted as an antidote against the contagion. The people in the city also, by the advice of physicians, filled their noses and ears with sweet ointments and perfumes. Nevertheless, nothing which they could do for themselves saved them from the deadly attack of the bubonic plague.

In the Fourteenth Century the scourge appeared in the East, spread rapidly to Asia Minor, thence to Northern Africa, and followed the trade routes into Europe. By the spring of 1348 it had entered Italy by way of Genoa, and soon had gripped the entire peninsula. Three-quarters of the population of Siena died; seven-tenths that of Pisa. Petrarch, who saw with his own eyes the Black Death at work in Florence, said, "We go out of doors, walk through street after street, and find them full of dead and dying, and when we get home again

79

we find no live thing within the house, all having perished in the brief interval of our absence."

Perhaps best of all contemporary descriptions of the Black Death is that by Petrarch's friend Boccaccio, which forms the introduction to his *Decameron.*

"There appeared certain tumors in the groin, or under the armpits, some as big as a small apple, others as an egg; and afterwards purple spots in most parts of the body; in some cases large and but few in number, in others less and more numerous, both sorts the usual messengers of death. . . . And the disease, by being communicated from the sick to the well, seemed daily to get ahead, and to rage the more, as fire will do by lying on fresh combustibles. Nor was it given by conversing with only, or coming near the sick, but even by touching their clothes, or anything that they had before touched. . . . These accidents . . . occasioned various fears and devices amongst those people that survived, all tending to the same uncharitable and cruel end; which was to avoid the sick, and everything that had been near them; expecting by that means to save themselves. . . . What numbers of both sexes in the prime and vigor of youth, whom in the morning neither Galen, Hippocrates, nor Aesculapius himself, but would have declared in perfect health, after dining heartily with their friends here, have supped with their departed friends in the other world!"

The Black Death took the Channel in its stride and wreaked such havoc in England that the dead were heaped into trenches, Parliament was suspended, and those who could flee the crowded cities did so. The Scots in derision dubbed it the "foul death" of the English, before it leaped their borders and wiped out one-third of them.

During this one year between a quarter and a half of the population of Europe died. An economic and social revolution which proved one of the great turning points in the history of the world followed in the wake of the plague.

The nature of mankind under extreme terror leads him to excesses. The convenient Jews were accused of poisoning the air and the wells. Some individuals considered that, since life was so uncertain, they were entitled to enjoy all license. Others believed that their only hope lay in placating an angry God. The sect of the Flagellants revived. In their despair the people regarded all efforts to stop the progress of the disease as sacrilege. The Duke of Reggio wisely ordered the isolation of the stricken, but "all were more grieved and terrified by this edict than by the fear of the pestilence which, when God permits it, cannot be arrested." During the next three hundred years the plague returned periodically. It reached its climax in England in 1665 when, after carrying off seventy thousand in London alone, approximately sixteen percent of the population, it spread South and East. Pepys faithfully recorded its onset in his diary for June 7th.

"I did in Drury Lane see two or three houses marked with a red cross upon the doors, and 'Lord have Mercy upon Us' writ there, which was a sad sight to me, being the first of the kind that, to my remembrance, I ever saw. It put me into an ill conception of myself and my smell, so that I was forced to buy some roll tobacco to smell and to chaw, which took away the apprehension."

The following year came the Great Fire of London, after which the plague disappeared from England, and shortly from Europe. But it remained endemic in the East.

Toward the end of the Nineteenth Century there was a recrudescence of plague. Hongkong, which had become the second largest port in the world, was the chief exporting point. The British, who were traders first and foremost, had shut their eyes to the need for sanitary control; consequently in the early days, few precautions were observed. From Hongkong the plague girdled the Pacific and, on its way, swept into the Philippines.

The human mind for centuries had been so handicapped by its ignorance of bacteriology that any hope of successful warfare against the plague was vain. But in the eighties some knowledge of microscopic life began to be acquired by the scientific world. The spread of the plague focused attention on Hongkong and there, in 1894, the bacillus pestis was isolated by Alexandre Yersin, the pupil of Pasteur, and Shibasaburo Kitasato, the pupil of Koch, working independently. This discovery marked the first great advance in the history of the conquest of the disease.

The association of rats with plague is so obvious that it was noted long before it could be proved. After the discovery of the bacillus it was a simple matter to identify the epizootic among rats as identical with the epidemic among men, and the close relation of the two was shown to be almost invariable. The problem was how to link them together.

There was a hypothesis, conceived by P. L. Simond of Spain, that plague was conveyed by fleas. He had no supporting proof for his theory; he merely imagined this was the way it happened. His claim was tested by the First Indian Plague Commission which, after investigation, announced that no connection could be found between the flea and the plague.

In the course of my work in Egypt, I had formulated certain theories of my own about plague, and could not reconcile them to the findings of the Commission. The subject had been extensively discussed at the Cairo Medical Congress in 1902. On my way thence to the Philippines I met Captain W. Glen Liston of the Indian Medical Service, and made the trip to India in company with him. He also was dissatisfied with the conclusions of the Plague Commission. As we sweltered in the Red Sea heat, we would lie on deck until late hours, and as we crossed the Indian Ocean pace up and down, discussing the pros and cons of plague theories. When we reached India, Liston enthusiastically took me to inspect the flood of plague cases coming into the hospitals.

One of the most interesting developments in India at the time was the plague vaccine developed by Professor W. M. Haffkine at Bombay. The religious tenet of the Hindus that the cow was sacred had interfered with his use of the beef broth, essential for culturing plague bacilli. He had surmounted this difficulty and had produced a vaccine which aroused the immunity forces of the individual into whom it was injected, though the immunity conveyed was relatively short. It was proving particularly useful for those compelled to work in plague stricken areas.

But while I was there, Professor Haffkine was in the midst of a great battle for his reputation. Part of his process had been to treat his culture with carbolic acid, which killed the bacilli but left the antitoxin. In the effort to fill a quantity demand from the Punjab, the acid was omitted. By an unfortunate accident tetanus germs were somehow included in a particular bottle and all inoculated from it died. However, after prolonged investigation by a special Commission, the Haffkine Laboratory was exonerated of all blame and he was reemployed by the Indian government.

Before Liston and I separated, we agreed to continue plague research, he in Bombay, and I in Manila. I established a laboratory at Mariveles where one of my assistants, Dr. H. S. Stansfield, began research on the flea transmission theory.

Every year came new evidence that fleas and rats were closely connected with the plague in human beings. Liston was surprised to find an outbreak of plague among guinea pigs at Bombay, and an examination showed they were infested with rat fleas. Guinea pigs do not usually harbor fleas, but dead rats were found in the vicinity. By keeping up a constant agitation Liston finally secured the appointment of a second Indian Plague Commission of which he became a member. In 1907 the Commission was able to announce that fleas definitely were the conveyors of plague, and proved its case to an incredulous world with a simple experiment. Cages containing rats were hung at different heights with plague fleas hopping about below. The rats which dangled enticingly above the fleas' four inch high jump record did not catch plague; the unfortunate ones which hung lower sickened and died.

In all my study of the rat I never was able to solve the enigma of his life's ending. It would seem he transported himself bodily to his heavenly granary. The statistics are incontrovertible. It is conservatively estimated that in every city of the world there is one rat for each two persons. I once made a determined effort to locate the tomb of the rat in Manila, which, at the time, had a population of three hundred thousand. Estimating the average life of a rat even at five years, there should have been a mortality from natural causes of twenty-five hundred rats a month.

The rat catcher gangs of over three hundred men seldom found a dead rat that had not died of poison placed for it, or from some other readily explainable cause. My curiosity was aroused; I stationed inspectors at the public crematories in which was incinerated the daily collection of all garbage, refuse, and street sweepings. They personally examined the contents of each container. Only one dead rat was discovered in the course of a month.

If dead rats had been found by householders they would automatically have been placed in the refuse cans or left lying on the streets. They would not have been burned, because stoves were unknown, and the small primitive fires of bamboo sticks would not have been likely to have consumed the carcasses entirely.

It was possible, of course, that a certain percentage of the rats had died in inaccessible places. But owing to the rapid decomposition in a tropical climate, the odors which would have arisen would soon have attracted attention; comparatively few nuisances of this kind were reported.

The rats were barred by fine gratings from access to the sewers. The generally swampy nature of the ground prevented burrowing, and the few spots where holes could not be flooded, we had sealed with concrete.

It was suggested that the dead rats were eaten by their brethren, but carcasses or even skeletons of partly eaten rats were not encountered. The riddle of the rat's last resting place still awaits its Oedipus.

With the links of plague transmission joined, research made rapid progress. Any rat may harbor the plague flea, but the chief danger comes from the long-tailed, blackish mus rattus, who, an unbidden guest, makes man's home and food his own. The reddish-gray short-tailed mus norwegicus is a fiercer fighter and seeks his shelter away from man.

The plague-stricken rat, like the human, has fever and septicemia. He moves very slowly. He shows no fear of human beings, but looks up at them without shying or running away. He may sometimes recover, and, after long years of exposure to plague, may even develop a certain immunity. In India this is greatest in places which in the past have suffered most severely. At Bombay, for example, local rats cannot be used for experimentation, but must be obtained from Madras, where the disease has never struck.

Out of the multitudinous varieties of fleas the principal culprit was proved to be the Pulex cheopis. Later research showed that on rare occasions others, such as the astia, might convey plague. But unless the rat acts as host to more than four fleas, there is little danger.

The flea has a hollow tube, called the epipharynx. With this it pierces the skin, and then with its jaws enlarges and lacerates the hole. It pumps saliva down its epipharynx into the wound, which rapidly becomes congested. The blood that collects is sucked up through the hypopharynx, or prolongation of the lip.

The oesophagus of many types of flea has a valve which retains the blood once it is swallowed, but in the cheopis and astia the apparatus is lacking, and an overdose frequently causes regurgitation. If the flea is infected, the fluid will contain plague bacilli. As many as five thousand may be lodged in the body of one flea.

When the rat sickens and dies his boarders leave him and hide in a crack or a pinch of dust. They may survive for two months, growing ever more hungry, and, if no rat appears, rather than starve, they will content themselves with a meal from a human or any other animal. The laboring class in tropical countries customarily goes barefooted and barelegged to the knee. This gives the flea the advantage.

When man is bitten, he scratches, inflames the wound, and makes a way for the plague bacilli to enter more easily. These multiply with appalling rapidity. Although the incubation period may last as long as seven days, plague normally appears within forty-eight hours. The toxin affects first the lymphatic system. One of the functions of the lymph glands is to repel invading poisons, but because they are unable to cope with the plague bacilli, the buboes, or glandular swellings, the sight of which had aroused such terror in the ancients, are formed, usually in the groin, more rarely in the armpit. After this system of defense has broken down, the whole body is invaded. Delirium shortly sets in, vital organs are poisoned, and the patient ordinarily dies between the third and fifth day.

In the septicemic type of plague, so much and so powerful a toxin is liberated that the body defenses are overwhelmed before nature's normal protections can become effective. These are brushed aside, and therefore no bubo appears. In most epidemics the mortality is over ninety percent, and no treatment has been found of much avail.

Only in pneumonic plague is the disease transmitted directly from man to man. The bacilli reach the lungs, and the fine spray from the coughing is charged with the deadly microbes so that those who breathe them are infected. The serum exudate in the lungs is so great that the victim is literally drowned. Death comes with shocking suddenness. None survives.

The Philippines were always threatened with plague. Once when the steamer *Zafiro* arrived in Manila from Hongkong the routine medical inspection was made, and no illness detected. But twenty-four hours later a Chinese member of the crew who had apparently been in excellent health the night before was found dead in his bunk of pneumonic plague.

Two days later the *Loonsang* arrived in the harbor, also from Hongkong, with a dead Chinese on board. While hauling spiritedly on a rope, he had toppled over in an apparent faint, and had died in the course of a few hours. He also had had pneumonic plague.

Chinese reports claim that tarbagans and marmots, as well as rats, are subject to plague in septicemic form. But when their fleas bite man, he contracts pneumonic plague. Every year Chinese laborers migrate to Manchuria in vast numbers. There they live huddled in dirty sheds. If only one laborer is infected with the pneumonic type, he may, by coughing, transmit the disease to a crowded trainload returning at the end of the harvest, and, as the coolies scatter to their homes, plague will spread like wildfire, sometimes wiping out whole districts. The coolies stop overnight, sleeping in crowded little shanties along the way, where they become infected, and travel on the next day, starting new foci of infection all along the route. Whenever they are segregated, or even made to wear gauze masks, the disease declines rapidly.

The plague had made its appearance in Manila in December, 1899. The measures adopted against it then were very strict and in full accord with the status of current medical knowledge. The sick were sent to the hospital, and the dead taken in charge by the Army Board of Health. The houses and their contents were completely renovated and disinfected. Partitions and cubicles were torn down, court yards opened up, and obstructions to sunlight removed. Circular letters were issued, giving the salient points of plague diagnosis, theories of transmission, and the course to be pursued when a suspected or genuine case had occurred in a locality. All vessels arriving during the epidemic were disinfected. Although it was not known at that time that the rat flea was the communicating agent for the plague, many of the measures taken had resulted in the destruction of the rats which carried the fleas.

Later, anti-rat measures were invoked and the Board of Health had spent $350,000 in the effort to wipe out all the rats of the city. But rats are difficult to exterminate because they breed so rapidly. Three to five times a year, after a gestation period of only twenty-one days, the female brings forth from six to sixteen young, and these in turn produce offspring when they are less than three months old. Thus a single pair in one year might be responsible for hundreds of descendants. At the end of five years when I took charge the rat population of Manila was apparently as plentiful as ever, and plague was still present.

At one time a bounty of five centavos was paid for each rodent whose tail was offered in evidence of death. But difficulties soon arose. Certain enterprising inhabitants of Manila began breeding rats. The outlay was negligible and the profits high; a tail was a tail, whether from a baby or a grandfather. The bounty system had to be stopped.

Experimentation showed that spring traps were seven times as efficacious as the cage type. We also spent much time and thought on the subject of poisons. Our greatest success came from mixing cheap and tasteless white arsenic with rice, which was the natural diet of rats in the Philippines. Every rice grain was impregnated with enough poison to kill one rat. But the rat was apparently able, in some mysterious fashion, to warn his brethren of danger. After only a short time the rats would refuse the poisoned tidbits, although their savor was unaffected by any detectible taint. We had to provide meals varied with such foodstuffs as fish and tomatoes.

To catch the rats was easy enough, but other factors complicated the campaign. It was always possible that a child might unsuspectingly swallow a portion of the poisoned bait. For the greater good we had to take this risk, but we used to provide for the contingency. When an epidemic broke out and intensive methods had to be used, antidote stations were located every few blocks so that, in case of a casualty, sesquioxide of iron could be administered immediately. As we had feared, a few children did succumb to the temptation of the rice, but due to our precautions no fatalities resulted.

Constant guard had to be kept to see that plague did not slip through our defenses. Manila was within a few days' steaming distance of badly-infected foreign ports. Passengers, crews, rodents, and vermin all might arrive well within the incubation period of the disease. Plague was detected from time to time upon incoming vessels, but such infections were invariably intercepted at quarantine. As a preventive routine measure, all ships which had not touched at plague ports were fumigated with sulphur at not greater than six month intervals.

We had big sulphur furnaces at the quarantine station, and Dutch ovens to take on board where we could not run the hose. The sulphur killed everything it reached, but, as a rule, it did not dispose of more than eighty percent of a ship's rat population.

Sometimes unwittingly we helped to smoke out other travelers, mostly Chinese who were always trying to smuggle into the Philippines. On one occasion, after the customs officers had examined a boat from stem to stern, my men started fumigation. Hardly had they battened down the hatches and turned the sulphur pots loose when suddenly there came a rap-rap. As soon as we could locate the sound, the hatch was opened, and three Chinese stumbled into the fresh air, spitting, "pfft, pfft, pfft," as they came. By signs we asked them, "Any more?" They shook their heads.

Again the hatches were battened down; a few moments later came another knocking. In front of our astonished eyes, forty coughing coolies, one after another, emerged with streaming eyes through a thick veil of billowing yellow smoke.

For the third time the hold was sealed. But in no more than a few moments the knocking began again. The remaining hardy souls in the coal bunkers who had thought they could stick it out tumbled gasping and nearly suffocated on to the deck.

The ship had carried one hundred and two stowaways.

Hydrocyanic gas, which is now employed instead of sulphur, is far more effective, but also more dangerous to handle. When the technique of applying it is not followed, an occasional fatality results, although we were fortunate enough in the Philippines never to have this happen. The customary routine was to fumigate a ship for several hours, and then expose everything to fresh air. But some drunken sailor would disregard instructions, find his bunk, and turn in; enough gas would still remain in the mattress to kill him. To avoid such casualties, ships are now completely ventilated with air jets before anyone is allowed on board.

Our primary concern in the Philippines was to keep rats from landing. Under exceptional circumstances rats will swim. I have seen them scuttle down the anchor chain of one ship and paddle furiously over to that of another. Vessels were made to remain at least six feet from the pier, special iron ratguards were placed on all lines leading to shore, and the gangplanks lifted at night.

As a final precaution, we built in Manila the first ratproof wharves. They were of concrete throughout so that no rat could gnaw his way through, and so flashed with steel sheathing underneath that the rat could not find a foothold. Clever as he is, he has never yet contrived a method of walking upside down on smooth metal.

Rats are noted travelers though their names never appear on the passenger list. For centuries their presence on ships was taken for granted. No one even inquired into the reasons therefor. When it finally became apparent that these rats were a menace to every port where cheopis fleas existed, all efforts were directed at clearing them out of ships and preventing others from entering. Over thirty countries joined in an international agreement to this end.

As I learned in my Philippines experience, the most effective way to deal with any pest is to interfere with its natural breeding places. A rat has to have a protected home and an adequate food supply. If he is not afforded harborage near man, his fleas are less likely to reach man. Thus the danger from plague can best be reduced by building him out.

The rat is expensive to get rid of, but even more expensive to maintain. The rats of New York cost the residents more than ten million dollars annually for meals. Crop destruction is also enormous, so that both urban and rural dwellers suffer loss. The world rat bill amounts to staggering sums. At least a cent a day must be expended to feed a rat on shore, and twice that on ships where the garbage is dumped overboard and where he must live on clean food. On shipboard also, there is the additional expense of fumigating twice a year. Almost fifty thousand dollars used to be spent on the *Mauretania* to keep her free of rats for twelve months.

In 1924 the United States Public Health Service placed a technical assistant on the *Leviathan,* and during a year's study of the rat problem he found fifty-three structural defects which were responsible for rat harborage. The ship was then ratproofed; thereafter no rats haunted the store rooms or lurked around the pipes. The British, the Germans, and the Dutch followed the American lead. Only the French, reluctant to spend money on new schemes, held out. But even they were convinced when the *Lafayette* had to be fumigated after her maiden voyage because of the many rats which had boarded her while she was on the ways.

The *Normandie* was ratproofed.

Building the rat out of Manila was a far more difficult undertaking, requiring the reconstruction of the city, and obviously was a matter of years. We began by having a municipal ordinance passed that all new houses or major repairs had to be constructed according to plans which would make it impossible for rats to find shelter. No hollow walls, partitions, floors, or structural parts were allowed. The foundation had to be of concrete, brick, stone, or mortar, extending three feet above the ground and several below it.

The house plan of the wild mountain tribe of the Ifugaos served in part as models for civilized Manila. The Ifugaos use their homes as granaries, and an economic rather than a sanitary motive had produced an efficient method of protection. Their thatched houses stood on posts, each of which was fashioned with a shoulder large enough to prevent the rat from creeping around it. It cost only a small sum to protect the nipa huts of Manila similarly by placing flashing along the sides of the building.

Rats are very fond of burrowing into the hollow ends of bamboo poles, out of which the floors of nipa huts are almost universally made. They did not gnaw through the smooth, hard, resistant surface, but could and did enter the open ends, biting their way through the joints until they found safe shelter. Such floors we ratproofed by cementing the ends of the bamboo poles. If the rat happened to be inside at the time, it was so much the worse for him. The bamboo fences were treated in the same way.

Most of the objections to ratproofing in Manila came from the Chinese, who controlled the mercantile trade and owned most of the rat-infested bodegas. The adobe walls of these warehouses were often several feet thick and contained rat burrows. Under the board floors the earth was honeycombed with runs. However, opposition began to lessen as soon as the caretakers of premises began to report unwonted freedom from rats and it became apparent that absence of rats not only meant immunity from plague but was also of great economic value.

Our problems in the Philippines were simple compared with the situation in India, where over a million persons were dying annually of plague. The Hindus would take no life. No rat could be killed in India; any live thing might contain the soul of an ancestor. Consequently, they stubbornly opposed the killing of rats. One method of driving out rats and at the same time compromising with religious sentiment was to lift off the roofs of the houses and let the sun in, so that the rats, who abhor light and crave privacy, would retire to some darker refuge. In other cases, a self-curing method was used. When plague appeared in a native village, the inhabitants were all moved out into the fields under temporary canvas shelters. At the end of six months the rats had moved out, and the townspeople moved in again.

Ratproofing was a preventive measure. An epidemic called for instant and concerted action. Plague slipped by the defenses in Manila, in 1905, and again in 1912. On the latter occasion we were prepared. One morning reports came in that plague had broken out in several widely separated districts of the city. But the flying squads of rat catchers, clad in flea-proof clothing, and with powdered naphthalene or kerosene on neck, wrists, and ankles, at once started as though to a fire.

Any block in which the disease occurred was regarded as infected. Radiating lines, usually five in number, were prolonged like the spokes of a wheel to the outskirts of the city. Plague rats were seldom found more than a few blocks away, but rats all along the lines were caught and examined. The furthermost points at which infected animals were detected were then connected with lines running from spoke to spoke, and the space enclosed was regarded as the area of infection. Instead of throwing a force of rat catchers into the house where the case of plague had occurred, which would have scattered the scurrying menace in all directions, the entire force of a hundred and fifty men was concentrated along the border of the infected section.

As the rat catchers closed in, the blocks were thrown out of commission. Every house was gone through in systematic fashion, starting at the top and moving down. Every box, barrel, or receptacle which might harbor a rat was opened. All dirt, filth, and straw in the yard was moved and burned. Woodpiles, which were favorite harboring places for rats, were invariably taken down and re-piled well above the ground and away from any wall, so that dogs and cats might keep the rodents out of them in the future. Rat nests, when found, were sprayed with insecticide.

When live rats were encountered, these were killed at once. Some of the rat catching gang had fox terriers, imported especially from Australia for their lightning-like swiftness. Others had trained ferrets which would come to their masters' call like dogs, and were even more effective. The rat stood no show. You could hear the crack as the ferret's sharp teeth severed the spinal column. He never shook the rat as the terriers did, and never attempted to eat him. He was a killer, pure and simple.

The Filipinos also grew unbelievably skilled in catching rats with their hands. As the animal would start to run from its hiding place, a man would grab it, and, before it could bite, would stun it against the wall and finish it off with a club.

Always as the rat catchers closed in, the ratproofers followed in their tracks, making it certain that the area would not be reinfected. One section after another was treated in this way. Once weekly thereafter, rats were caught in previously infested sections, and at other places which were known to be insanitary.

By the practical application of this system plague was twice wiped out of Manila, the only large city until recent years where an imported infection has been thus completely eradicated.

THE BLACK DEATH

In the Philippines, as elsewhere in the East, Europeans and Americans who lived in more cleanly surroundings were rarely attacked by plague. But there was one outstanding exception. One day William Crozier, editor of the *Manila Daily Bulletin,* was taken violently ill, and forty-eight hours later died at the San Lazaro Hospital. While the sanitary squad was carrying out the insecticidal and other anti-plague measures in his office, an inspector pulled the upper drawer of his desk out to the end. Live fleas were seen hopping around, and in the very back lay the body of a mummified rat. A hole in the rear of the drawer showed the manner of its entrance. After the rat had died its fleas had deserted it. Crozier, who was presumably working in his shirt sleeves because of the heat, must have reached into the drawer and been bitten by one of these fleas. We found a wound on his arm later. Plague bacilli were recovered from the fleas and the rat in the drawer.

Plague remained of vital interest to me long after I had left the Philippines. The Rockefeller Foundation, generously recognizing this, was always glad to make my services available to any government which requested aid in dealing with the disease.

One of my visits to Ceylon happened to coincide with a bad outbreak at Kandy. People in Ceylon were generally accustomed to having natives die horribly of plague, but when members of the nice clean English club also began to die horribly, consternation reigned. Some had already died, many more would die, and the instant the news became public, the tourists, on whom the material prosperity of Kandy largely depended, would seek a safer playground.

Immediately upon my arrival at Colombo, I was called in as a consultant. I repaired to Kandy and went over the ground with the plague expert of the Health Department. We spent hours poking about in native houses and dirty narrow alleys. I could point to nothing which had not been done. Sometimes, however, the obvious is overlooked. A large English store on the main street backed upon the plague area. At the end of a long day, I asked, "Have you investigated that?"

"No," my colleague explained. "That is a European store which is kept perfectly clean. If there had been any sick rats around, they would have been noticed."

93

"I'd like to go over it just the same," I said.

Accordingly, he introduced me to the manager. I examined the first and second stories without finding any suspicious indications. Then I asked, "What else do you sell?"

"We have a feed department in the basement," he answered.

No further information was needed. As soon as he had taken me downstairs, I singled out the piles of baled hay and straw. "We ought to take those down," I suggested.

Inside were dead and dying rats by the dozen. Some traveler rat or flea, plague-stricken, had entered with a grain shipment and infected the local rodents. The English club had been well within the radius of the infection.

Stamping out the focus stopped the plague in Kandy.

I really enjoyed the detective work often involved in completing the deadly triangle of the rat, the flea, the man. It was extraordinary but true that incredulity as to the relationship still persisted. Only a few years ago, Sir Herbert Samuel, governor of the Palestine Mandate, sent word to me that plague had broken out and that he desired advice. On my arrival, he presented his particular problem. "Our health service says it will take a half million dollars to get the plague under control. That's an enormous sum for a small government to spend. Before embarking on this program, we'd like an outside opinion, although, of course, we'll spend the money if it's necessary."

"I'll talk it over with your Health Officer," I said.

This official showed no resentment at what might have been regarded as interference with his duties on my part; instead, he gave me a hearty welcome. However, he said he did not agree with my published report that dead rats were always associated with plague. No rats had been found during the present outbreak, and, therefore, he was forced to conclude that my deductions must be wrong.

"Where is the plague center?" I asked.

"Jaffa."

"Could we go there?"

"Certainly," he agreed.

Accordingly, he conducted my young North Carolinian assistant, Dr. W. P. Jacocks, and myself to one house in Jaffa where seventeen people had just died of plague, but where nobody had seen a dead rat.

"Where did the first person die?" I asked.

I was shown a bed against a wall in a downstairs room.

"I'd like to have a hammer," I said.

I began to tap the walls, listening carefully to the sound. As I was working my way towards the large crack which I had noted above the bed, the Health Officer interrupted me.

"You're evidently not familiar with house construction methods here. There are no hollow walls."

"I'm probably a damn fool," I replied, "but, if you don't mind, I'd like to satisfy my own curiosity."

He made no further objection, and I continued tapping until I reached the crack, where the wall gave forth an unmistakably hollow sound.

"Will you have a man dig into the wall just here?" I asked.

In a few moments the workmen had uncovered an open shaft, and in the shaft was a small shelf on which lay a dead rat. "The flea came through the crack," I explained.

"You seem to be right," the Health Officer admitted, "but how would you account for this one?" and he led me upstairs to a bed set squarely in the middle of a room.

I glanced at the ceiling and located another crack. "If you'll send a man to the attic, you'll find a dead rat just about there," I said, pointing to a particular spot above the bed.

The corpus delicti was there.

I glanced at Dr. Jacocks, but instead of the expression of satisfaction I expected, I saw that his face was as white as his linen suit. I was startled. "What's the matter with you? Are you ill?"

"Look at me!" he shouted.

"What is the matter?"

"Look!"

To my utter horror he was literally covered with fleas. They were crawling all over him, black spots against his white clothes. Everybody rushed to pluck them off, and we soon had them in bottles which were hurried to the hospital laboratory. After an hour of great anxiety, we received word that they had been identified as merely dog fleas.

When we had recovered from our fright, we returned to the search for the focus of plague infection. Two dead rats did not explain the origin of the epidemic.

The house we had just examined was one removed from the corner, around which was a blacksmith shop. We repaired thither. I engaged the owner in conversation and casually inquired, "Do you ever see any rats around here?"

"Oh, yes," he replied. "Lot's of 'em. But they're the funniest rats I ever saw. They come out of that hole over there and just stand. They don't seem to be afraid or run away, and all we have to do is hit 'em with a hammer and throw 'em in the fire."

"That's very interesting," I commented. "Where does that door lead?".

"Into a vacant lot."

I promptly followed it through and behind the high wall enclosure found from three to four feet of débris remaining from the wreckage of a house. I procured some Arab laborers at once. Underneath the rubbish they came upon a wooden floor, ripped it up, and uncovered hundreds of dead rats.

But my work was not yet done; these mute bodies offered no explanation of the tragedy which had overtaken them.

I scouted further, and came upon a grain store across the street. Such an establishment is always suspect, because the mus rattus is an epicure, and loves best the food which humans eat. I learned that this store had been importing rice from Rangoon, one of the plague centers of the world. Since vessels there were loaded from lighters coming direct from the heavily rat-infested godowns, or warehouses, it was safe to assume that plague rats, or fleas, had been unwittingly imported, and had brought the infection to Jaffa.

The final step was to have specimen rats collected from towns and villages in Palestine. The orders were sent out for this to be done.

I was suddenly awakened two nights later by the jangling of the telephone bell. "Dr. Jacocks is very ill," I was told. While I was hurriedly pulling on my clothes, I kept thinking, "There must have been some cheopis fleas that were missed." In the full realization that it was I who had been responsible for taking him to the plague house, I spent some harassed moments before arriving at his bedside.

To my intense relief, the dread triangle was incomplete, and he was in no mortal danger. His illness was malaria with chills and fever contracted in his own Southland.

Meanwhile the fleas of Palestine were coming to the laboratory. Out of them all only the rats of Jaffa and Haifa proved to be infested with the cheopis variety, and the plague was cleared out of Palestine for a few thousand dollars.

A far greater amount has been expended in the effort to eradicate the plague menace in this country, gradually spreading eastward from California, where it had landed in 1900. It is reasonable to believe that, if proper measures had been taken, the disease could have been wiped out at that time. The Federal government, which had been steadily assuming more and more responsibility for the entrance of dangerous communicable diseases into this country, sent Dr. J. J. Kinyoun there to take charge. But the people of California so bitterly resented the suggestion that bubonic plague might be present in their midst that he was publicly assaulted and even spat upon in the theatre.

At first the disease was confined to Chinatown, where Dr. Kinyoun asserted plague-infected persons were actually found. When the California authorities denied this, a plague commission was appointed to go to California, headed by Dr. Simon Flexner, then Professor of Pathology at the University of Pennsylvania. The Commission found unmistakable evidence of the bacillus pestis among the Chinese, but California was still unconvinced, and the press was almost unanimous in denying it.

Then the Federal government delivered an ultimatum to California: "You are a sovereign state. You may do as you please within your borders, but if you do not take steps to control this vital danger, we will establish a quarantine entirely around you, and every person and every piece of goods crossing your state line will have to go through this quarantine."

Only under this duress did California finally surrender.

But the capitulation came too late. The rats had infected the ground squirrels. In spite of the expenditure of millions of dollars, these infected ground squirrels have not been eradicated. They do not live near human habitations as do rats. Carbon bisulphide, poisoned fruit and grain, and sharpshooters have not sufficed for their extinction. Always some get away to infect others. In the fall of 1919 fourteen cases of pneumonic plague occurred in Oakland, and all but one of these died. In the epidemic at Los Angeles of October, 1924, thirty died out of thirty-two cases.

Even now there is an occasional case of plague in California. The ground squirrel infection has extended over the Coast Range, which barred the way for a long time, and has recently crossed the Rockies. In 1935, plague-infected squirrels were found in Nebraska. Plague will probably never flourish in this country, but its prevention may become exceedingly costly. The great hazard lies in the possibility of the squirrel, which avoids the presence of man, transmitting his fleas to the rat, which lives with man. This danger might have been avoided had the people of California been reasonable in 1900.

It is now beginning to appear that if plague has been endemic for thirty years in a community, it tends to vanish by itself. I noted this first in Basra, and later in Canton, Hongkong, and Bombay. In Canton the disappearance was certainly not due to direct prophylactic measures, because none was taken. At Hongkong, on the other hand, by 1910 a housewifely sanitary force had cleaned and dusted the whole town twice a year; every piece of furniture had been set on the street while the fumigation, cleansing, and airing was proceeding. But the plague mortality in slovenly Canton was no higher than in tidy Hongkong.

Bubonic plague, a name synonymous with disaster to the Ancient and Mediaeval World, need not exist in the Modern. This is a great human achievement. The scourge had seemed to attack blindly and without reason; neither rich nor poor, high nor low, old nor young, knew who might be the next victim.

People no longer need wring their hands in futile terror and despair at the appearance of plague. The mystery of its cause has now been solved by the laboratory worker; the link in the chain of transmission has now been broken by the prophylaxis of the watchful and resolute sanitarian. If plague does creep by the outer defenses, it can still be dealt with swiftly and with certainty. Finally, the health officer, who stands sentry at the port, knows when it is safe from any attack. Flea surveys are now made to show what species are present among the denizens of the rat underworld. A port may be considered non-infectible when the flea population of the average rat contains no more than one cheopis.

New York is a safe port. The New Yorker may seek his Sabine Farm as a pleasant refuge; he need never be driven there by the blind panic which possessed the citizens of Florence when the Black Death had stormed their walls and taken their city in "a sad and wonderful manner." But the citizens of San Francisco, Mobile, and New Orleans must still exercise vigilance if they wish to sleep in peace.

CHAPTER 8. EAT, DRINK, AND BE MERRY

I HAVE been walking along a street in Manila, and ahead of me have seen a man, as though jerked by some inexorable force, leap into the air, and then fall back sprawling on the ground. He would be dead before I could reach him.

But although the toxin of cholera, like strychnine, sometimes stops the heartbeat ·with the swiftness of lightning, it is not always so merciful. More often into the few days of its fearful course is compressed an infinity of suffering. The victim of cholera is a terrible object. A cold, clammy sweat is upon him, his skin shrinks and grows dark grey from the terrific purging. Cramps of unbelievable intensity occur in the calves of the legs and in the arms. His thirst is unquenchable. His circulation finally grows so sluggish that even cutting the veins fails to produce a flow of blood.

Little can be done for the sufferer beyond alleviating his agony. The injection of salt solution in the veins replaces some of the lost fluids and relieves the cramps. The cholera patient never loses consciousness. His face is puckered into an expression of anxiety, due as much to the draining of the fluids from his body as to terror.

I well remember one afternoon at the cholera hospital when, in the course of my rounds, I entered the ward in which eight American Negroes had been placed. Each bed had a number and, by one of those strange coincidences which become more striking because of the macabre nature of the occasion, the Negro in bed No. 1 had died first, to be followed rapidly by the inmates of beds Nos. 2, 3, 4, and

5. Beds Nos. 6, 7, and 8 were still occupied when I entered the room. Fully expecting that he would be the next to go, the Negro in No. 6 had pulled the sheet over his head to shield himself from the sight of the gruesome succession of corpses being taken from the room. I drew it aside. His eyes were at first tight shut. As he gradually opened them, I could see the whites shining in the semi-darkness of the room.

"Boss, is I daid?" he inquired anxiously.

He was fairly close to it. Death, however, had paused by his bedside. He and his two companions left the hospital on their own feet, none the worse for their harrowing experience, but with no assurance that they might not find themselves in beds Nos. 1, 2, and 3 the next time.

In all my experience in the Philippines not one medicine ever proved of any great value in the treatment of cholera. Many so-called specifics were recommended. An old doctor in far away Ohio dogmatically proclaimed that it was unnecessary for anyone to die of cholera; that our wanton disregard of his quinine cure was unjustifiable.

Because we had ourselves been vainly searching for a remedy, we had already given his treatment a trial, hoping that by some miracle it would prove beneficial. Convinced it was worthless, we had discontinued its use. When the old doctor received no satisfaction from us, he wrote President Theodore Roosevelt to the effect that the bureaucratic physicians in the Philippines were prejudiced against him. He knew his remedy would cure and we were sacrificing thousands of lives by failing to use it.

President Roosevelt, in his forthright manner, cabled us suggesting that the treatment be given a trial at once. The epidemic of 1905 was in its most virulent stage, and patients were dying in large numbers. In any event, quinine could do no harm, and the suggestion had come from the President of the United States.

The medicine was given in strict compliance with the inventor's prescription. But it failed to save the life of the first man upon whom it was tried. The second man died also. A few days later we cabled the President saying we had tried the quinine remedy on six patients, and that all of them had died. "Do you wish it continued?"

"No!" came the quick reply.

Iron bars and thick stone walls had served for centuries to protect the cloistered nuns of Santa Clara from the prying eyes of the outside world, but could not guard against the entrance of the penetrant cholera. One nun after another was stricken, until the bodies of half a dozen had been placed outside the great wooden doors. Then terror became so great that the Mother Superior appealed for help to Archbishop Harty. He advised that the rules be abrogated and that I be asked to attend. On my way to and from the Ayuntamiento I had often passed these lofty walls, but it was with a sense of dread that I stooped to enter the little door set within the larger one, and placed my feet upon the stones over which no man had walked for a hundred years or more.

The Mother Superior, of commanding presence, conducted me down the long hall, grim in its austerity, where through years of poverty the once white walls had grown darkly stained. The corridors seemed alive with restless, swishing, grey-robed figures; eyes which had long forgotten how a man appeared stared curiously from white faces. I passed the chapel, gleaming with many flickering candles, where nuns knelt silent in perpetual adoration. At last I entered the dormitory and there, with what meagre facilities science had to offer, ministered to the desperately sick nuns.

But something could be done for those as yet untouched. I turned to the overshadowing problem of seeking the way by which the disease had crept into these forbidden precincts. In the long bare inner court I found the nunnery well from which all had drunk. As so often before, in so many countries, cholera had sprung from this unguarded source.

I sterilized this death-dealing menace, explained the simple rules for avoiding cholera, and took my departure, leaving the nuns once more to their cloistered seclusion. There were no more cases.

The first suggestion of the connection of cholera with contaminated water had come in 1855 from Dr. John Snow of London. The previous year he had traced an epidemic to a pump on Broad Street. He found that only those who had drunk of this water were attacked by the disease. He ascertained that a cesspool drained into this well, and that there had been a case of cholera in the house served by the cesspool. He proved that the intestinal discharges of the sick had polluted the water supply. His classic reply to the query, "How can we stop this cholera epidemic?" was, "Remove the pump handle." Dr. Snow wrote an account of his discovery that seemed of such little interest to the publishers of his day that he was forced to print it at his own expense. Nevertheless, though recognition was late, the English people, goaded by fear, began to install uncontaminated water supplies.

In 1884 Robert Koch, often referred to as the founder of bacteriology, after having already isolated the bacillus of anthrax and of tuberculosis, discovered the cholera vibrio. Although it creates such great damage, it is subject to many inimical forces; like the rare orchid it must be nurtured in exactly the right environment. In one hour the sun can destroy it, acid kills it, drying sterilizes it, almost any other bacteria can choke it out. If it is to flourish, it must somehow or other get from one human intestine to another. In spite of these serious handicaps, the vibrio manages to find transportation, and has circumnavigated the world more than once, and always without a ticket.

Cholera has been one of the great scourges of modern times. At four different periods in the Nineteenth Century it was pandemic. In the sixties it was taking toll through large parts of the United States. Terrified England was twice swept by the disease.

Seven great epidemics since 1820 ravaged the population of the Philippines. When the deaths in Manila reached a thousand a day, not enough people could be found to bury the dead. Nightly the streets to the cemeteries were blocked. The priests, leading the religious processions of atonement, could with difficulty find a path through the calesins, carromatas, and slow carabao-drawn carts, all bearing the dead for burial.

Mediaeval theologians had taught that all illness and deformity were manifestations of divine wrath; plague, pestilence, and famine were visited upon the people for their transgressions. Where this doctrine had become powerful enough to regulate the life of the Christian world, the progress of medicine had come to an almost complete standstill. The Filipinos were still living in this mediaeval atmosphere; they were resigned to their angry God, were used to his punishments, and preferred their own ways to those of strangers.

Beyond establishing free medicine stations, the Spanish authorities had been powerless. Instead of taking those simple measures of health and sanitation which would have prevented these destroying epidemics they had bowed their heads and prayed while the death rate mounted to its inevitable peak.

When the Americans came, they were not disposed to tolerate such resignation. Because they had to protect their troops, they decided that something must be done about cholera. March 3, 1902, the attention of the Chief Quarantine Officer at Manila was called to the existence of Asiatic cholera in Canton. Five days later came news of it at Hongkong, from which large quantities of fresh vegetables were constantly being shipped to Manila. In the effort to ward off infection, the port authorities at Manila immediately placed an embargo on low-growing vegetables. This step was necessary because the Chinese were accustomed to sprinkle human excreta in liquid form on growing cabbages, not only for fertilizer, but also for protection against insect pests. If cholera were present in the vicinity, it was always possible that each fresh, crisp, tender leaf would enfold a myriad cholera germs.

Under the terms of the embargo, a large shipment of cabbages from Canton was refused, and the angry shipmaster thereupon dumped the cargo into Manila Bay and sailed off, leaving the surface of the water literally covered with the bobbing heads. From the nipa huts of Farola, Tondo, and Meisic, the Filipinos swarmed to the water front, launched their praos and bancas, and went fishing for cabbages. They welcomed the succulent vegetables as manna.

In the light of subsequent knowledge it is doubtful whether cholera entered the Philippines in this way. There is no doubt, however, that one of the most terrible epidemics of modern times had begun. A few days later two cases of cholera were admitted early in the afternoon to San Juan de Dios Hospital, through whose ancient portals so many thousands had preceded them. Before the day was over, two more arrived. Within forty-eight hours doctors and nurses were rushing about distractedly trying to find beds in which to put the sufferers.

Responsibility devolved upon Secretary of the Interior Worcester.

He was a man of magnificent physique, respected by the Filipinos for his size and courage, but feared and disliked for his personality. He was brusque, and did not ask for cooperation; he demanded compliance with his orders. He always insisted that the established sanitary fact of the morning must be the rule to be observed for the evening. In following out what he considered right, he paid no heed to Filipino public opinion.

Worcester was taking vigorous steps, and cholera was not claiming so many victims as in Spanish days. The more ignorant of the populace, therefore, said this disease could not be cholera because not enough people were dying. Many Spanish and Filipino physicians, who, under the old régime, had been the most influential class politically and socially, jealous of the authority of the Board of Health, criticized its measures and fanned the antagonism of the people.

A land quarantine was established around Manila in the effort to keep the disease from the provinces. In the state of resentment over what seemed the dictation and ruthlessness of a military occupation, the Filipinos could not comprehend the theory of paternalism which said, "We are doing this for your own good." Eluding the futile cordon at night, or slipping across the fields by day, people already sickening of the disease escaped to start new foci of infection.

Within a few weeks seven thousand temporary employees of the Board of Health were in the field. But the force was new and untrained, and undoubtedly in exercising its duties it was guilty of discourtesy and even abuse of power.

The Farola district, a narrow neck of land along the Pasig River running out into the Bay, covered with warehouses, coal piles, and a crowded mass of small filthy nipa huts, was the apparent focus of the disease. Worcester ordered it evacuated and burned. Under a blazing sky the terrified and resentful owners watched the shooting sparks as shack after shack crackled and collapsed. The report spread about that the homes of the poor were being burned to make room for future dwellings and warehouses of rich Americans. Further rumors that the foreign doctors had poisoned the wells were also widely credited; it was even said the American aim was to annihilate the Filipino race.

It was true that, in the effort to stop the spread of infection, the Americans sometimes may have overridden the private rights of individuals. Uniformed men clattered up with ambulances and without ceremony lifted the sick from their mats and carted them away from their wailing families. The husbands, wives, and children could not understand why they were forbidden to follow. Four times out of five this was the last they ever saw of their loved ones until shortly they received a curt notice to come to the hospital and claim their dead.

The severity of this treatment gave rise to even more extravagant rumors. It was said that in the detention camps where contacts were segregated all sorts of horrible abuses were being perpetrated, and at the emergency hospitals the sick were being deliberately murdered.

The state of popular apprehension amounted to hysteria. Whenever possible, the sick were concealed by their families and the dead thrown into the esteros or the Pasig River or the Bay, thus adding further poison to the already poisonous waters.

Measures were taken to control sea traffic. All vessels leaving Manila were quarantined five days at Mariveles, and for a longer period if cholera broke out. A water patrol was established on the Bay, but here also many small boats evaded the watch. At the time of my arrival the emergency was so great that the quarantine service was extended to cover the Manila waterways.

The people were often, in their pitiful ignorance, hastening their own destruction. One morning I came down to my office. My first glance, as always, was towards the big map on the wall. I was startled to see that, according to the arrangement of the colored flags which marked the location of every case, cholera had suddenly burst forth in little isolated groups all over Manila.

An investigation was begun at once. This soon revealed that two days earlier a fisherman had come in from the Bay with a marvelous story of how he had seen bubbles rising in the salt water which, as they rose, formed the vague outline of a great cross. He had tasted the water and found it sweet. Crossing himself, with wonder in his heart that he had been chosen to discover this portent, he paddled furiously to land. Others, at first incredulous, tasted and then believed. The fisherman escorted to the spot a priest, who blessed

106

the water and declared it a miracle. The Filipinos were such ardent seekers after wonderworking that they would cry out "I believe" when any prophet proclaimed, "Lo! A Miracle!" Dwellers along the shore poured themselves out on the Bay in anything that would float and eagerly scooped up the holy water in bottles, jugs, pans, and pails.

Together with the Manila health officials I was soon on a launch, which nosed its way through the conglomeration of native craft. A glance was enough to show us that this was no miracle but a dire calamity. The sewer line, which emptied far out in the Bay, had broken. If access to the miracle were shut off immediately, we knew that, in the prevailing state of incipient rebellion against health measures, the believers would feel deeply outraged and would be ready for any violence; the health service would be attacked for interfering with divine providence itself. On the other hand, action was imperative if cholera were not to run riot in the town.

We went to the Governor General and asked for constabulary to patrol the area and keep the people from committing mass suicide. Instead of acceding immediately to our request, he hesitated. "It's quite possible there'll be a minor insurrection if I do this," he argued.

"It's quite certain there'll be a major catastrophe if you don't," I retorted.

"Well, I don't know," he drawled. I was well enough acquainted with the Governor's legal turn of mind to realize that he was weighing all contingencies before making a decision. To me there could be no question as to the necessity, and, moreover, speed was of the essence.

"We are advising you in the strongest terms that the constabulary be called out. The situation is serious, and if you want to assume the responsibility, we can't do anything further about it. But we want to have it plainly in writing that it is you who are responsible."

We could state our position no more plainly.

The Governor did realize the danger, the police and the constabulary prevented the collection of the water until the sewer was repaired, and, on this occasion at least, the disturbances which ensued were of only a minor character.

When I took charge of the Bureau of Health in 1905, cholera had broken out again. If a fire is to be kept under control, it is imperative

107

to prevent a state of panic. My experience in the previous epidemic had taught me that quiet, effective measures and persevering kindness were far more potent than martial law and armed forces.

Beyond placing guards on the Benguet Road and trails leading to the Mountain Province from badly infected towns, no attempt was made at a land quarantine. An efficient blockade would have required an army of fifty thousand and the expenditure of vast sums of money. If we could keep the populace from becoming alarmed, they would perhaps stay in Manila.

Simultaneously with our efforts to keep the infection localized, we were isolating the sick in hospitals as quickly as possible. Most of them were taken to the newly completed San Lazaro buildings which, I believe, harbored more pests than were ever before concentrated at any one spot in the world. But instead of barring the friends and relatives, we built glass partitions so that they could see and realize the patients were being properly cared for. However, memories of old wrongs die hard. In spite of our efforts to calm the panic, the vernacular press accused us of exercising the same ruthless measures as had been enforced in the previous epidemic, and of being lacking in pity and humanity. One article described how the naked bodies of the dead, tagged and with feet tied together, lay about the entrance. Widespread terror among the lower classes was prevented only by Worcester's prompt action in compelling the paper to print a public retraction.

Isolation was the most important weapon against cholera, but our inability always to locate cases in their early stages prolonged the epidemic. Even with house to house inspection by police and constabulary, from two to twenty-four hours often would elapse before the Bureau of Health was informed. A quarantine guard was at once placed upon an infected house and its inmates, and from that moment the particular focus was adequately cared for; yet in the hours before these measures could be taken, other individuals almost inevitably had been infected.

In order to reduce the risk as much as possible, we mapped out the city of Manila in districts, and disinfecting carts were maintained like fire apparatus. At the sound of an alarm, the disinfectors would set out on a mad gallop, and in most cases would be at work in a few moments. Nothing but prepared food was destroyed or damaged. Clothes, blankets, mats, crockery, all went into a tub filled with carbolic acid solution. There was rarely a second case in a house which had been thus treated.

The spread of infection was often due to the kindly Filipino habit of visiting any neighbor who fell ill. Friends and relatives literally crowded to commiserate with him. But upon discovery of the nature of the disease, or upon notice from the doctor that he had to report the case, they promptly scattered and went to their meals without washing their infected hands. Many times they carried from the house mats, clothing, food, and drink, to save them from the disinfectors. We tried to trace the homes to which these articles had been carried, but it was always difficult and often impossible to locate them all.

In giving foremen their instructions, we laid great stress upon the necessity for displaying courtesy at all times. They were told to take part in no argument with householders or anybody else, and to do their work with consideration, but none the less thoroughly.

In one epidemic we had six hundred men working. The daily consumption of disinfectants was enormous. About seven hundred gallons of carbolic acid and seventy-five tons of lime were used. The entire stock of the former was consumed in one month and emergency shipments had to be secured from Hongkong and Japan. In this crisis Dr. Paul Freer, the Director of the Bureau of Science and a brilliant chemist, suggested that sea water could be electrolyzed, forming a disinfecting fluid which, according to laboratory tests, would kill cholera vibrios promptly. This provided us with a cheap and inexhaustible supply of disinfectant.

To sanitate people with fixed abodes was comparatively simple when compared to the problem presented by the harvesters of rice, sugar, and tobacco. These semi-nomads moved rapidly from place to place seeking employment. They stubbornly persisted in stating that the disease was not cholera, but poison introduced by *los Americanos* under the guise of disinfectants.

In addition to active opposition, we had passive obstruction to deal with. At times when the immediate isolation of a case of cholera would have saved a town, factional disputes might either prevent the Municipal Council's convening for lack of a quorum, or, if it did meet, it might decide that guava water was a more desirable disinfectant than carbolic acid. If the town health officer happened to be persona non grata through religious, political, or personal differences, his salary might be reduced to the lowest possible limit.

Doctors were still reluctant to settle in the provinces, so that there were many sections without skilled medical aid. Even where they were stationed, I had occasional difficulties with them. The following exchange of telegrams is self-explanatory:

"Dr. ——, San Fernando, Union: Governor, Zambales, reports cholera San Narciso. Proceed immediately take charge situation. Answer."

HEISER.

The reply came, "Health, Manila, am sick. Impossible for me to travel."

"When will you be ready?"

"Have itch: am making house my office. Shall advise when cured."

The telegrams were sometimes even more laconic. A young Filipino graduate of Rush Medical School in Chicago had returned sartorially garbed in the height of American fashion with the latest thing in neckties and toothpick shoes. His first assignment was to a cholera outbreak in an isolated town ten miles beyond the end of a railroad line. He found not even a carromata taxi at the terminus.

"No conveyance. What shall I do?" he telegraphed me at once.

"Walk!" I wired.

But I am reminded of an earlier occasion on which the zeal of a subordinate had created unexpected difficulties. The first indication that I had of anything wrong came in the form of a summons to an interview with Governor Taft. Trying to compose his jovial features into an expression of severity, he began the conversation. "Look here, Doctor, I want to help you all I can, but your department is going much too far."

"What's the matter?" I asked.

"They've been stopping the ringing of church bells in Batangas. Why?"

"I'm sure I don't know," I answered, "but I'll find out at once."

I summoned the inspector and asked for an explanation. He admitted readily that he had stopped the bells. "But that's not a sanitary measure," I pointed out.

"Oh, yes, it is," he insisted. "When the church bell rings, it lets everybody know another person has died of cholera. This news casts a gloom over the whole community. You know, yourself, Doctor, that any depressing news interferes with the secretion of the gastric juices, and that one of the best protections anybody can have against cholera is strong gastric juice. Now, when the church bell rings, the gastric juice of all those who hear it is reduced in strength, and they are much more likely to get cholera."

Still inexperienced with Oriental sophistry, I was taken aback by his reasoning. It is true that a deranged digestive system and a weakened hydrochloric acid offers a happy hunting ground for cholera germs. But even so, I was well aware that the inspector was moved by anti-Church feeling rather than true scientific spirit. I accepted his explanation, however, merely admonishing him that he was not in the future to interfere with religious observances.

I relayed his explanation to Taft who roared with laughter, and admitted the logic was incontrovertible.

The basis on which I worked in attempting to control cholera was that it could only be contracted by the introduction into the mouth of contaminated food or drink. "You can eat cholera, and you can drink cholera, but you cannot catch it." Almost absolute safety against infection could be secured by the simple precaution of using safe, potable water and cooked food. My greatest task was to convince the Filipinos that this assumption was correct.

Large portions of the population were ignorant and inaccessible. Much superstition existed, one of the most popular beliefs being the supposedly injurious character of boiled water. The time-honored custom had been to keep water in large earthen jars into which anyone who was thirsty dipped his half cocoanut shell and, incidentally, his fingers. The eating habits were equally simple and primitive. Food was conveyed to the mouth with the fingers from a general bowl used by all the household. The sterilization of water and the preparation of hot food was difficult and expensive, because all heating and cooking had to be done over infinitesimal fires of bamboo sticks.

The question of the perishable food supply of the inhabitants of Manila was almost as important as water. It had to be inspected so that nothing diseased, unsound, or unfit would be sold or consumed. We erected large airy buildings of concrete, which were to serve as central markets. This system of distribution proved to be one of our few innovations which pleased everybody. The city liked it because of the income, the dealers because of the cheap rents, the housewives because of the wide choice of foods and the convenience of being able to buy all their supplies in one place. Finally, it served the purposes of the Bureau of Health because it gave us an opportunity to control the sale of foodstuffs. Manila has the distinction of being the only city in the world where perishable food may be sold only in a public market. We also took advantage of these gathering places to teach the Filipinos habits of sanitation by instructing them in the use of public latrines.

The low-growing vegetables, as usual, were barred, but the sale of fruits that grew high on trees, such as bananas, cocoanuts, and mangos, was not dangerous and not interfered with. Forks were provided in the meat stalls, but much education and patience was necessary before the old custom of handling one piece of meat after another could be stopped.

Every market had a large number of stands which catered solely to the chewers of betel. The kernel of this nut, fruit of the Areca palm, is taken from its thick husk, much like that of a walnut or butternut, and is then cut into disks. The pieces are covered with lime, wrapped in moist green buya leaves about the size of those of a morning glory, and placed in an earthen pot. They are thoroughly sprinkled every few hours, but the old water at the bottom of the vessel is seldom replaced.

The Filipino purchaser is very particular as to the tenderness of the leaves. He puts his hand into the jar and feels them all carefully before making his selection. Naturally, if his fingers are infected, he spreads the contagion throughout the pot.

The habit of betel nut chewing was so ingrained among the Islanders that any attempt to forbid it would have been useless. Its mildly stimulating effect was apparently no detriment to health, although it was incidentally injurious. The Filipino would push the cud between his teeth and cheek, and the pungent essence of the nut would irritate the mucous membrane, often causing buccal cancer. Since we could not stop this habit, which was more common than gum chewing in the United States, we prohibited the sale of the nut outside the markets.

In an epidemic we used to rope off the market so as to leave only one possible entrance. There we stationed a uniformed guard, and placed by his side a barrel filled with a weak solution of bichloride of mercury, mild enough to be harmless to human beings. The guard saw to it that each person entering the market rinsed his fingers in the barrel. Since no towel was provided, the disinfectant perforce dried on his hands.

The Filipinos regarded this procedure as a rather childish American practice which hurt nobody. They dipped in their hands and then, with shouts of laughter, splashed one another with the disinfecting solution. Nothing could have served our purposes better.

Even more important than bullfighting to the Spaniard is cockfighting to the Filipino, because every man, no matter how poor, can participate in the sport. In many homes the cock is the most valued possession. In case of fire the Filipino is popularly said to rescue first his cock, then his wife, and lastly his children. A cock costs money, a wife nothing, and children are easily come by. One of the commonest tableaux in the Islands is that of two men holding their cocks by the tails and letting them scratch and pull towards each other to strengthen their muscles.

Around the cockpits, which are in every village, amphitheatres are built of bamboo and nipa, and each Sunday the seats are filled from dawn to dark. Usually a white cock is matched with a colored one, so that each may be readily distinguished. Before a contest begins, the owner brings in his cock and, holding it firmly by the tail, allows it to struggle and strain in order to display its fierceness and strength. The audience of inveterate gamblers makes its appraisal promptly and the betting begins. Cries of, "Five on the red," or, "Ten on the white," alternate with the clink of money thrown into the pit. The attendant shouts, "Any more bets?" and when none is forthcoming, he sweeps up the silver and paper with a broom.

Each cock has fastened on one leg a steel gaff of razor-like sharp-

113

ness, and one of the combatants is disemboweled quickly or runs away. The slain heroes, although tough, eventually find their way into the family soup pot. The pay-off, which takes place without any apparent system of accounting, is a most amazing performance. A man comes up to a little window and merely says, "I bet five on the red," and receives his money. I never saw a single dispute about the amount of the wager.

In times of epidemics any gathering of people was dangerous. We could not ride roughshod over the customs and the religion of the people; often we had to compromise. The fiesta is a time-honored institution in the Philippines, and the principal event in the yearly history of each town. Save for its religious aspect, it resembles one of our county fairs, bringing together thousands of people of all ages and conditions, who, for the time being, lose themselves in festivity.

The greatest single hazard to health during the year came from the annual celebration of the feast of *Nuestra Senora de Paz y Buen Viaje* at Antipolo. For several weeks ten thousand persons or even more would congregate in the small town containing the shrine. Feasting was one of the essential features. Food was brought from cholera-infected districts and even from invaded homes, and, with that sincere hospitality so characteristic of the Filipinos, was distributed to all who would partake. There was a natural tendency to excess in eating, and the indigestion thus induced might have afforded just the opportunity for the development of a case of cholera or typhoid or dysentery.

Patients in the incubation state of cholera often mingled freely with the well, and, since the means for the disposal of the excreta of so many people were usually inadequate, it was quite obvious how the disease might spread. After visiting the Virgin, the pilgrims used to bathe in the Mariquina River, which was nearby, and the drinking water was scooped up farther down the stream.

Almost immediately after Antipolo, cholera would crop up simultaneously here and there about Luzon. The villagers could find no other explanation than that some mysterious fermentation was working in the soil. But to the members of the Bureau of Health who were studying the route maps of the returning pilgrims, it was apparent that the lines of infection radiated in all directions like the spokes from a hub. The devout travelers might have escaped contagion at Antipolo itself, but too often it was obvious they had stopped at Pasig, where they must have purchased low-growing vegetables fertilized with human excreta alive with cholera organisms.

Quarantine as an emergency measure and, as more permanent preventives, the disposal of excreta and the provision for pure water, were our only prophylaxis against cholera in the early epidemics. But it was obvious that other factors, as yet unknown, entered the equation.

Cholera had always broken out at crowded Bilibid Prison in every epidemic. When I was first called upon to cope with this disease, the prison medical service was under the complete control of an official called the Director of Prisons. As the death rate was mounting to over two hundred per thousand, Governor Wright asked whether I would find out wherein lay the trouble.

"I'll try," I said, "but I can do this only if I have the necessary authority. Will you instruct the Director of Prisons to carry out any reasonable requests I may make?"

"But that would be infringing on his domain. I don't see how I can do that," said the Governor.

Realizing that my work would be useless without complete control, I said I was sorry, but that I should have to decline. Governor Wright considered for a moment, and then decided that the emergency required the cutting of red tape. "This outbreak must be stopped. I'll do as you say."

I went to the prison and, after searching all morning, had discovered nothing. The sick had been promptly isolated, the food was cooked, and the water was pure; there seemed to be no reason for the constant recurrence of cases.

Then the dinner gong rang. The prisoners trouped into the dining room, and I noticed the flies from the toilets went with them. In those days little was known about the possibilities of carriers and insect transmission. Flies, however, were a danger in any epidemic, because they might carry on their feet any intestinal disease. They frequented disease breeding spots and purposely hunted for filth. If there were no filth, there would be no flies. I ordered the toilets to be screened and the entrance to be provided with a vestibule and spring doors. Within forty-eight hours the cholera epidemic in Bilibid Prison stopped with dramatic suddenness.

The prison medical service was shortly thereafter placed under the Bureau of Health, and Bilibid became a laboratory where we could study disease under controlled conditions. The death rate there dropped to the level of the most famous health resorts.

Flies might explain an outbreak in an institution, but could not make clear why, in spite of all our sanitary measures, cholera kept cropping up in widely scattered districts of Luzon. An epidemic would start in Hagenoy, and a few days later break out in Pampanga. By rigorous methods we would be able to declare Hagenoy clean, but while we were concentrating on Pampanga, Hagenoy would somehow be reinfected. And no sooner would Pampanga be cleared up and we would proceed to another district than it would be reinfected from Bulacan. Often cases were few and dissociated, but the endless chain went on. An infection dispersed so broadly, so elusive, and so slight as to be scarcely noticeable, could with great difficulty be combated. Nevertheless we knew that any relaxation in vigilance would surely be followed by a major outbreak.

In studying the causes of the tragic Hamburg disaster of 1892, when eight thousand people had died in three months, the doctors of the period had offered as a theory the possibility of cholera carriers —people who, though themselves not ill, were yet able to distribute millions of germs and infect many others. The explanation had not been proved and was lost sight of until Dr. Allan J. McLaughlin, one of the outstanding members of my department, working on the German hypothesis, determined the existence of carriers in the Philippines. Thereafter, in our measures for controlling cholera, we took cognizance of the potential danger from this source.

If the bacteria carrier washed his hands often enough and at the proper times, he would not transfer infection from his dirty fingers to the food or drink of others. Otherwise, he was a great menace to the public. We kept very close track of all carriers and isolated them whenever they gave positive results. Even when they were negative, it was possible that they might become positive at any time.

Consequently, before the season for cholera came around, we used to have them examined.

Once in possession of the fact that cholera carriers existed we were able to guard the Philippines against the entrance of cholera from other countries. We required bacteriological examination of all passengers at quarantine, a system which has now become an essential part of safeguarding any port from cholera carriers or those slightly ill with the disease.

In 1911 I happened to be in New York on my vacation when cholera broke out at Brooklyn. Three thousand immigrants were coming in almost daily, and it was assumed cholera carriers among them must have brought in this infection. Wholesale bacteriological examinations were obviously necessary, and, because of my previous experience with cholera, I was asked to help. An emergency appropriation was secured, a laboratory was set up at Rosebank, New Jersey, and thirty women technicians were employed to find the carriers. Instead of sweeping the country as had so often happened, cholera was stopped in its tracks.

The system we installed at Rosebank has now become the recognized one throughout the world. Although it is most useful in preventing cholera, it does not give absolute assurance. All threatened towns or sections must always be prepared to fight the disease.

Combating epidemics was temporarily stopping the leak in the dam, and cleaning and renovating were essential, but all would be of no lasting value unless the coming generation were educated in the necessity for and knowledge of prophylaxis through inculcating cleanly habits in eating and the disposal of feces.

The children made the handiest tools to work with. The little Filipinos were exceedingly studious; such a thing as a child not preparing its lessons was unknown. There were never enough schools to go round, and it was pathetic to see them standing outside the schoolhouse looking longingly in, hoping that some boy or girl would not appear and one of them might enter in his or her place. Teaching by precept and example and literature did a great deal. We organized Knife and Fork Societies among them. In some cases they carried this lesson in table manners home, but the older people were seldom affected; their eating habits were fixed, and the danger quite beyond their comprehension. Nevertheless, we continued to encourage the children to repeat what they learned to their parents who, although they themselves could neither read nor write, were also eager for learning.

Simple rules of hygiene were placed in the newspapers and on handbills in English, Spanish, Tagalog, Ilocano, Visayan, and various other native dialects. With the cooperation of the Bureau of Education, these circulars were sent to every school teacher in the Islands. They were to be taught to the children so that they could repeat them verbatim to their parents. We also had the rules printed on large flaring red posters which were placarded on municipal and other public buildings.

We spent much time in the preparation of a primer of sanitation, destined for the bending of these young twigs whose homes possessed no running water, no stoves, and no bathrooms. When it was put in words of one syllable, it became the standard for schools throughout the tropics.

To get the best results in our campaign of education we concentrated on one subject at a time—beriberi, cholera, tuberculosis, or whatever was most important at the moment. Talks, pamphlets, newspaper articles, and demonstrations were all used. We would gather the people together wherever we could and illustrate our points with lantern slides. We secured a car from the railway, and made it into a traveling exhibit with a Filipino lecturer to accompany it. Later a Healthmobile and good roads enabled us to reach many more. To those who were still inaccessible we sent miniature exhibits on porters' backs, and a lecturer went from house to house expounding.

A prime requisite in the campaign was the cooperation of the churches, because of the great respect which the Filipinos generally paid to the words of their religious instructors. I first went to Archbishop Harty, a very intelligent man without whose help I could have accomplished little. I explained to him the highly infectious nature of cholera, and pointed out that it did not make any difference whether a Catholic or a Protestant swallowed the germs—they both died. Our aims were identical. His priests were intelligent men, but as long as they taught their flocks that cholera was a punishment for transgression and merely commiserated with them, they helped rather than hindered the spread of the disease. Every death was furthering destruction by bringing together large groups of people, and during an epidemic it was vital to stop these wakes.

"I do not want to ban them arbitrarily," I explained to the Archbishop, "because I should gain nothing in that way. The people would probably hold their wakes in secret. But you can instruct your priests and they will faithfully obey."

He agreed to help me.

I then broached an even more important subject. I wanted him to distribute simple rules for cholera prevention. He promised that they would be preached from every Catholic church in the Islands.

Armed with Archbishop Harty's assurance, I approached Monsignor Aglipay, the head of the Independent Catholic faction. "Your Grace," I began, "the Roman Catholics are sending out cholera circulars. Don't you want to save the lives of your people also? If you do, here are the handbills which will teach your parishioners how to avoid this disease."

In his eagerness, Father Aglipay almost snatched the circulars from my hands.

I then made the rounds of the Protestant denominations and said to Episcopalian, Methodist, and Presbyterian in turn that the Catholics were sending out circulars, and suggested they might wish to do the same. They also promptly agreed.

In this manner I brought into my camp the best educational and religious forces of the country.

Month after month and year after year we labored by every possible means to persuade the Filipinos to boil their water, but with no great success. One of my American doctors, valuable because of his knowledge of the Tagalog tongue, was especially good at coping with cholera outbreaks. I knew that wherever he went he would stress the necessity for sterilized water. When the cholera rate remained high in his province of Pampanga, I went in person to investigate. I began making the rounds of the houses and in each one I asked, "Do you use boiled water?" and in each received an affirmative reply. By the time I had reached the fifth house, I decided I had better go into the question somewhat more thoroughly. "How do you use this boiled water?" I inquired.

"We take a teaspoonful three times a day."

The wise Chinese are the only Oriental people who apparently do not suffer from cholera. They know the use of boiled water and cooked food. They drink tea and eat hot rice. Perhaps far back in the Shang, or the Chou, or the Tsin, or the Han dynasties, certain Chinese preferred fragrant tea to insipid water when they were thirsty. Cholera passed them by. But those who did not practice the delicate art of brewing and drinking tea, in the course of time perished, leaving a nation of tea drinkers.

In the Philippines it was found that the Chinese who were stricken had betrayed their ancestors by adopting the Filipino mode of living. In Manila there was one case of cholera out of a thousand Chinese, one out of seven hundred Americans, and one out of two hundred and fifty Filipinos.

The Chinese always drink boiled water, the Americans generally drink boiled water, and the Filipinos seldom drink boiled water.

CHAPTER 9.   WATER, WATER, EVERYWHERE

FOR many years the indifference of the Filipinos toward the question of better water seemed almost impossible to overcome. If a bridge fell down and ten people were killed, the public would be wrought up to fever pitch, and an investigating committee would at once be appointed to fix the responsibility, but the deaths of hundreds of people who died of poor water went totally unregarded.

Whether water was safe and potable seldom seemed to have been inquired into from a scientific standpoint, nor was the enormous amount of labor to be saved and the convenience which would result by having it delivered through pipes seriously considered.

The Spaniards had put in a pumping station for Manila which elevated water from the Mariquina River to a reservoir and then distributed it by pipes. But this system did not reach all the people in Manila. As a result, the poorer classes, among whom the danger from cholera was greatest, were accustomed to take water from shallow wells, ponds, esteros, or other questionable sources, not only for washing clothes and kitchen utensils, but in many instances for drinking purposes. We tried to forbid this practice, but more often than not our orders were ignored because some barrios were located so far from the nearest hydrants that the people had to carry water a long distance in bamboo tubes or the emptied Standard Oil tins which litter the East.

One of the first steps in a cholera epidemic was to guard the water supply from pollution. We closed all the wells, except a few in the more distant barrios. These we treated with permanganate of potash; nobody would then drink the blood red water. Wherever possible, all stagnant places were drained by digging ditches, and certain small infected esteros were patrolled by the constabulary. Until simple disinfection with chlorine became available, the United States Army was also called upon in emergency to guard the banks of the Mariquina and prevent soil pollution. Communities aggregating ten thousand were located along the banks of the river, and from time immemorial had been accustomed to bathe and to wash there.

In the 1905 epidemic, a few days after the first cases of cholera appeared in Manila, reports of an outbreak came in from San Mateo, one of the towns in the Mariquina Valley. A certain young Filipina, living nearby and called by her admirers the Queen of Taytay, was performing miracles. She was bathing in a galvanized iron garbage disposal tank which had been abandoned by the Army. Villagers from near and far were standing in line all day long waiting to drink the water after her ablutions. They believed that she was endowed with such miraculous curative powers that the hundreds of those who drank would be healed.

No doubt some who came to drink had cholera germs upon their hands and, as they dipped in their containers, the water had become infected. Cholera organisms remained in the residue, which was not removed, so that each fresh tankful was reinfected.

Faith healing has always had a tremendous hold over all people of all times. This is particularly true of a country which has been disease-ridden for centuries. To tamper with the Queen's miracle when Rizal Province was in such a state of emotional excitement would, as in the case of the broken sewer in Manila Bay, have been a hazardous undertaking. But it was even more dangerous to let her continue.

Although the Queen of Taytay was invading my precincts, I could think of no legal way in which she could be stopped. The Bureau of Health always tried to proceed along the lines of law and order, but every avenue in this case seemed to be blocked. The Attorney General went through the Philippine statute books, and he also was unable to offer any solution.

WATER, WATER, EVERYWHERE

I had to resort to guile. I repaired to Taytay and went into conference with the father and mother of the Queen. I conceded that she might be doing good, but I pointed out that in the capital she would have wider scope for her activities. Where hundreds could drink in Taytay, thousands could drink in Manila. I promised here and cajoled there, and in the end I persuaded them. Even the Queen, after a day of earnest argument, consented to come to Manila. In addition, I made solemn affidavit to the whole village that she would be given ample opportunity to bathe as much as she pleased, and that we would take good care of her.

A procession was formed. The Queen and I led the van during the twelve mile walk to Manila, and many of the inhabitants of Rizal accompanied us to make sure no harm should befall her. Before she disappeared within the hospital, I addressed the multitude, which, after the manner of crowds, had increased enormously in numbers.

"Your Queen," I said, "must go inside to do her bathing and perform her miracle, but once an hour she will come out on the balcony, so that you may see that she is safe."

Though the assemblage did not seem to be altogether convinced, no open protest was made.

Curiously enough, we had no difficulty with the Queen herself. At first she took her baths regularly, and regularly we let the water run away after she left and drew a new one for her. She seemed to have no concern over the disposition of the water. As time went on, she bathed less often. Since she was being fed well and having a pleasant time, her interest in miracles rapidly waned.

For the first few days the Queen's balcony appearances had been dutifully made. At night we had even turned a flood light on her so that her faithful watchers would have hourly reassurance. But gradually they grew tired of their long vigil and went home. She walked on less and less frequently as the numbers of her followers diminished. By the end of a week she had played her final performance. After two weeks we told her she might go home, but that she should bathe in the tank no more. If she were overpowered by the need for performing miracles, she should come back to us and perform them at the hospital.

The Bureau of Health did not subscribe to miracles. We put our faith in a new water system. We went thirty miles farther up the Mariquina to a sparsely inhabited watershed, and across the pure white marble gorge of Montalban we built a dam. Necessarily, the few inhabitants had to be moved elsewhere; not all wanted to go. I can still see Worcester in his customarily forceful language talking to one recalcitrant whose stables and sty stood beside a small stream which emptied into the Mariquina above the dam. He said this little river belonged to him, and refused absolutely to budge.

"All right," said Worcester. "We can't put you out of your home. But we can forbid you to let one drop of your polluted water flow over on our area." The farmer could not very well keep his river at home, and surrendered.

After the new water supply was turned into the pipes, eight hundred fewer deaths annually occurred in the city of Manila than ever before. We were to be given even further proof of the vitally important role played by water in the tropics. The Filipinos were always dynamiting the streams to get fish, and by chance they once set off a charge directly above the water main where it crossed the river bed. We had to send all the way to Glasgow for new lengths of pipe. This accident, combined with a severe drought, compelled us to go back to the old Spanish system. Although we tried by every means to induce the people to boil their water before drinking, yet three hundred and ten more died than in any similar period since the new system had been completed. As soon as the pure water was in use again, the death rate came down, not only from water-borne, but from all other diseases.

This was directly in line with Hazen's statement that when drinking water was made safe, each death avoided from typhoid fever caused the avoidance of two or even three other deaths from diseases not regarded as intestinal-borne.

It would never have been possible to guard all the streams and shallow wells of the Philippines against pollution. Furthermore, if pure water could be provided, we should be spared the never-ending task of inculcating the boiled water habit. We asked the Legislature for twenty-five hundred dollars with which to bore a few experimental artesian wells. With the greatest reluctance this money was appropriated. The members, almost to a man, regarded this as a new-fangled notion of the Americans which could not possibly be of any utility to their constituents.

The first well was drilled in 1906 in the province of Pampanga. It came in successfully and began flowing large quantities of pure, potable water. But the people would not come near it. They said, "If God had intended us to drink water out of a hole drilled in the crust of the earth he would have put it there." According to their ancient custom, they continued drinking out of the streams in which carabao wallowed, and the wells into which filth drained.

We sent a Filipino doctor to explain to the Pampangans in their own dialect the virtues of this new water. In the effort to give them a practical example of its benefits, he almost water-logged himself, but to no good. The people remained indifferent. Other doctors were despatched; hostility grew. One of them had to flee for his life, pursued by bolos. Rumors began to circulate. "If you drink this water," the villagers said, "your hair will fall out. If you don't believe it, look at the Director of Health at Manila. He drinks this water. Look at him!"

I could make no valid defense to this conclusion. It posed a neat problem, because the Filipinos are so proud of their hair that they will go to almost any lengths to conserve it.

For several months the well bubbled invitingly, but none partook. We had led the Filipinos to the water but they would not drink. Then we were ourselves vouchsafed a lay miracle which brought to pass instantaneously and simply the results we had so long struggled for. This well was located a short distance from a town. A weary and sick stranger was passing along the road, and in his great thirst drank of the water. Almost from the first sip he began to feel his sickness leave him. He sat down beside the well and drank more. The more he drank the better he felt, until finally he was entirely recovered.

The traveler hastened to tell the villagers what had happened to him, and of the great medicinal value possessed by this water. Nothing could have been better adapted to Filipino psychology. The villagers streamed to the well. The parish priest blessed it. The news spread to the surrounding districts by grapevine telegraph. Inside of a week people were coming from points as distant as one hundred and fifty miles to get some of this marvelous water, taking away as much as they could carry.

We went again to the Legislature for money, and this time encountered no difficulty. In a few years "artesian wells" became one of the leading public questions of the day. Assemblymen who wanted to be elected would always come out in their platforms for artesian well appropriations. The demand became far too great for the supply of money, although three hundred thousand dollars was appropriated in 1915 gladly and willingly.

We watched very carefully to see the effect upon the mortality in villages where wells had been drilled. It was gratifying to observe that a death rate of forty to fifty per thousand would drop in one year to twenty or twenty-five. Nevertheless, the villagers still did not understand the true purpose of the wells, although they liked them and used them. We would sometimes find upon investigation that the pumps had been primed with water from the nearest ditch.

There were many deaths in the Philippines traceable to intestinal causes which did not find their way into the statistics under this head, and in addition perhaps even a greater number which were indirectly due to lowered resistance or other factors not clearly understood. For each death directly ascribable to intestinal disease, there are at least ten cases of illness which incapacitate an individual for ten days. Practically every Filipino had some form of intestinal parasite; often several varieties in combination. This condition was directly due to soil pollution, which for centuries was responsible for more deaths and illness among soldiers than have ever been slain on the field of battle. In recent years vaccination against typhoid and cholera has greatly reduced the military danger.

As far back as there is any historical record, the disposal of human wastes has been a sanitary problem. Nomadic peoples, such as the Indians of North America, would move on to a new place as soon as their camp grounds became filthy. Those who lived on the seashore depended upon the tides to keep their abodes in a cleanly condition.

Moses, the leader of a wandering people, was among the first, as far as history shows, to make written sanitary regulations for the proper disposal of human wastes. For many years his laws were in operation throughout the world, and even today are practised by those who live a camp life. The pit system used in the armies of the world is but a slight deviation from that enforced among the Ancient Jews. Moses had no knowledge of disease germs, but he had learned from experience that if he did not keep his camp grounds clean, his people became sick.

Cholera, typhoid fever, and dysentery are due to soil pollution. No one would think of throwing a substance known to be poisonous into the yard, or leaving it uncovered in the house; yet human wastes are more dangerous than arsenic or strychnine, and a thousand times more likely to be carried to the supply of drinking water, or to be brought in contact with the food, than are vegetable and mineral poisons.

The public generally is not interested in the subject of soil pollution. The excreta of a great city can be safely disposed of with a modern sewer system, but in the Philippines there were no sewers. In the nipa hut districts of Manila, houses had been built promiscuously all over an interior plot of ground without regard to street or alley lines. Access to many was only by means of a narrow path, not even wide enough for a cart. Others had to be reached by going under the neighboring houses.

In these closed barrios, made up of collections of miserable shacks, without proper kitchen facilities or even surface drainage, and with overcrowding worse than the old "lung" blocks of New York or Chicago, the difficulty of finding and combating epidemic disease was very great. Kitchen refuse, and even human excreta, were dropped through the interstices in the bamboo floors; the waiting pigs were the only sanitarians.

Pigs are omnipresent and offensive in the Philippines, but as scavengers they are invaluable. These starvelings ran loose in Manila until the olfactorily-sensitive Americans passed a law whereby they had to be locked up. Thereafter most Filipino homes had bamboo runways under the houses. The gastric juices of a pig are so powerful that they destroy practically any bacteria he eats. Cholera vibrios which would have killed a human being in a few hours, were as nothing to the pig. We concluded he was a help rather than a hindrance.

In a way the cholera epidemic helped us in our efforts to reclaim the nipa hut interiors. The attention of the better class of Filipinos was thus called to sections of their city into which few of them had previously penetrated. Many had honestly considered that the Bureau of Health was only persecuting an inoffensive class of poverty-stricken unfortunates.

As soon as cholera had disappeared from Manila we set about a determined effort to do away with these districts. But it was only after years of effort that we succeeded in securing sanitary barrios, on easily drained land and subdivided into streets, alleys, and lots according to a definite plan. It was interesting to note that the criminal rate, which had been highest in the insanitary sections, went down as soon as health was improved.

The installation of a new sewerage system in Manila also did a great deal to reduce health hazards. But many people would not obey the local ordinances, and we had to go to the Supreme Court of the United States to enforce sewer connections. The opposition came chiefly from the owners of large tenement houses, but, once the legal decision was made, we had no further major difficulties.

In contrast to the dread inspired by cholera everywhere, there is the greatest indifference to typhoid. Yet the presence or absence of typhoid is often regarded by many as the chief index of the sanitation of a given locality. Typhoid is usually thought of as a disease of civilization, and when the Americans first came to the Islands, Filipinos apparently suffered very little. But as communications improved, it began to spread, and with thousands of miles of good roads the infection was scattered broadcast. It circulated rapidly, was extremely virulent, and caused a high rate of mortality.

Since typhoid is conveyed in much the same way as cholera, the same measures of prophylaxis are applicable, although the typhoid bacillus is not so easily destroyed as the cholera vibrio. The administration of typhoid vaccine is a preventive, but it is expensive, and immunity grows less after two years. The principal way to combat the disease is through a pure water supply.

The study of health records in the tropics shows that the great enemies of man are diarrhea and dysentery, and not the spectacular cholera and plague. Dysentery caused more deaths, more disability, and more time lost from gainful occupations than all other tropical diseases combined. Annually dysentery assumed an epidemic form in a number of localities, shortly after the beginning of the rainy season. Curiously enough, it usually did not spread by extension as did cholera, but kept within certain bounds. Sometimes it appeared simultaneously over a widespread territory. It might break out on an island which had had no communication for weeks with the mainland at the same time as in the thickly inhabited Dagupan Valley.

Dysentery is of two kinds. It may be caused either by a bacillus or an amoeba, although the symptoms are much the same. The amoeba is a slightly greenish, microscopic, unicellular parasite, which is able to move around with considerable freedom. In the early days we thought all amoebae could convey dysentery, and, since all water in the Philippines contained amoebae, we would have to sterilize it all. This would have been so costly as to be practically prohibitive. The problem was turned over to the Bureau of Science, and its experts proved that amoebae were of pathogenic and non-pathogenic types. Since the ordinary amoebae did not hurt anybody, this made it possible to exclude from treatment a great many water installations.

It was long known that the drug ipecacuanha was useful in treating dysentery. In 1658 it had been brought to Europe from Brazil and sold as a secret remedy to the French government. But the use of this drug caused disagreeable and exhausting nausea as well as actual vomiting, because of the large doses essential to obtain full curative effects. Many vain efforts were made to coat the pills with salol or keratin, so that they would pass through the stomach undigested, or to check the vomiting with opium, chloral hydrate, or tannic acid.

Ultimately, Captain Edward Vedder of the United States Army Medical Corps, in the Philippines, discovered that emetine, the principal alkaloid of ipecacuanha, had the power, even in high dilutions, of destroying amoebae in test tubes. He did not, however, experiment with this drug on human beings.

Leonard Rogers of the Indian Medical Service, later knighted for this distinguished contribution to science, happened to read on shipboard the pamphlet in which Vedder described his experiments. He could hardly wait to reach India and try emetine on dysentery patients. By administering it hypodermically, he obtained results that seemed scarcely short of miraculous. He hastened to make the discovery known before the impending rainy season brought the inevitable increase in cases. The new treatment was immediately adopted and proved of inestimable benefit.

It was generally assumed by powers which colonized in the tropics that the native populations were immune to dysentery, but we made one thousand consecutive autopsies on Filipinos who had died of other causes, and found that three hundred of them had ulcers in their intestines from this disease. We knew then that dysentery was a problem among the Filipinos as much as among Europeans and Americans. There was a certain difference in its course, however. Among Filipinos and Chinese the tendency was toward recovery, and the abscesses of the liver which so often occurred among white victims were not so frequent.

Curing disease has never seemed to me of equal importance with its prevention. But I could not agree with the British, who always insisted that woolen belly bands protected them against intestinal diseases and guarded them against chills. I ridiculed the practice, saying it was much better to harden yourself against chill, and what would happen to you if you went out some time without your belly band? In any case, it was hot and uncomfortable, and it took more than a belly band to kill an amoeba.

There were certain omniscient ones among Americans, also, who said it was all foolishness to drink sterilized water; they never did. I always replied mildly that their luck would hold only so long, but the chances were that sooner or later they would have their bouts with dysentery. There was scarcely ever a transport or liner leaving Manila that did not carry back invalids who had caught dysentery as the result of not drinking boiled water.

On the month-long inspection trips through the Mountain Province I always had servants bring my canteen to me as soon as it had been filled. If it were not piping hot, I would know the water had not been boiled. I also saw to it that each member of the party took half-gallon canteens. He was thereafter supposed to make sure only water properly boiled was placed in it.

We could carry no ice, of course, on such trips, and the contents of the canteens were often warm and unpleasant. But those who disobeyed the instruction to partake only of boiled water invariably became sick. One by one the foolhardy ones would succumb to temptation. We would arrive at a mountain stream which rippled invitingly across the trail. They would be so hot, and the water would look so clean and cool, that they would lie down and put their dry thirsty mouths into it and drink. For the moment they would be refreshed, but they would soon find to their cost that they had been imbibing contamination from the villages above. I remember one particular expedition when out of twenty men Forbes, Worcester, and myself were the only ones who did not have to be carried in litters to the coast and shipped back to the Manila hospital.

Among the wild tribes, who had the best opportunity to disseminate infection, there existed dense ignorance in regard to the nature of bacteriological cleanliness. To them a germ was a bug, something that could be seen and dealt with by means of a bolo. The difficulty of explaining to a primitive race the nature of microbes and their wicked doings was excellently illustrated by the endeavor of Winfred T. Dennison, Secretary of the Interior under Harrison, to teach the Igorots about the amoeba.

Mr. Dennison was a little man, and therefore not so much admired in the Mountain Province as his predecessor, the gigantic Worcester. He was convinced that he could turn the Igorots' belief in evil spirits to good account, and asked that a motile amoeba be mounted for him on a microscopic slide. A lusty specimen was accordingly provided.

We went on the annual tour of the Mountain Province, and, at one of the chief towns of the Igorots, Mr. Dennison decided to give his demonstration. He had one of the chiefs brought over and said to him, "I want to show you an evil spirit that causes diseases. The white man can control him. If you look through this you will see him."

The *Apo* looked as directed, and grunted.

"What do you see?"

No reply could be elicited.

Mr. Dennison then handed the *Apo* a pencil and paper, and said, "Draw what you see."

The *Apo* produced a very good likeness of an amoeba jumping about.

Mr. Dennison then triumphantly exclaimed, "That's what causes diseases that kill you, but we can kill it."

"You say that little thing can kill a man?" queried the *Apo* incredulously.

"Yes," came Mr. Dennison's confident reply.

"Well, it might kill a little white man like you, but it wouldn't hurt a great big *Apo* like me."

I have followed my own rules of exercise, cooked food, and boiled water faithfully for years in the tropics, and only once have I had any so-called tropical disease. This was in the nature of an experiment. I was attempting to test my thesis further. I began to drink water casually on ships and in hotels without making precise inquiries into its source. After two months of this nonchalance, I came down with amoebic dysentery at Calcutta.

CHAPTER 10.   NOT WITH BEAT OF DRUM

I HAVE always found that, no matter what the color of a person's skin, if you can relieve him of pain, he becomes your friend. This is especially true among primitive races, who are more lavish in their gratitude than many civilized people I know.

In the mountainous interior of Northern Luzon lived three hundred thousand wild tribesmen, untamed wards of the government who, for lack of a better name, were commonly called non-Christians. But they were not savages and, because they had so recently abandoned the practice, they were sensitive to the opprobrium conveyed by the term head-hunter. The principal reason for their long isolation was geographical. The narrow passes which led into the mountains could be easily defended against a considerable military force. Furthermore, the land was poor and the people fierce and warlike. It had never been worth the Spaniards' time or money to conquer them. For centuries also a feud had smoldered between Christian lowlander and animistic mountain dweller, and for a long time it was questionable whether friendly relations between the two could be established.

In general, the mountain people were exceptionally healthy and sturdy, and the normal death rate from disease was not so high as in the lowlands, although many children died of malnutrition or improper feeding. The mothers used to chew up rice, camotes, and meat, and feed infants of a few days directly from their own mouths, as a squab is fed.

All five tribes suffered appallingly from a disease called yaws, which is communicated under conditions of filth and poverty, and by actual contact. Although not venereal, it had many of the pathological characteristics of syphilis, among them a positive reaction to the Wassermann test. It usually began with a large cauliflower-like excrescence known as the mother yaw, and thereafter the lesions spread over the entire body. In later life it often caused paralysis and deformities. Children were particularly susceptible to this disease, which frequently and tragically robbed them of their childhood.

Our first step in peaceful penetration was to provide medical service for these mountain dwellers whom civilization had overlooked. In the Igorot country, which lay just beyond our doors, we began the attempt to relieve some of the suffering caused by yaws. We were making slow progress with the old potassium iodide treatment for syphilis, when luck unexpectedly came our way. Dr. Paul Ehrlich sent some of his newly developed salvarsan (606) to Dr. Richard P. Strong, who experimented with it, and found it marvelously effective in yaws, working miraculous cures. Armed anew with this discovery, we opened a small dispensary on the edge of the Igorot territory.

The healthy Igorot wore nothing but a breech clout, but when he fell ill he immediately took his blanket and wrapped himself into his misery. There was no clock, no sun-dial, no hourglass in the Mountain Province, but the sun rose every day. Every medicine man, brown, black, yellow, or white, often practises hocus-pocus. To an Igorot whose sufferings had overcome his suspicions, we handed a stick with fifteen loops of string tied around it.

"Be up at dawn each morning," he was admonished solemnly. "Have your bolo ready. Watch carefully. Just as you see the first yellow tip of the sun, cut off one loop. Do not take off your blanket. Do not look at your skin. At every sunrise cut one more loop. When the last one is gone, throw aside your blanket. You will be well."

Having pronounced these words, we injected the 606, and sent the Igorot on his way.

One of our doctors was most anxious to describe the magic treatment for a medical journal. He had selected six particularly interesting cases, and sent for a photographer from the Bureau of Science, asking the six Igorots to be present on a certain morning. The morning came, and so did the photographer, but no Igorots.

"That's just the way with these ungrateful people," the doctor irritably exclaimed. "You cure them with great trouble and cost, but when you ask some little favor, that's the last you see of them."

Two weeks later the doctor heard a great hullabaloo. He went to the door of the dispensary, and there were his six "ungrateful" patients, triumphantly leading several hundred of their afflicted brethren, all coming for their sticks with the fifteen loops.

By healing the people we gradually extended our dispensaries, until we had penetrated into the heart of the non-Christian country. The tribesmen began flocking to them, carrying their sick in litters and welcoming physicians and nurses into their homes.

Eventually at Bontoc, the capital of the Mountain Province, we built a modern hospital, made of brick baked in the hills. It took much time to teach the people our new and strange ways. Just after the hospital was opened I remember making an inspection visit one night and finding all the beds empty. I had seen the ward full only a few hours before. As I was looking around for some explanation of the phenomenon, I noticed a pair of bare brown feet sticking out from under a bed, and stooping down, I found all the patients in similar positions. We had to permit them to sleep on the floor until we could convince them a bed really had its advantages.

The non-Christians were much averse in the beginning to staying in an enclosed space for any length of time, ignored the advantages of quiet in producing a cure, and abhorred all treatment which limited the usual quantity of their daily food. They much preferred to remain in their homes and enjoy the *canao*, or feasting, which, according to them, was the best cure for their infirmities.

But in the end they turned out to be excellent publicity agents. A man who had been operated on for a large benign tumor would say to a friend in the same sad case, "You go down to those American doctors. You go to sleep in a room. When you wake up, it is gone."

When we first went into the mountain country, tribe warred against tribe, all hunting each others' heads. The mutual ferocity and hatred was unbelievable. The people were compelled to huddle into villages for protection from their head-hunting neighbors, and spent hours traveling from their distant fields to their homes. Men from Village A would not even carry our baggage as far as Village B. They would go half way, lay down their loads and retire, whereupon those from Village B would come forward and pick them up.

Almost every house had its head rack, and the number of skulls, which might range from two to several dozen, indicated the social standing and prestige of the owner. Head-hunting was a sort of game; if one village took three heads, the enemy village had to prove its manhood by securing four in return. There were great ceremonies, with speeches and songs, when the heads were carried home in triumph. Any warrior decapitated in one of these encounters was considered to have cast such discredit on his community that he was buried under a trail where his resting place would be trampled upon. The Igorots had a fundamental sporting instinct; they would send timely warning to the village to be attacked, and sometimes met by mutual appointment.

In later years the warriors would stage sham head-hunting battles for us with spear, head axe, and shield of stout wood lashed with rattan. It was a beautiful sight to see with what accuracy they could hurl the wickedly barbed, long steel-tipped spear, but gruesome to watch them manipulate, even in play acting, the terrible head axe, pointed at one end to puncture the enemy's skull, and fashioned and sharpened at the other to cut off his head.

Head-hunting was forbidden by law, but the enforcement of such laws is not easy. In most backward countries, the white man's usual method is to shoot the offenders; we did it chiefly by changing the nature of the rivalry. We substituted athletics, reduced to their simplest terms. Instead of allowing the villagers to cut each others' heads off, we would say to those of Village A, "Choose eight of your strongest men. Village B is going to do the same. Then you will meet in a tug of war and whichever team can pull the other over the line has proved that he belongs to the better village." These contests became life and death matters; in this way the tribesmen sublimated the violent emotions which formerly had found outlet in bloodshed.

I made many solitary trips into the Igorot country, usually fore-warned by anxious friends that I would certainly be killed, because I could not tell when the savages would turn upon me. I was going along one day in a remote part of the country when my ears were startled by the most stupendous uproar of yelling and shouting. It sounded ominous, but there was no help for it. I had to go on. These agile runners could have outdistanced me and cut off any possible escape had they been so minded. The only thing to do was to keep quietly on as unconcernedly as possible.

The din increased as I proceeded. Suddenly I emerged into a clearing, but, instead of spears and bolos, my eyes were startled with the sight of bats and balls, and the fantastic picture of a savage, naked save for a string around his middle and a great wire catcher's mask before his face. An inter-village baseball game was in progress. Nobody paid any attention to me; nobody knew or cared whether I had arrived. The teams were fairly matched, and I was soon raised to almost the same pitch of excitement. With one man on first base, a young Igorot came to bat and, with a resounding crack, hit the ball into left field. The man on first started for second, but it seemed almost certain he would be put out. With one accord the cry arose from the throats of the wild men, "Slide, you son of a bitch, slide!"

The Igorots had watched the games of the American soldiers at the hill station, and were letter perfect in their lines.

The mountain tribes had some characteristics and habits sharply distinguishing them from one another. The Igorots, largest in numbers and highest in the scale of development, were still not far removed from barbarism. Their bodies were strong and lithe, but around their tattooed limbs they often wore coiled brass rings or bands, which in time became so tight that they impeded the circulation and made the veins stand out in snakelike ridges. Their teeth were filed to sharp points as a mark of beauty. Their hair was banged on the forehead and long behind, confined in a little basket-woven cap of scarlet, yellow, and brown. When matches were introduced, they were kept with the tobacco in this tiny hat on the back of the head. On their chests hung necklaces of dogs' teeth, saved from their feasts.

On the Benguet Road I often used to see Filipinos, bound for the Saturday dog market at Baguio, each dragging along on a leash six to ten yellowish-brown curs. It was hard to imagine why these lean and hungry beasts, which had never been fed anything beyond the scraps of garbage and refuse they had picked up, were so prized as articles of diet. But the meat hunger in this country which had little game or fish, had given the Igorots a keen appetite for proteins. The favorite method of preparation was to feed the starving animal with rice till his belly bulged full and round. When he could swallow not one grain more, he was promptly killed and, thus neatly self-stuffed, was roasted and eaten. The undigested rice was esteemed the greatest delicacy of all. General Wood remonstrated with the Igorots, and, partly due to their fondness for him, and partly to the tinned salmon with which they were then being supplied, they agreed to give up the practice.

Since meat could not be preserved, whenever a family had an animal to kill, it was the occasion for a *canao*, to which all friends were invited. There was no wastage; viscera and head disappeared with the flesh as everybody gorged. When the head of a family died, according to the Igorot "Share-the-wealth" plan, all his property was given away or consumed. If he were rich, if he had plenty of carabao, pigs, and camotes, the native tubers, there would be a splendid festival which would continue until the fortune was entirely eaten up. The feasting mourners would squat in the house of the deceased, and custom demanded that the corpse be there with them, propped up in a rude chair with a smoke fire going under him to keep him. I have known these affairs to last six months, and in that warm climate the corpse, even in its smoked condition, was likely to become rather high.

The neighboring Ifugaos had an unattractive practice of eating their carabao alive. The beast was turned loose and hamstrung with the first blow so that he could not escape, and then everybody attacked him with bolos, cutting the raw flesh from the living animal. In a few moments, the carabao was chopped to pieces. I have often seen the crowd so frantic with meat lust that the flailing bolos inflicted serious wounds, even cutting off fingers. It was a job for several doctors to sew up the injuries after one of these affairs. Later the practice was forbidden and, instead, the meat was properly slaughtered.

Igorot and Ifugao were obliged to depend for their daily food on camotes and, more particularly, on rice. Both were hard-working agriculturists and cultivated the land to the limit of maximum productivity. Each year during the dry season thousands of acres of rice paddies were planted in the dry river beds, the stones were cleared out, dikes were erected, and earth was carried in by hand, and each year during the rainy season they were destroyed by the floods and all had to be done over again the following year.

The land in the river beds was only a fraction of that required for sustenance. There was little level ground elsewhere, only hill after hill, the soil of which had no adhesion or cohesion, and slipped incessantly. With marvelous engineering ability the tribesmen had terraced the sides of the high, steep slopes, and had led water to them for irrigation, building stone and clay walls from four to ten feet high to keep the rice paddies from being washed away. From the very top of the mountains they stretched, "Down, down, and away over the mighty hills like stairways of the hosts of heaven."

The Ifugaos displayed the greater skill in all building operations. The Igorot house was merely a depression in the ground with logs and stones heaped around and covered with a high grass roof. But the Ifugao dwelling, built on stilts with board floor, wooden sides, and thatched roof, was a remarkable structure. The door posts had interesting designs carved upon them, and invariably the supports had the projecting shoulders to keep the rats and vermin from getting into the granary and store room. Chickens were hung at night in cages, like parrots, from the beams underneath the hut. Below these prowled the scavenging pigs, the dirtiest, leanest, and hungriest specimens I have met with on my travels.

In the Igorot country the girls and unmarried women lived in one large house, where young men of the village sought companions for the *oolug,* or trial marriage. Most of these were successful from the beginning; the partners in the experiment really wanted to see whether they could live happily together, and childlessness was usually the only cause of dissolution of unions made in this way.

As far as I could observe, the Igorots possessed a natural sense of morality. If pregnancy occurred, the mother and father married. Abortion was not popular; those who were compelled to practise it regarded themselves as prostitutes. The Igorots claimed knowledge of a certain vegetable extract which would help to cause abortion during the first two months of pregnancy. But under controlled conditions this drug was tested and proved ineffective.

The animistic religion of these tribes was as uncomplicated as their sexual customs. The spirit of life and death was the beneficent Lumawig who, they believed, appeared to them in ghostlike form. But they had always to propitiate the *anitos*, or spirits, which were embodied in everything alive and inanimate—bird, beast, snake, grass, wood, or stone.

The folklore of the mountains was extremely limited. The most common story was that of an old woman who had two boys. She was never satisfied with anything they did. They brought in all kinds of wood, but she always said it was either too green or too old, and for punishment began depriving them of food. The boys grew thinner and thinner until one day one of them climbed a tree and called to his companion. "I'll get some wood to satisfy the old woman." First he threw down one leg, then another leg, then one arm, then the other arm, then his trunk, and lastly his head. "Take those to the old woman," he said. He had given up his whole body and was now an *anito*. In the form of a bird he directed the other boy by the shortest path back to the house.

To the Western mind this story, in its incompleteness, adorns no tale and points no moral. But it is typical of the simplicity of the primitive mind which demands no explanations.

Far more backward and more difficult to make contact with than Igorot or Ifugao were the Ilongots, who suffered agonies from their superstitions, and propitiated the evil *anitos* with shrines. They were forest dwellers, small in size and numbers, who lived by hunting game with their large bows and arrows, and waged constant war against the more civilized peoples. Lying concealed along traveled trails, hiding behind their light wooden shields of dull brick red, they attacked from ambush, rushing upon the enemy and decapitating them. Worcester called them "a good deal more than half devil, with the balance half child, but peculiarly treacherous, vicious, and savage man."

Penetrating north, further and further from the settled territory, was like pushing back the curtains of time. Each successive tribe was one step backward in progress, and ferocity increased with each onward step.

The small tribe of the Kalingas, Mongolian in appearance, lived on the open spaces and the bare hillsides. Their houses were, however, often nested in trees, and even when on stilts were cleaner and more orderly than those of Igorot or Ifugao, so often grimed with soot and ashes. Their costume was especially colorful; they ornamented their hair with tufts of scarlet feathers, tipped with yellow. Their fighting regalia was as gay as their dress. They had black shields, quite different in shape from those of their neighbors, and brilliantly ornamented with scarlet and yellow, or black and white.

In making the first overtures among them, one of the white Constabulary officers formed a bundle of the lances thrown at him, and sent them back to the Kalingas, suggesting this was not the proper way to treat a would-be friend. Ultimately these tattooed devils, whose name means "enemy," were turned into effective agents for the maintenance of law and order.

Once the Kalingas had accepted the proffered amity, they showed a childlike curiosity in the devices of modernity. One of the officers displayed a phonograph to a Kalinga chief who could not believe that the sound which delighted him came from the machine, but ascribed it to some supernatural origin. When the phonograph was taken away, he dug deep into the ground with his bolo, attempting to locate the pipe which had conducted forth the sub-terrestrial harmonies.

Fiercest of all the mountain tribes, and the last to be persuaded of our peaceful intentions, were the Apayaos. They were supposed to be the remnant of a band of Moro raiders whose wild natures had been attracted by the wildness of the country, and who found as good hunting there as in Mindanao, a thousand miles away. The result had been a strange people, warlike, but fond of fiestas and gaudy clothing.

Forbes took a paternal interest in the welfare and happiness of the five tribes, and each year went on a tour of inspection, accompanied by his aide, Secretary Worcester, in whose department lay the care of the non-Christians, Governor Pack of the Province, the five sub-governors of Benguet, Ifugao, Bontoc, Kalinga, and Apayao, and a few favored visitors. I went along to keep everybody healthy, as well as to inspect medical progress.

The trip, which had to be made on horseback, required about a month. The baggage train would consist of carriers from the local province. Igorots, for example, would meet us at the edge of their territory. They would all pick up their fifty-pound loads and dash off over the hills, rarely following the regular trails, but taking a short route of their own. We never gave a thought to our unlocked baggage thereafter. It was invariably safe when we arrived in camp for the night; in my experience I have found that primitive peoples seldom lie or steal. Not merely was everything in its place, but the carriers with huge banana leaf umbrellas had kept everything dry in a country where rain fell almost daily.

Before Governor Forbes was to make his first inspection trip, he suggested that we ride his thoroughbred polo ponies. I had been over the rough, precipitous trails on other occasions, and was practically certain that I would have difficulty in handling the high-bred nervous animal assigned to me. Two weeks before we started, therefore, following a presentiment, I began to practise mounting and dismounting on the wrong side. By the time we set out I was quite adept at getting on or off either side of the horse.

On such trips I was frequently stopped by urgent requests to visit the sick. Medical attention was still rare; we had not yet had time to establish enough dispensaries in these almost inaccessible mountains. I happened to be delayed one day by one of these professional calls, and the main party went on ahead. While I was hurrying to catch up with them my skittish horse shied at a fluttering leaf, slipped, and left the trail. I leaped from the off side to safety. As he fell, he rolled over and over down the mountainside, loose rock clattering and banging after him. I peered over the edge, never expecting to see him, but by some miracle his forefoot had caught on a vine just at the edge of a sheer drop of hundreds of feet.

I was standing helplessly pitying the dumb animal, when the baggage train came trotting around the bend. Here was a possible solution. The sure-footed Igorots clambered down goatlike to the edge of the precipice and, while five or six held the poor beast, one cut the vine with his bolo, and others hauled the pony by the bridle. He came scrambling up the steep hillside, badly scratched but with no bones broken.

The most forlorn mountain village at news of our approach would be transformed into a bower of bamboo and greenery. The reception parties would come to meet us and escort us in under the triumphal arch with a grand hurrah. Always a *canao* would be held and native dances to the rhythm of an Umpah, Umpah, Umpah, beaten on an instrument that looked like a copper skillet, sometimes assisted by a nose flute or a stringed instrument of bamboo. Although the warriors would seem mirthful and gay at such a reception, we always had them stack their spears, over which two of our party were told off to keep a close eye, because in case of trouble their first movement was toward their weapons.

One of the essentials in the welcoming ceremonies in any Ifugao village was the passing of the *bubud*. To the foreigner this fermented rice drink was a vile tasting mixture, but to refuse the proffered loving cup as it made the rounds was an unforgivable offense. It had to circulate until it was emptied. Furthermore, if anyone entered the company before the ceremony was completed, he had himself to down an entire bumper. I had observed that Dr. Strong always happened to be absent while we were undergoing the ordeal by *bubud*. This made it necessary for everyone else to imbibe just that much more of the fearful stuff. I called Forbes' attention to Strong's defection; he nodded meaningly.

We reached Banaue, the next village, in a driving rain storm, and were received in a fragile lean-to. Dirty muddy water was rushing through a ditch past our feet. Just as the inevitable *bubud* made its appearance the prudent Strong, as was his custom, melted away. Manfully the rest of us kept at the container until finally we saw the bottom. At this point Strong returned unobtrusively and sat down debonair and smiling. The moment Forbes caught sight of him, he turned to the Apo and said, "Dr. Strong has not yet had his *bubud*."

With his dirty toes, the chief immediately retrieved the cannikin from the ditch, poured *bubud* into it, and offered it to Strong with a fine gesture of courtesy.

Strong was now in for it. He would take a swallow of the nauseating stuff, but it would not stay down. It would have been a bitter insult to have spit it out. We gloated fiendishly over his predicament. Large tears appeared in his eyes, and he had many chances to taste it both going down and coming up before it finally stayed down.

Strong was never again late for his *bubud*.

143

Presents had always to be given at a *canao*. Since there were thousands who had to receive them during a trip, this might have seemed a difficult job for anyone but Santa Claus, but these grown-up children were perfectly satisfied with strips of white paper, which they tied gleefully around their black hair. A big strong man might obtain two, or perhaps three, in the grab. Such shouts of joy were never heard even on Christmas morning.

Needles and skeins of colored yarn spread equal delight among the women. At one time Worcester who, because of his regal manner, was regarded with special deference, took along suitcases of such yarn for the women. To handle the expected rush, he used a large cabin into which they were admitted one by one, and passed out by another door. But after half a dozen had secured their yarn, the women, unable to restrain their excitement, stormed the guard, threw themselves into the room and buried the worsted, and Worcester as well, in a tremendous scrimmage.

A number of us rushed to the rescue. Only waving arms and legs could be seen; it seemed quite likely that the Secretary of the Interior would be suffocated. We seized the Igorot ladies bodily and tossed them through the window until we had dug down to where Worcester lay helplessly tangled in the skeins.

By such means as the giving of simple presents and entering into their festivities, we worked toward winning the friendship of the non-Christians, and bringing them law and order. But only little by little could tribal hatreds be broken down. Once when we arrived at Ifugao we found that an Igorot, in an attempt to escape from the jail, had been caught by the Ifugao guard, who had reverted to their ancient tribal hatred and cut him up badly, even breaking some of his bones. Taking no chances, they had then put irons on him.

Dr. Strong, after working over the prisoner for some time, was of the opinion he would probably die within eight hours, and could almost certainly live no more than ten. Since there was no possibility of his escape, Dr. Strong asked to have the irons removed, and laid him on the veranda of the guard house to die in peace. But because the feeling against Igorots was so strong, Captain Galman gave strict orders to the Ifugao sentry that the prisoner was not to be harmed in any way. If an Ifugao were given a direct order by his commanding officer, he would never disobey.

For a time all was quiet. The sentry paced up and down outside the guard house and Governor Pack sat inside doing his accounts. Then suddenly warned by a slight sound, Pack looked up to see the delirious prisoner, given up for dead, coming at him with leveled bayonet. With a convulsive and almost instinctive leap, he was through the window, calling to the sentry, "Shoot! Shoot!"

The sentry paid no attention, but continued placidly walking his beat. Governor Pack dodged in through the door, the "sick man" after him, and in a second leaped through the window again, closely followed by the small dark figure. The foot race continued. Round and round they went—from the garden into the guard house and out again through the window. Governor Pack was a big man and easily winded, so that he could never gain a safe lead over the prisoner who, wounded though he was, kept at his heels. The Governor was staggering when Captain Galman arrived on the run to see what all the noise was about.

"For God's sake, tell the sentry to shoot!" panted Governor Pack.

Captain Galman gave the order. The sentry came to attention, raised his rifle deliberately, and shot the prisoner through the head. Then he put the gun back on his shoulder, and resumed his beat as though nothing at all had happened.

The behavior of these Ifugaos was an exception. In general, the men of that tribe formed the best Constabulary companies, and practically always won the annual rifle competition. When the Americans came, the undress uniform was "back and side go bare, go bare." The government had to consider this prejudice in forming the constabulary. The Ifugaos liked the nice blouses with shiny buttons, but drew the line absolutely at trousers and shoes. As they strode along, it seemed like the march of civilization—strong splay toes gripping the ground firmly, brown legs twinkling in the sun, buttons on their blouses shined according to regulations, uniformed hats jauntily perched on their heads, and Springfields over their shoulders instead of bolos in their hands.

As soon as the health service was well entrenched in the hearts of the people, the educators followed through this opening wedge. The young Igorots learned English rapidly, the school idea spread quickly, and the mountain people often erected their own buildings with free labor. The most promising pupils were sent to Normal School, and are now teaching their own people.

After the schools were established the Church brought up the rear, both Catholic and Protestant, and began to capture pagan souls.

I once met a most disconsolate looking old Igorot sitting by the roadside. He looked so absolutely wretched that I stopped and asked, "What's the matter?"

"I feel so bad," he answered.

"Why? Tell me about it."

"Oh, Bishop Brent is coming here tomorrow."

"He's a nice man," I said reassuringly. "He won't hurt you."

"Oh, yes, I like him too," agreed the Igorot.

"Then what's wrong?"

"When he was here last he gave me a hat and I became an Episcopalian."

"That's fine. It's a good religion."

"Well, a little later a Catholic priest came along and gave me a pair of pants, and I became a Catholic."

"Catholicism is also a very good religion," I assured him.

"But what is Bishop Brent going to say? I don't want to make him unhappy."

The Igorot meditated until finally I asked, "Well, which are you going to choose?"

"I think I'll give the bishop back his hat and the priest his pants, and just be an Igorot again."

Far more primitive than any of the wild tribes were the Negritos. Only in August, during the dry season, was it possible to cross the East Coast barrier reef of Luzon to the country where most of them lived. They had once spread through the Archipelago, but they were a vanishing race, only scattered remnants of them remaining. They were dwarfish, with thick lips, knock knees, and black kinky hair. Many of them had curly beards. Their arms, like those of the African pygmies, were disproportionately long. That they were true Negroes was shown by the one piece cartilage in their spreading noses; all other races have a split cartilage. Even the octoroons show this negroid characteristic, which is regarded as a reliable test for Negro blood.

As far as health work was concerned we could do nothing for the shy, mild, little people any more than we could for the deer in the forest. They spoke neither Spanish nor English—only a gabble of their own. They had no houses; for shelter they ripped the bark off a tree and stood it against another tree. They used bows and arrows smeared with deadly poison, the merest scratch from which was supposed to be fatal. Like the natives of Yap, they made scar patterns by cutting their skins with sharpened pieces of bamboo and rubbing dirt into the open wounds. They were wonderful woodsmen but good for little else. The Filipinos had tried to use them as house servants, but they were hard to domesticate. Though they did not slave-raid themselves, these improvident people, when they suffered from hunger, used to sell their children into slavery. Sometimes they came into the cultivated country during the harvest season and worked in return for rice; otherwise they lived on game, fruit, and roots.

A small colony of them had settled back of the quarantine station on the slopes of Mount Mariveles, where on Sunday afternoons I used often to go for a stroll in the hills. On one occasion I had proceeded but a mile or two along a trail when I met a little naked Negrito girl about ten years old.

"Hello," I said without thinking.

"Hello," she responded with an American accent.

I did not believe I could have heard aright. To test my ears I said, "What would you like to have?"

"A chocolate ice cream soda," she answered without the slightest hesitation.

I would have granted this simple wish had it been possible. Instead, I inquired further and found she had been one of the exhibits in the St. Louis Exposition of 1903, and there had learned English so that she could speak it as well as any American child.

One amusing old fellow in her tribe used to call himself a chief, but his sole distinguishing claim to such rank was an ancient silk hat, his only article of clothing, given to him by a Spanish official. It always remained a mystery how he kept it dry and prevented it from molding in a country where dampness and heat were so incessant. But

147

in the course of years it became tattered and torn. Worcester was so delighted by the chief's unusual costume and afraid that it would not last indefinitely, that he brought a new silk hat from the States and presented it to the Negrito.

The hat must long since have passed to the old chief's descendants, but to this day I have no doubt that its lucky owner is accorded a position of honor and dignity among the shy Negrito survivors of the Mariveles Hills.

During my first years in the Philippines I had little to do with the Southern Islands of Mindanao and Jolo and the other Mohammedan lands. They were administered by the Army, and their health service was also under military control. It was always the endeavor of the civil régime to extend its sway to these Islands as soon as they could be pacified. This was difficult, because the Spaniards had been shooting them for several hundred years, and our Army and Navy was similarly engaged for over ten. Pershing had "subdued" them, and Wood had led a great attack to the center of Mindanao. Each time the Yakan Moros, more savage, more cruel and more aggressive than the Ilongots, had retaliated in kind.

The chief potentate to whom all the *dattos* were subject was the Sultan of Sulu, who lived on the island of Jolo, but was also Sultan of Borneo under British jurisdiction. The remnants of his former power could only be exercised over petty offenses and religion. In spite of being subsidized both from Philippine and British sources, he was always notoriously hard up.

On one of my visits I was accompanied by Professor John Mulholland of Columbia University who, in his lighter moments, practised magic and was expert at this art beyond most professionals, always maintaining that it consisted solely of trickery. Together we paid a call on the potentate and, in order to entertain him, I asked the Professor to work some of his magic. He agreed and went through the usual rigmarole of making things disappear and reappear, and then turned to the Sultan with the remark, "I can't possibly understand why money should be so scarce in Jolo when even the air is full of it."

He thereupon took off his coat, rolled up his sleeves, and pulled silver dollars out of the air until the floor was littered with them. The Sultan's eyes popped so far out of his head that they could have been

148

knocked off with a stick. To think that the air was so full of money and he who needed it so much had not been able to discover it! He was inarticulate with amazement, and I do not know to this day what he really thought of the performance.

It was not until we changed our policy to one of peace that any real progress was made among the Moros. In 1914 the change from military to civil government was finally brought about, and Frank W. Carpenter was put in charge. As Governor he showed the same sagacity as he had displayed when councillor to the successive Governor Generals of the Philippines. Tremendous progress was made toward pacifying this race of warriors under his administration; the bolo and the rifle were replaced by the hoe and the plow. Much time was also spent trying to organize schools to which the Moro women could go, but the men always retorted, "We don't want our women educated."

The Moro health service was brought under the central office in Manila and reorganized by Colonel E. L. Munson, who had done so much to help formulate the sanitary laws of Manila. Hospitals and dispensaries were established, and produced the same calming and civilizing effect as among the wild tribes. Colonel Munson was succeeded by Dr. Jacobo Fajardo, who carried the work yet further and accomplished it so well that he eventually became Director of Health of the Philippines.

With three hundred islands to inspect, scattered in a huge thousand mile crescent from the tip of Luzon in the North to the Celebes Sea in the South, much of my time was inevitably spent upon the water. Some of the Islands—Cebu, Mindoro, Negros, Samar, Leyte, and Panay—were large and easily accessible. Others seemed lost in the immensity of endless sea and sky. Once a year only the mail boat went to the rocky Batanes, tiny Christian outposts anchored firmly in the windswept Bashi Channel. The tidal maelstrom which separated them from Formosa rushed by with such fury that no swimmer and no boat propelled by oars could make headway against it.

One of this isolated group, only ten miles in diameter, was the curious and remote coral islet of Ibayat. It formed almost a perfect circle, cupped around a lake in the center which furnished the few thousand inhabitants with water. Ibayat rose sheer from the sea; an ocean liner could steam close to its edge and still find no anchorage.

Fierce as was the tide below, the wind on top was even fiercer. The houses had to be tucked half into the ground, and the roofs fastened on securely. In some areas, each stalk of sugar cane had to be pegged to the ground.

There was no break in the circular rim; not even a goat could clamber up. The island provided unexcelled grazing land, and the herdsmen had devised a method of exporting cattle which, although it seemed cruel to Western eyes, served its purpose. The animals were driven to the edge of the precipitous cliff and then ruthlessly prodded into space. I have watched them drop with helpless legs asprawl, all the while bawling in mortal terror. There would be a splash and a thud, and a splash and a thud; then bobbing heads would emerge and the poor frightened creatures would swim madly in all directions. Rowboats from the steamer would close in to pick up the short ropes previously tied around their horns, and when five or six had been towed within reach of the steamer's winch, one by one they would be hauled aboard by the horns. As many as three or four hundred would be taken away on a trip.

At rare intervals I paid a visit to inspect the work of the resident medical officer. To admit the visitor, the Ibayat hermits, like the monks of Athos, let down a basket dangling at the end of a long vine. We maneuvered underneath and, what with the rocking of the boat and the swaying of the basket, almost simian agility was required to scramble in. I clutched its sides firmly as it swung perilously back and forth; the vine stem seemed a fragile hold to life. I watched the top of the cliff slowly approach and could not prevent a sigh of relief when the basket bumped on solid ground.

CHAPTER 11.   FOR THEIR OWN
GOOD

THE Bureau of Health was like the tree of life, Yggdrasill. Worcester, Forbes, and I were the three Norns who assiduously watered its roots, which pushed their way around stones and through clay into the not too clean earth of Filipino existence, so that it might reach from the Hell that was to the Heaven that might be.

Necessarily we had to invade the rights of homes, commerce, and parliaments. We had to guard against the entrance of dangerous communicable diseases by strict measures, even when they conflicted with convenience or personal necessity, and segregate the cases of leprosy which might endanger the health of the greater numbers. Hospitals for the sick had to be built, and doctors and nurses trained. The physical welfare of the morally ill had to be cared for. The helpless insane and orphans had to be provided with homes. Births had to be recorded and resting places found for the dead. What the people ate, what they drank, where they went, and how they traveled had to be safeguarded. Finally, the great majority had to be taught how to arm themselves against disease and death.

But always we tried to tangle the threads of Filipino lives as little as possible.

When we arrived the hospitals were of the most primitive type. There was not a good operating room in the Islands and no laboratory facilities. Modern medicine had not penetrated far. To remedy this condition Worcester, in 1900, had formulated a plan on a noble scale to build a hospital, a medical school, and a laboratory of science all in one integral group—the medical center idea adopted in the United States so much later.

After the Bureau of Science was started in 1901, the next step was to train doctors. The ancient Santo Tomas University already had a medical school attached to it, but it was inadequate. In 1905 we secured an appropriation for a government institution with American curricular requirements, which later was to become part of the government-owned University of the Philippines. When the Church school saw the more modern one in operation, it raised its standards so that, in addition to turning out our own graduates, we were, by our example, assuring a further supply of well-trained young men. The Filipinos made excellent physicians, once their dislike of dirtying their hands was overcome.

But the project was not yet completed. Session after session and year after year Worcester presented to the legislative body a request for money with which to build a modern hospital in Manila. As often as he came away disappointed, he returned to the charge. After eight years of steady pounding he was rewarded with success. The Philippine General Hospital was authorized in 1908 and completed in 1910.

Hospitals are too often bare and bleak. We tried to make ours, built on the pavilion system, open on all sides, cool, pleasant, and cheerful as well as practical. By polished molave and media aguas we endeavored to soften its white austerity. For the first time hospital beds were equipped with wheels; they could be rolled on to the spacious verandas so that the eyes of convalescents could be made glad by the sight of royal palms and the gorgeous acacias, which twice yearly made the grounds a sheet of flame. What the patients ate at home was not good for them, and we had no wish to make them adopt our food, which they did not like; we handed over the problem of modifying their diet to imported dieticians.

But a fine hospital was not enough. The imported American nurses would soon go home and it was essential to have Filipinas to take their places. In the effort to train them, we came up at once against the strongly rooted social custom which decreed that women should do no manual work. My constant endeavor was to interest the Filipinas in health work; through them we could reach the men also. Rarely did a Filipino take any action without first consulting his wife. She held the keys to whatever there was of value in the house. She was the business manager and, as a rule, she was the more intelligent. The man cooked, washed the dishes, made beds, and also labored in the fields. Hospital nursing was foreign to the Filipina of the upper social strata. This prejudice had to be overcome.

I first persuaded five girls at the Normal School to include a course of nursing which in the beginning was to be entirely theoretical. They seemed to enjoy learning out of a book how much of this or that drug should be given for this or that ailment, but luring them into practising their knowledge was another matter. Only after much cajolery on my part did they consent to wander around the wards of the hospital for a few hours each day. But then they struck. It took candy and flowers to bring them back, and no sooner had I shepherded them into the hospital than they walked out again. After this had happened three times, I effected a compromise by installing a small sick bay in the Normal School, where a few students would pretend to be the patients. Half-heartedly for a few days the girls practised bed making, giving baths, and dishwashing, and then declared, "This is servants' work. We'll have no more to do with it."

At this turn of affairs, I threw up my hands. Not even Miss Mary Coleman, who was in charge, could, by any form of persuasion, get the young ladies back. Finally, in a moment of inspiration, she announced, "We'll have to write a play."

"But I don't know anything about playwrighting."

In the end, however, we composed a remarkable drama. I supplied the technical details and Miss Coleman the plot. We engaged professional actresses to play the roles of the nurses, who were all co-starred.

The performance was attended solely by invitation and sparkled with social tone. The wives of the highest ranking officials were all patronesses, and the tickets were distributed to a specially selected group, including our former pupils. The play, which was produced before a capacity audience, proved an unbelievable success. Crisis followed crisis. Almost every instant a situation arose where a nurse saved the day. Whenever one of the numerous heroines would rush in and snatch half a dozen lives from the jaws of death, loud and enthusiastic applause would shake the hall.

The next morning the five girls were back again, this time to finish their preliminary course.

As soon as it seemed safe, I ventured to send them to the hospital, with the intention of having them practise two hours a day in the wards. The morning after their first experience, I was sitting at my office desk when the attendant brought in a sheaf of cards. The briefest glance informed me that I was in for a mass attack from the parents of the girls.

As they stormed through the door, the leader said, "Our daughters have been humiliated and disgraced. We are taking them home at once."

"Why?" I inquired innocently.

"My Rosita was asked to go into a room where a man was in bed. She never can hold up her head in society again."

I tried reasoning, but with no success. Nothing I could say would cause these offended parents to change their minds. I then played my last card.

"I've been very patient with you," I said. "Now I'm tired of all this nonsense. Our American women are just as fine as yours, and they take up nursing careers without loss of dignity or self-respect. If you're so far behind in the scale of civilization that you can't realize this, take your daughters out of the school at once. I don't want them there any longer. I've given them the opportunity to learn an honorable profession. But you're just exactly what your critics—"

"Wait a moment," they interrupted in concert, "let's consider this further."

"No! Not for a second," I asserted firmly. "Take the girls away."

They began to plead with me. Their arguments turned to entreaty.

"No!" I said haughtily. "There's nothing more you need say."

But they said much more. Only after an hour's ardent effort were they able to persuade me not to dismiss their daughters.

The next year the class increased to thirty. Finally we had to make provision for two hundred. We distributed application blanks among the schools, which were to select the most desirable girls. Not only the chosen ones put in an appearance, but an additional one hundred accompanied them. I was pleased with their enthusiasm, and told them I genuinely regretted we had no room for the extra ones.

All Filipinos, men, women, and children, petition the Legislature when anything displeases them. The hundred rejected girls appealed to the Philippine Congress. They said I was refusing them an education, and demanded entrance to the school.

The Legislature subpoenaed me, read charges against me, and intimated that my resignation was in order.

When this ceremony was over, I asked, "Will you hand me that digest of laws over there?"

In the course of my professional duties I had been obliged to familiarize myself thoroughly with the volume in question, because such contingencies were apt to occur at any moment. I flipped the pages to the paragraph I wanted and read it aloud. It was to the effect that any public officer who incurred an expenditure not specifically authorized by the Legislature would be subject to fine and imprisonment.

I closed the book with a bang, laid it down, and struck an attitude. "I am acting in accordance with your own law," I told them. "If I admit these girls, I shall have to feed and house them. You have given me no money for this purpose, and I refuse to disobey the law!"

"We see that, we see that," they chorused eagerly. And immediately a law was passed appropriating the money necessary to include the extra hundred students.

In a way the question raised by the Legislature was most gratifying. It showed that nurses were making a place for themselves in the life of the community and that there was a desire on the part of the law-making body to give them protection. The long struggle to establish nursing in the Philippines on a sound basis with standards that would compare with the world's best now began to look as though it could be won. In this I was not only thinking of the Philippines but other countries in the Orient. There was hope that the sick of China, Japan, Siam, Java, and other Eastern nations could have much more adequate care. A career was in prospect for the women of the Orient through which they might have an important part in alleviating unnecessary suffering. If nursing on a proper basis could be established in the Philippines there was much reason to believe that it could be done in other Asiatic countries.

Once the nurses had accommodated themselves to Western ideas, they worked faithfully and fulfilled our highest expectations. They were invaluable because they knew the local language, customs, and prejudices far better than we, and, therefore, could teach the people how to apply the sanitary regulations. During a major outbreak of bacillary dysentery at Cebu they went from house to house, showed the inhabitants how to dispose safely of bodily excreta, sterilize water, prepare food, and demonstrated the importance of clean hands; dysentery disappeared almost in their wake.

In the midst of our worst cholera epidemic four young Filipina nurses not yet graduated volunteered for duty at the San Lazaro cholera hospital. With the dead and dying all around them they performed coolly and capably some of the most disgusting services that could be demanded of any human being, and with full knowledge that any slip in disinfecting themselves would change them in a few hours from cholera nurses to cholera victims.

Many of the graduates ultimately came to this country to study higher nursing. Some passed the United States Civil Service examinations with high marks and occupied nursing positions in America with great credit, and some returned home to teach in newly established nursing schools. Many of the nurses became adept public speakers, and were powerful politically. Whenever I wanted to have a particular health measure enacted into law expeditiously and inexpensively, I would request a committee of these women to talk to the legislators.

Until Filipino doctors also could be trained I necessarily had to depend to a tremendous extent on my American staff. These were of many types and gradations, but one and all supported me loyally. Efficient in a medical way, but one of the shyest and most retiring men I have ever known, was one of my quarantine officers, Dr. Turnipseed. It was the custom when going on board an incoming vessel to call on the captain first to have him sign the quarantine papers. One morning Dr. Turnipseed boarded a big ship from the Pacific Coast, went to the bridge, and knocked timidly on the captain's door.

"Come in," commanded a big gruff voice.

Turnipseed edged through the door and said apologetically, "I am Dr. Turnipseed."

"Well, you haven't anything on me. I'm Captain Garlic."

FOR THEIR OWN GOOD

Many of my doctors later attained eminence in the medical world, but one of the greatest geniuses among them achieved no such reputation. Dr. Gilbert I. Cullen could do more things well than anyone I have ever known. Whenever any place was mentioned, he had been there; whenever anybody was in a tight spot, Cullen was able to extricate him. His feats of legerdemain sounded so improbable that many people considered his experiences fabricated. But I saw him often in action, and I am sure the things I did not see must also have been true.

Cullen had come out in 1899 with the Philippine Volunteers, and had served in Hell Roaring Jake Smith's contingent at Samar, where the insurrection was raging most violently. All the signal men had been killed in the initial fight, and there was no way of communicating with Manila. Somebody familiar with Cullen's versatility suggested he might be able to use a telegraph key.

"Oh, yes, I can telegraph," Cullen admitted readily. For a month he alternated clicking out messages in Morse with dressing wounds and tending the sick. The Army was so grateful that a line was diverted to his tent from the main cable, through which all the news of the world came to him. It was always possible that Cullen, in the course of satisfying his curiosity, might stumble upon information of value.

Cullen served the Army well not only by his varied knowledge but also by his physical courage. When it was almost certain death for any American to set foot in the Pulajan country of Samar, the Constabulary asked him, because he had already familiarized himself with the native dialects, to undertake a mission into the interior. He went alone, and by methods of his own arranged for the surrender of the rebels.

When Cullen came under my jurisdiction I appointed him Health Officer of Samar, where his really thorough knowledge of medicine coupled with his unrivaled knowledge of the Island made him invaluable. His intimate acquaintance with Army affairs often stood us in good stead. One day he walked unannounced into my office at Manila. "What are you doing here?" I asked. "I didn't give you any orders to leave Samar. You're supposed to be there attending to your job."

Government appropriations were meagre, as Cullen was well aware. "I know how important bargains are to you," he replied. "There's going to be a big clearing out sale of Army medical supplies. I wanted to tell you ahead of time."

"How do you know?" I asked.

All Cullen would vouchsafe was, "I've ways of finding out."

That same noon I met the Quartermaster in charge of Army supplies and remarked, "I hear you're having a big sale of medical articles."

"Oh, no, we're not having any sale," he assured me.

I sent for Cullen. "I've just seen the Quartermaster and he says there isn't going to be any sale. I assume you had some private reason for coming up here. The best thing you can do is to get back as fast as possible."

"You'll get notice pretty soon," Cullen replied confidently.

Two days later the Quartermaster approached me. "Do you remember you asked me about a medical supplies sale? Well, I don't know how you found out, but we've just had a cable this morning telling us to clear them out."

Thereafter I believed in the accuracy of Cullen's information, though I never did find out how he obtained it.

Cullen had also had training as a lawyer. He was able to plead eloquently in court, and often defended the poor without thought of a fee, usually winning his case. But whatever his extra-medical activities might be, he never allowed them to interfere with his work. He was one of those rare individuals who require only a few hours of sleep; he did his reading and experimenting at night. Furthermore, he was so proficient mechanically that he was able to start a stubborn fire engine when Iloilo was burning up, and even build himself a radio set out of odds and ends when he was confined to a hospital bed.

After Cullen had served at Samar for some time, I had him transferred to the laboratory of the Bureau of Science with the idea of having him acquaint himself with the more recent developments in science. He had been there no more than a week when the head of the department asked me, "Why did you send Cullen here? He knows more laboratory procedure than we do."

FOR THEIR OWN GOOD

At another time a plan for the Coast and Geodetic Survey of the Islands was being developed by George Rockwell Putnam, who wanted to determine the exact spot in the Philippines on which to base his survey. This problem in triangulation was extremely difficult, and an expert in geodesy was brought from the United States.

Dr. Cullen happened to drift into the Survey office at Manila and asked inquisitively, "What are you fellows doing?"

"We're trying to plot a base position," he was told.

"Let me see what I can do," said Cullen.

With some merriment the data were handed over to him, but he surprised the experts by rolling up his shirt sleeves and setting efficiently to work. Their amazement grew as he completed step after step and arrived at the correct solution.

Cullen was past master of practically all branches of higher mathematics. A coast guard cutter was once about to leave Samar when the officers decided they needed a purgative. Somehow they confused a bottle of bichloride of mercury with Epsom salts; several died and the others were completely incapacitated. Nobody was left on the bridge. When Cullen volunteered the information that he had officer's papers, he was thankfully told to take command, and he navigated the ship safely back to Manila.

Cullen was always immaculately dressed. When everybody else was hot and untidy, he was clean and cool. Dr. George Shattuck of Boston went with me on one of my leper collecting trips. When we were off the East Coast of Samar, he said, "I'm terribly embarrassed, but I've left my toothbrush behind. I don't suppose there's any possible way of getting one here."

The place was remote and the nearest shop many miles away. But I automatically said, "Cullen will be able to take care of you."

Cullen did not let me down. To my question he replied, "Certainly, I have a new prophylactic brush right here," and reached into his dufflebag.

"How about some chocolates? Got some of those too?" I asked jocularly.

"Would you like a box?" he asked, and, like a magician producing rabbits from a hat, he handed out a pound carton.

One of the inevitable duties of any department of health is the compilation of vital statistics, which are an indispensable measuring rod of sanitary progress. Before we took charge in Manila not over forty percent of the births there were recorded, and the percentage was far lower in the provinces. By persistent efforts we gradually collected the necessary data. Sanitary inspectors on their rounds would make inquiries as to whether there had been any new births, and baptismal information was obtained from churches.

The cemeteries proved to be one of the most vexatious of all our administrative problems. In Spanish times the practice had been to deposit bodies in rented graves or in leased niches, the lease period being usually five years. When the time expired, the well-to-do would renew their leases or remove the bodies to their final resting places in the crypt. But unless another cash payment were made the bones were thrown out.

When the Americans came to the Islands their first messages to the homeland told of the ossuaries, or human bone piles, back of every church, and many a femur and tibia found its way to the United States as a relic from this far away and very odd country. In less than two years all the bones in the ossuary of Paco cemetery disappeared. Sometimes a section of a skeleton would turn up under queer circumstances, and we were never quite sure whether a murder had taken place.

No records seem to have been kept as to the exact location of bodies in the majority of cemeteries, which were scattered helter skelter over Manila, and mourners not infrequently had to witness the uncovering of remains in the same graves in which their own dead were about to be laid. Five or more bodies had sometimes been interred in one grave.

Governor Taft was amazed and distressed at the condition of the cemeteries, and had a law passed which compelled each one to secure a license. Being able to think of no other agency, he put the enforcement of the ordinance into the hands of the Health Department, even though the problem was one of esthetics and not of disease.

We had to examine each cemetery and listen to complaints which, in some cases, led us into legal complexities, and many times into conflict with the people, a situation we were most anxious to avoid.

As the schism in the Church proceeded, the followers of Father

Aglipay were not allowed to bury their dead in the Roman Catholic cemeteries. Constant fights and reprisals took place. An Aglipay health officer would declare a Catholic cemetery insanitary and close it. A Catholic of the old faith would complain to me there was grease on the top of his well, which must have come from some grave in the Aglipay cemetery near his house.

Whenever we had to close a filled cemetery, the Church had to find new ground. Formerly the government had supported the Church; now fees had to be collected directly, so much each for baptism, marriage, and burial. The Filipinos were not used to paying fees, and paid them seldom if ever; the priests had very little to get along on.

An Aglipay cleric one morning came to my office, and begged for a permit to bury a rich parishioner whose family ardently desired to have him placed in a cemetery I had ordered closed.

"I'm sorry I can't open this cemetery for you," I said. "It's far too crowded already."

"Oh, I should so like to eat some meat," he moaned. "I've had nothing but rice and dried fish for so long a time. You could make it possible for me to get some meat. All I need is a temporary permit for this one burial, and I could get some meat again."

I could not make an exception for him, but compromised by buying him a meal with meat included.

I not only had to watch over the cemeteries, but also concern myself with allied activities. There was an undertaker in Manila named Dell who had erected a new and first-class establishment for which he had to get a license from the Municipal Board. But all was not plain sailing, and he sought aid.

"You've helped me with the plans for my mortuary, and you know I've fulfilled all the health requirements. But the Board is going to vote me down. I don't know what I'm going to do. All my money is invested in this, and I'll lose it all."

"How do you know you're going to be turned down?" I asked.

"They've got a petition signed by a thousand people saying my establishment would be inimical to business and bad for trade."

"How much time have you before the hearing?"

"Only three days."

"That's time enough. Write yourself a flowery petition. Tell how your establishment would enhance values and be an asset to the city. Show how desirable it would be. Make it elegant."

"But all the people in the neighborhood have signed the other petition."

"Get their signatures first of all and then go further afield."

Here was an opportunity to test the truth of the current belief that anybody in the Philippines could get any petition signed for anything pro or con. There was a story of how, far back in Spanish times, charges had once been filed with the Governor General against a Provincial Governor. When shown the scroll with thousands of signatures affixed, the latter had asked, "May I have a week to answer?"

At the time specified he had returned with a long petition signed by twice as many people, which read, "To our personal knowledge the Governor General is a son of a jackass."

Dell accepted my advice and had his lawyer draw up a beautiful petition which he circulated. Every shopkeeper and householder whose signature was on the other paper was equally complacent when asked to affix his name to the new one.

At the hearing Dell's opponents read a petition signed by a thousand citizens against granting him a license. His lawyer thereupon rose and read a petition in favor of granting him a license, signed not only by the thousand who had endorsed the other, but by many others as well.

Dell obtained his license.

As a person wielding much authority over many activities, I was constantly being importuned for favors of one type or another. A gravestone manufacturer once came to find out whether I would let him print his advertisements on the back of the official death certificates; in return he promised to cut and erect me the finest tombstone in the cemetery.

I also had the usual difficulties in warding off ambitious salesmen from the States. A shrewd Irish American named Kelly, realizing it was a problem for our small staff to be in all necessary places at once, was constantly after me to buy some of the new-fangled motor bicycles for our sanitary inspectors. His argument was that they would be able to cover more ground with these contraptions. He had the proverbial pertinacity of his kind, and it was not easy to avoid him.

On my way to lunch at the Army and Navy Club I used to pass by the old Luneta, which during the late afternoon and early evening was filled with carriages and promenaders. One noon as I came across the park, practically deserted during the siesta hour, Kelly hailed me from his motorcycle.

"Please give me a minute. I want to show you how well it runs."

I had done some amateur bicycle racing, and was naturally interested. He inveigled me on to the seat. I was admiring the gadgets and fiddling with them when, without meaning to, I pressed something, and the thing started off like a shot. I had never been on one before, knew nothing about it, and had not the faintest idea how to stop it. All I could do was to guide it around and around the Luneta.

Kelly shouted directions at me, but the machine was making such a racket that I could hear nothing as I tore past. He rushed across the oval to intersect me, cupped his hands and yelled at the top of his lungs, but still to no avail. I sped along wondering how much gas there was in the tank and praying that nothing would get in my way before it was gone. I lapped the Luneta at least ten times, while Kelly shuttled back and forth, his face getting redder and redder, still screaming futile directions.

Suddenly a carromata loomed ahead. I swung sharply to one side to avoid it, and in so doing I happened to twist the handlegrip. To my amazement the machine increased its dizzy speed. This astounded me. In my bicycling days it had been essential to have the grips firmly cemented, and it would never have occurred to me that a grip could serve as a control on a motorcycle. But such was obviously the case.

Feeling safe in the knowledge that I had mastered the infernal machine, I thought I would have a little fun. I turned the rubber grip until I was going sixty or seventy miles an hour. Kelly was nearly crazy. There was no use now in his racing back and forth; he merely jumped frantically up and down.

After three or four turns, I took pity and pulled up to a neat stop right beside him.

"These things are very nice," I said as I dismounted nonchalantly and strolled on toward my lunch.

The Bureau of Health depended to a great extent on the Bureau of Science for aid of all sorts. Worcester's greatest achievement had been to assemble under one administration, as far as practicable, all the scientific work of the government, building up in one unit the most modern organization in the laboratory field that any country had ever evolved. Under the able direction of Dr. Paul Freer, discoveries were made which are even now just beginning to be utilized elsewhere in the world.

The Bureau of Science Biological Laboratory performed all the microscopy for the general hospitals, and diagnosed specimens of all kinds. Four hundred thousand rats were examined for plague bacilli. A routine examination was made for all cholera carriers. When a cure for any disease was announced the laboratory would test its value. Quack native remedies were often advertised as being cure-alls, and the people were apt to have more faith in them than in foreign importations. For any type of experimentation prisoners from Bilibid would always volunteer, because they would receive perquisites and even have their sentences commuted if they were to incur serious risks.

All vaccines or serums developed in any part of the world against disease were manufactured at the laboratory. Diphtheria antitoxin and the Pasteur treatment for hydrophobia were kept in readiness. Over two million units of vaccine against smallpox were made annually.

In addition to the routine at least half the laboratory was working on independent research. Extensive studies were made for eradicating the locusts which caused hundreds of thousands of dollars damage to agriculture annually, and years were spent in developing a rinderpest serum. Dr. Marshall Barber investigated the role played by cockroaches and other insects as carriers of cholera, bacillary dysentery, and typhoid. Dr. E. L. Walker worked more than a year on amoebic dysentery, and succeeded in differentiating pathogenic from nonpathogenic types. Over three thousand examinations were made of Philippine water supplies to determine their biological content.

The botanists combed the Islands, and for the first time classified the flowers and plants and studied the insect pests and the fungi, the forest products, fibres, seeds, dyes, and tans. The entomologists studied methods of exterminating mosquitoes, flies, and termites. They also conducted extensive research on the possibility of introducing silk culture, though the industry never gained a foothold because of too keen competition from China and Japan. The ornithologists collected the common forest birds, and showed which ones were injurious and which helpful. Worcester himself discovered the nesting place of the frigate bird, an enormous creature like the albatross. The Island of Bancanan was thickly covered with these strange birds, which refused to give the human trespasser the right of way, biting when any attempt at force was made.

The *Philippine Journal of Science* became rapidly one of the leading publications of the world in its field. The central scientific library, the largest East of Suez, was accessible to anybody. In the museum were assembled the tools, weapons, agricultural implements, costumes, and basketry of the various peoples. One of the most valuable collections of pictures in the world was gathered by the photographic department. A proof of each was filed so that the negative could be procured for use at a moment's notice. The wild peoples were photographed at regular intervals, showing the stage of civilization to which they had arrived year by year.

The chemical laboratory also had a vital function to perform. Ten thousand samples of cement were tested to see which would best stand the tropical quakes and downpours. Paints were tried out against Philippine sun and rain. The first steps were taken in developing industries. Soils were analyzed, copra production improved, gums, perfumes, and essential oils tested and experiments made in the extraction of sugar from the nipa palm.

The Food and Drugs Act in the Philippines could not be enforced until definite knowledge became available; first, of the effects of certain substances upon the human organism, and, second, until laboratory methods for examining foods had been still further perfected. But it was obvious that lime juice adulterated with five percent sulphuric acid, jellies with formaldehyde, peas with copper, cheap flavoring extracts with wood alcohol, and coloring matter with arsenic or mercury were highly deleterious to health. Moreover, the people were not being fairly treated when they bought butter with rennet added to increase the weight, or baking powder with starch added up to fifty percent, or lard with water added up to twenty-four percent, and mixed perhaps with starch, lime, alum, and salt. Sausage often contained nitric acid. Many shipments of milks contained formalin and other preservatives which might readily have been responsible for much of the indigestion among children.

Ice cream made in Manila had almost everything in it except what the name indicated. When brought to book the dealers claimed it was impossible to make proper ice cream in a tropical climate. Such claims were promptly disproved by the chemists, who demonstrated beyond question that good ice cream could be made as well in Manila as anywhere else in the world.

The chemists of the Bureau of Science were exhaustive in their search for these adulterated foods. One of them determined, for example, that certain imported lard contained cocoanut oil. Although Armour & Company denied categorically that it had been adulterated by them, our chemist stuck to his guns. It finally developed that the lard in question had been rendered from Oregon hogs fed on copra, and that the cocoanut oil globules had been deposited by nature in the tissues of live hogs.

When another of the chemists stated he had discovered salicylic acid in Hires root beer, that company almost burst with indignation. They said their chemists were as competent as any in America, and they could certify on their honor that their extract contained no salicylic acid. However, it turned out oil of wintergreen had been included among the flavorings, and when the extract had been shipped through the hot tropics the wintergreen had been chemically transformed into salicylic acid.

Then formaldehyde was found in Swiss strawberry jam. The Swiss said this was impossible, but it eventuated that certain sugars in the strawberries of Switzerland had the peculiar quality of turning into formaldehyde under the influence of heat.

The Chinese were naturally the great food importers, and controlled ninety percent of the business in Manila. They knew that a hundred centavos made a peso and paid more attention to the one which they did not have than to the ninety and nine which they had safely hidden. When we found adulterated articles on their shelves, we had to seize and destroy them. They meant to be law abiding, but they could not understand what we were trying to get at. In his bewilderment, one of them approached me and exclaimed plaintively, "The green the peas, the green the peas, the green the peas," over and over again. It was hopeless to try to explain to him that the peas contained copper.

We made life fairly miserable for the poor Chinese. On one occasion I stopped a shopkeeper on the street. Divining from my uniform that I was an official of some sort, without a word he brought out from under his shirt the leather bag in which he carried his valuables. First he presented me with his certificate of residence. I shook my head. Then out came his immigration certificate. I assured him I did not want to see it. He kept hauling out more papers—the cedula which proved he had paid his head tax. I shook my head again. He produced his merchants' tax receipt, looking up hopefully at me. Again he was wrong. I had given up trying to stop him by this time. His plague inoculation certificate did not satisfy me, nor did the license which showed he owned a stall in the market. Finally, he pulled out his vaccination card, which happened to be what interested me at the moment. I had never realized before what a bale of papers the poor Chinese had to carry about with him in the Philippines to prove his right to exist.

At the time the civil régime was instituted in Manila, there were two hundred or more places where the Chinese could buy a pipe and table space for twenty cents. Their contention was that opium, as they used it, was no more detrimental to their health than whiskey and soda to a foreigner. But while they were satisfied with the drowsiness and visions they obtained from their tiny pipes, the Americans and Europeans, when they took up the drug, wanted the full effect. In the fear that the Filipinos might become addicts to the opium habit unless some means could be found of preventing its spread, a commission was appointed. After studying the opium question throughout the East, it recommended that the drug be excluded entirely from the Islands two years from that date.

The first day of March, 1908, was "Black Sunday" for opium habitués. The truth and seriousness of the situation finally dawned on those who had sinned away their two years of grace between the passage of the law and its going into effect. The behavior of the victims in the face of the government's determination to save them by legal force would truly characterize them as fiends. The term fiend is used liberally by the laity, but becomes appropriate when a victim is deprived of the drug.

In sheer desperation the sufferers sought the hospital treatment provided by the government. The rush was so great and the task so hard that the San Juan de Dios Hospital, which had previously cared for drug addicts, asked to be released on the ground that it lacked proper facilities for the accommodation and restraint of so large a number of frenzied patients. Accordingly, to meet the emergency, the government made ready several wards of the new insane department of the San Lazaro Hospital. There the addicts fought, screamed, threatened, and sulked until they realized that the government meant business, when they quietly submitted.

Experience demonstrated that the opium habit was not particularly difficult to treat, especially among the smokers. Those who took the drug by mouth experienced more inconvenience, and those who were in the habit of taking it hypodermically suffered considerably. We used the Towne treatment as recommended by Dr. Alexander Lambert. Severe as it was, it was justified by the results. As soon as the craving for opium was gone, we proceeded to build up the patients. How many relapsed after being discharged from the hospital was, of course, unknown, but many habitués professed profound relief at being cured. Alcoholism could also be similarly treated. It gave me great satisfaction to pick up beachcombers and by the same method turn them once more into self-respecting citizens.

Upon the exclusion of opium and the closure of the public resorts, the price of opium promptly went up, which made it prohibitive for Filipino purses. Moreover, the Chinese were not particularly anxious to force the habit on the Filipinos, once they had to depend on illegal sources for their own supplies.

The Chinese are, without doubt, the world's most adept smugglers, and they soon devised ways and means of satisfying their simple needs. We were always finding opium in the most unheard-of places. One day, in my routine examination of imported foods, I made an unannounced inspection at the Customs House. A huge shipment of jam had just arrived. I had no reason for being suspicious, but as my eye traveled over the stacked cases I said to one of the inspectors without knowing exactly why, "I'd like to see one of those tins."

I took it in my hands, looked it over, and saw it was correctly labeled strawberry jam. Nothing apparently was wrong. Nevertheless, "Bring me a plate, please," I asked the inspector. When I emptied out the contents of the tin, it seemed an unusually small amount compared to the size of the container. Examining it more carefully, I found it had a false bottom. Every one of the forty-eight tins in the crate was then opened, but only four contained opium. An examination of the several thousand crates in the shipment showed that the Chinese, mathematically computing the probabilities of detection, had filled just four cans out of each forty-eight in every case.

Other smuggling devices were even harder to cope with. Although the Filipino backyards were overrun with chickens and roosters, eggs were comparatively scarce. Consequently, huge quantities were shipped from China. A favorite ruse of the opium smugglers was to insert a hypodermic needle into an egg, withdraw carefully all the albumen and then refill the cavity with opium. When the hole was expertly sealed, the illicit contents could only be discovered by breaking the eggs. Thousands of dozens were shipped by each Tuesday's steamer from Hongkong, and for a time the customs inspectors broke every single egg that came in.

But it was obviously impossible to open every tin of food or break every egg that passed through the various customs houses, and undoubtedly a great deal of opium must have slipped through, no matter how alert the inspectors were. In fact, the Chinese succeeded in getting large shipments of bulky and perishable lettuce and cabbages passed in right under our noses. They could always be bought in the Chinese quarter. Once we found a case labeled shoes which, under the first layer of slippers and boots, was made up of forbidden vegetables.

In 1908, just before sailing for the United States on leave of absence, I went to say goodby to Governor General Smith.

"I'm sorry you're not going to be here for our monster opium bonfire," he said. "It's going to impress the Chinese tremendously, don't you think so?"

I explained to him that in my opinion the Chinese, instead of being impressed with our high moral purpose in burning the seized opium, would think we were merely playing a colossal trick upon them. It would be inconceivable to them that we would destroy anything so valuable. I illustrated my point with an experience I had once had. At the request of the State Department, I had gone to China to carry out a diplomatic mission. I had no sooner arrived than I was offered fifty thousand dollars by one group of litigants. Although I paid no attention ultimately I had, in fairness, to decide in favor of the disputants who had offered me the bribe.

Hardly had I returned to Manila when I began to be besieged by Chinese wanting my advice. They would be sitting in my office every hour of the day and would ask my opinion on every conceivable subject—whether they should get married, whether a certain investment were good, whether they should buy more land. I could not understand it.

Then one day a Chinese came in who had been born in America and could both speak and understand English better than his compatriots. I asked him, "Why do all your countrymen keep coming to see me? They never used to."

"They think you are a very wise man."

"That's nonsense. What really is behind all this?"

He hemmed and hawed but finally told me the truth. "We all know you were offered fifty thousand dollars in China to decide that case the way you did. We also know you did not take that offer so that you must have received a better one. We had your bank accounts and all possible hiding places searched, and we have not been able to find a trace of it. Anybody who could successfully conceal so much money must be a wise man."

"That," I said to the Governor General, "is typical of the Chinese attitude. They'll never think you're burning opium, but will be sure you're pocketing the profits and substituting molasses."

"Then what would you suggest?"

"I'd have the opium shipped to the United States and made into pharmaceutical products which we could use for the poor in our dispensaries."

He accepted this suggestion, and for years thereafter the Bureau of Health had an ample supply of the drug.

FOR THEIR OWN GOOD

The Filipinos, in spite of our best efforts to persuade them of the value of the Bureau of Science in the development of the Islands, had never appreciated it fully, regarding it mainly as a place for the white collar class to earn an easy living at the expense of the populace. Governor General Harrison encouraged them in this misapprehension and his Cabinet naturally reflected his own attitude.

I remember the indignation of the new Secretary of the Interior Dennison, upon receiving an estimate of some sixty odd dollars for the photographing of certain molluscs. He even made a speech on this subject, which aroused great antagonism and a storm of articles in the press. His theme was that since the Filipinos were not interested in the Department of Ichthyology of the Bureau of Science, why should they pay money to provide a few scientists with pictures to gloat over?

"I could pay the whole share of the insular government in one teacher for the Mountain Province for the cost of these photographs. I am not unaware that the world outside of the Philippines may possibly prefer the photographs of the molluscs to teachers in the Mountain Province, but can there be any doubt in the mind of anyone that my duty is to spend that money for the interest of the Philippines rather than to further what may be considered the interests of the scientific world at large?"

Mr. Dennison, however, had not taken the trouble to inquire into the purpose of the appropriation. In the Philippines there was no window glass; in its place the window frames were filled with three-inch panes of the translucent mollusc shell. The Department of Ichthyology had learned how to propagate the mollusc and was trying to extend the market for this purely Filipino industry to the United States where other uses could be developed. To this end the disputed photographs were to be sent to the Smithsonian Institution. Mr. Dennison assumed that it was his function to determine whether the money should be spent on what the Americans thought was good for the Filipinos or for what the Filipinos themselves wanted.

During the years of Governor Harrison's administration the Bureau of Science almost entirely lost its reputation, and so many unscientific reports were published in the *Philippine Journal of Science* that its professional standing also was undermined. If the Bureau of Science were to be of utility, it was necessary to have on its staff men who loved research for its own sake. Such men could not do good work in the midst of the political atmosphere which existed from 1913 to 1921 in the Philippines, where almost every newspaper issue brought rumors of reduction in their salaries or even abolition of positions, and where scientific work was subject to constant hostile discussion by members of the Legislature. In a few years the Bureau was dismembered, its staff dispersed, and its appropriations for research restricted almost to the vanishing point.

The Bureau of Health suffered almost equally from the change in administration, but it was strangely due to Governor Harrison himself that one of the most advanced pieces of legislation in health was put through. My personal relations with him were always extremely pleasant. He probably found me useful as a consultant, because I had been through all the preceding administrations. I was accustomed to have breakfast with him often at Malacañan, and afterwards we would ride downtown together.

One particular morning Governor Harrison's attention happened to be attracted to a peculiarly lurid example of patent medicine advertising on a billboard. He pointed it out to me. "Isn't that a bad idea?" he asked.

"Frightful," I agreed. "Poor people waste their small savings on things which are useless, expensive, and often habit-forming. Here in the Islands the credulous population will accept as truth the wildest claims to a panacea, and the patent medicine evil flourishes like the green bay tree."

"Why don't we stop it then?"

"I'm surprised you ask that question. There's the red clause in newspaper contracts."

"What of it?"

"Your experience in the American Congress must have taught you nothing effective can be done in legislating against the proprietary medicine interests because they are too powerful."

"Anyhow, you draft a bill and bring it to me tomorrow."

"That's only twenty-four hours. I can't do a good job on it in that time."

"I want it quickly. Tomorrow."

I sat up all that night pounding out a draft on my typewriter, and then marking out here and inserting there with a pencil until I myself could hardly make sense of it. I worded it far more stringently than was really necessary, but wanted to have enough extras in it so as to be prepared for the inevitable and necessary compromises. At daylight I had a rough draft ready which I took to the Governor General's office as soon as it was open.

Governor Harrison glanced through it hastily and said, "That's fine. Just what we want."

"Then I'll take it to the Attorney General and get his advice."

"Oh, no, no, no. The bill is all right as it is."

"But it may not be in the proper legal phraseology. I'd much rather have him go over it."

"You've written lots of laws, Doctor, and I'm a lawyer myself. This looks all right to me."

"Well, at least let me make you a clean draft."

"No, I want it just as it is."

He was Governor General. He kept the document.

At six the next morning a boy knocked timorously on the door of my room at the Army and Navy Club, and said some gentlemen had called to see me on business.

"Tell them I'm in my office every morning at eight," I replied crossly. "I'll transact business with them then."

The door was shut. I was preparing to resume my slumbers when the knock came again. "They won't go away, Doctor," the boy explained, looking a trifle scared. "They say it's important and they must see you immediately."

With resignation I put on my dressing gown and started down the long stairway to the lobby. Even before I had reached the bottom, the waiting group spied me. All had papers which they began waving excitably in my face. "You're the fellow who committed this outrage," one of them shouted.

"What are you talking about?" I asked in amazement, and then suddenly recognized two or three representatives of the patent medicine interests.

"You had this outrageous law passed," another shouted.

"I don't know anything about any law. When the proposed patent medicine bill goes to committee you'll have an opportunity to present your views."

"How can we? It's a law already. It's been enacted." He shoved a paper into my hand and there was my bill, word for word as I had drawn it up, the strictest of its kind ever passed.

It was undoubtedly a law, but the history of its mysterious passage still required explanation. Subsequently I learned that, as soon as I had departed from the Governor General's office, he had had it copied and sent by special messenger to the Upper House. The President of the Senate had said, "Here's a bill which our very good friend Governor General Harrison has sent down. He's apparently much interested in it. It doesn't affect any of us, and I propose that, if he wants it, we suspend the rules, read it by title, and pass it."

The motion had been made and seconded, and the bill had been passed by acclamation.

When the House had met at four that afternoon, the Speaker had risen and announced, "Here's a bill which our very dear friend Governor General Harrison wants. The Senate has just passed it. Let's show our respect for the Governor General and pass it also."

By six o'clock the bill had been back on Harrison's desk. He had signed it immediately, and it had become a law. I was given the job of enforcing it.

The law was so stringent that magazines containing patent medicine advertising could not be shipped into the Philippines unless the formulae were published. Patent medicine concerns from all over the earth raised a howl. Our only counter to this was that we had not attempted to prohibit the sale of nostrums, but merely required publication of formulae. If this were done, however, anybody could see that the ingredients of pink pills at one dollar a box were probably nothing but Blaud's carbonate of iron which could be bought in any drugstore for fifteen cents.

Because the measures of the Health Bureau had been so criticized, when Governor Harrison had arrived and had begun dismissing Americans on every hand, it was assumed that I should be among the first to go. When the weeks passed and I still remained, a newspaper war began to wage around the rumors. The United States press, of all shades of political opinion, and even the trade journals took part. Telegrams, letters, and newspaper clippings made a pile waist-high, all protesting against my being interfered with and stating that my dismissal would be an outrage. Finally President Wilson stilled the troubled journalistic waters by issuing a statement that I was not to be removed. Governor Harrison then broached the subject for the first time by echoing the President's words and saying such an idea had never entered his head.

Paying no attention to the clamor, I proceeded with my duties.

CHAPTER 12.   THE HEAVENLY FLOWER

SMALLPOX is as loathsome as leprosy and claims many more victims. Millions of people, who could so easily have been saved, have died of this disease. Hundreds of thousands have been doomed by smallpox to lifelong blindness. Every bazaar in India is filled with these helpless and pitiful martyrs, groping their way through eternal darkness, or led stumblingly about by those who are already overburdened with poverty and sickness.

This heartbreaking condition is due to the stubborn refusal to accept the simple and effective remedy that science has to offer. The world, if it so willed, could be free of this most horrible disease.

One of the most satisfying successes of the Bureau of Health in the Philippines was the almost complete obliteration of smallpox. It was the more satisfying because it need never be feared again. Forty thousand people, most of them children, were alive at the end of each year who, in times past, would have been dead, and thousands upon thousands were saved from blindness and disfigurement.

The microbe which causes smallpox has never been discovered. But the disease is one of the most contagious of all human afflictions. The eruption on the skin, the breath, and the clothing of the patient can apparently convey the disease to others. There is even a strong possibility that the infection may be carried through the air. Smallpox patients used to be kept on board hulks anchored in the Thames, and it was noted that people who lived on the lee side of the smallpox

176

ships suffered badly from the disease, while among those to windward there were few cases.

Smallpox has existed as far back as we have any records. It was
in India and China in 300 B. C. In the sixth century A. D. it was epidemic in Southern France and Northern Italy. Among the Crusaders
it wrought fearful havoc. The first settlers brought it to this country
where it killed more Indians than the bullets of the Puritans. In virgin territory it reaped a frightful harvest. With the increase in travel
during the Eighteenth Century it was spread far and wide.

Long before vaccination was discovered, attempts had been made
to lessen the ravages of smallpox. It had already been observed that
anyone who had once had the disease would never sicken of it again.
The Hindus, Chinese, and Persians practised inoculation; that is, they
transferred pus from the pock of a sick person to one who was well.
This "sowing the smallpox," as it was called, caused a true case in the
person so inoculated. One most unpleasant Chinese method was to
soak a shirt in smallpox pus and put it on the victim; another was to
blow the dried pus into his nostrils. The hope, often futile, was that
smallpox thus contracted would be milder in form, but too often the
procedure ended in fatalities.

In India, where inoculation was directed by Brahmins, it was
somewhat better managed. The prospective patient, to get him in the
best possible physical condition, was placed on a special diet and rest
routine before the ordeal. The Brahmins would then soak a pad in
pus mixed with holy water from the Ganges and apply it to the upper
arm.

As time went on and attempts to reduce mortality spread westward, methods of inoculation began to approach the modern idea of
vaccination. In Turkey a wound was made in the upper arm, the pus
inserted, and a walnut shell tied over it. Lady Mary Wortley Montagu, wife of the British Ambassador, indefatigable observer and
chronicler of everything and nothing, described the inoculation parties
at Constantinople in 1716. Groups of people would gather and arrange to have an old woman come "with a nutshell full of matter of
the best sort." Lady Montagu's correspondence with friends at home
was responsible for introducing inoculation into England.

Macaulay wrote a particularly graphic description of smallpox during the Seventeenth Century in England, where it had been estimated that only five out of every thousand escaped, and one out of four died.

"The smallpox was always present, filling the church yards with corpses, tormenting with constant fears all whom it had not yet stricken, leaving on those whose lives it spared the hideous traces of its power, turning the babe into a changeling at which the mother shuddered, and making the eyes and cheeks of a betrothed maiden objects of horror to the lover."

More than half those living had borne pockmarks. To be without them had been conspicuous; an unmarked face had been useful in describing a fugitive. Two-thirds of the inmates of the early blind asylums of London were there because of smallpox. The disease could not be shunned and each new generation had brought new victims.

The English fashion of inoculation was to take smallpox virus from a fully developed pock and insert it under the skin of a well person. It was found the disease when induced in this fashion was much milder, and gave a mortality of only one percent, but since it was as contagious as smallpox normally contracted, this method involved isolation for a number of weeks. Friends used to be inoculated at the same time and pass the period of seclusion in each other's company.

Apparently the Sanskrit texts made mention of the protective qualities of cowpox. But although this vital fact may once have been known, it had long been buried in an oblivion from which it did not emerge until the end of the Eighteenth Century when Edward Jenner investigated the dairy maid's chance statement that persons infected from sores on the udders of cows with cowpox escaped the more fatal malady. In 1796 he vaccinated eight-year-old James Phipps with virus taken from the sore on the hands of a milkmaid who had been infected while milking a cow. Six weeks later he inoculated this same boy with smallpox, and the disease did not take.

Jenner's paper, announcing his discovery, was rejected by the Royal Society, and he, like Dr. John Snow, had to publish at his own expense. However, unlike many of his confreres, he attained high honors during his lifetime from universities, learned societies, sovereigns, and even from the American Indians. The enlightened ones of a world who had so long suffered from this blight recognized that his contribution, differing from so many which had been mere steps in the conquest of a disease, heralded the possible annihilation of smallpox.

Immediately after Jenner's announcement a storm of controversy, for and against vaccination, arose. It was possible that, having seen the too often fatal effects of inoculation, the great mass of the people accepted this heritage of fear and classed vaccination with previous experiments towards immunization. Professor Benjamin Waterhouse of Harvard University took up the cudgels for vaccination, as Cotton Mather had done almost a century before for inoculation. He vaccinated his own family, only to find that the newly born but already lusty anti-vaccinationists were at once up in arms. He had to take his children to the smallpox hospital and actually expose them to the disease before people would believe they were immune. When he was asked to argue the merits of vaccination, he always rejoined that one fact in such cases was worth a thousand arguments, and he was ready to demonstrate the fact. Waterhouse sent some of the virus to President Thomas Jefferson in 1801, and himself vaccinated some of Jefferson's family.

Spain, often considered an unprogressive country, has been a leader in introducing vaccination into her colonial empire. In 1803 a ship sailed down the Guadalquivir with twenty-two children on board. During the voyage they were vaccinated by passing the contents of the vesicles from arm to arm so that it could be preserved until they reached Manila. Three years later that city had a Bureau of Vaccination, and in 1850 an institute for the manufacture of virus. Systematic vaccination was inaugurated in many of the provinces, but at best the work was sporadic and often interrupted by lack of funds.

Smallpox existed throughout the Philippines. Under a Spanish law vaccination had been compulsory, but lack of efficient organization preceding the American occupation had made it largely ineffective. Each year during the dry season a huge temporary hospital had to be erected at Manila to take care of the hundreds of victims, the great majority of whom died. The Filipinos were not against vaccination per se, but they had become accustomed to see the law not observed. The strong fatalistic philosophy which ruled their conduct permitted them to take chances that their better judgment condemned as unnecessary and hazardous.

When the Division of Vaccination was reorganized in 1905, my aim was to vaccinate all the seven million inhabitants of the Archipelago, including every new-born baby by the time it was a month old, and, furthermore, to see that everybody was kept vaccinated. For the safety of all each newcomer had to be included also.

The authority under which I acted required that every person in the Islands who could not furnish satisfactory evidence, either by certificate of recent date from a president of a municipal board of health, public vaccinator, duly qualified physician, or such other person as I might designate, to the effect that he was immune against smallpox, should have to submit to vaccination as often as might be required by the above-mentioned authorities. The greatest error with which any person can delude himself is that because he has been in the presence of the disease and has not taken it, he is immune. Many lull themselves also with the idea that one successful vaccination, perhaps in infancy, is protective for all time to come.

The first plan was to have the local Filipino health authorities take charge of vaccinating everybody who lived in their districts; but it did not work. In most instances, the health officer did not appreciate the necessity and importance of vaccinating every individual, without exception. He often would permit his friends, or perhaps influential caciques, to go unvaccinated.

As soon as it was demonstrated that Filipinos were often negligent and were apt, under pressure, to break rules, a new system was organized. An American physician, with some twenty or thirty vaccinators, began at one border of a province and literally marched across it, only going forward when all behind could display the evidence on their arms.

Reliable vaccinators were hard to get in sufficient numbers. Not until they were taught antisepsis were they allowed to go to the provinces and use the vaccine. Fortunately for our expense account, a Filipino who was learning any trade was willing to work for very little money, and we were able to accomplish a great deal at small cost by taking on *aspirante* vaccinators.

In 1905, the first year of the campaign, the stupendous number of

1,687,767 people were vaccinated. It was not all smooth sailing. In some districts the vaccinators were regarded as busybodies interfering with the routine of life. In Iloilo much patient effort was required to overcome the false rumor openly circulated by the mal-disposed that vaccine had been purposely infected with leprosy and that all those whom the lancet touched were doomed to the living death. In another outlying district, it was necessary for the mayor, the head of the police force, and myself, to be publicly vaccinated before the timid were reassured.

In provinces where violent objections were encountered, the vaccinators were as a rule withdrawn at once. We bided our time. In six months an unvaccinated pueblo would turn its eyes enviously from its own sick to the fortunate neighboring pueblo where tiny arm scars had taken the place of horribly disfiguring pocks, blindness, or death. The chief men in the unvaccinated pueblos would themselves request that the vaccinators return. For example, in the province of Albay, bitter opposition was encountered in Tabaco and Malinao. Many of the inhabitants fled before the vaccinators. But in the following year there were forty deaths in those two localities alone, and not another one among the 234,000 population of Albay.

Similarly, great opposition was encountered at first in Antique Province from intransigents who even threatened the lives of the vaccinators. However, by the use of tactful persuasion, a number submitted. Shortly afterwards smallpox broke out, and the death rate mounted. Here was visible proof that those who had been vaccinated, even when they were nursing the sick, did not contract the disease. The people of Antique cried for help and welcomed the same vaccinators whom a short time before they had driven away.

Patience worked wonders in Albay and Antique, but the outlying districts presented an entirely different type of problem. Bagac was an isolated barrio of two thousand inhabitants in the province of Bataan, situated in the path of the monsoon, accessible by sea only during short seasons, and by land requiring strenuous travel over a wretched trail. From 1896 to 1901 the district had been in the throes of war and rebellion and therefore neglected. But in the 1905 epidemic of smallpox, there was an outbreak at Bagac, and it would have been criminal negligence had we not attempted to protect it. As soon as one of the villagers had brought the news that every house in the barrio had one or more cases, I immediately loaded a launch, sturdy as a tugboat, with vaccinators and supplies. We plowed down the Bay, through the Boca Chico, and up the coast until we arrived off the village. Twenty-four hours a day, while the Northeast Monsoon blew, the great rollers piled up on the sandy beach where great boulders protruded here and there. The shore shelved so steeply that anchorage was out of the question. We had to lower a boat in the open sea, and thought ourselves lucky to surge through on top of a huge comber and land on the beach without upsetting.

The results proved worth the effort. Two weeks later there were no new cases of smallpox in Bagac, and soon the disease had disappeared completely.

Many regions in the Islands were so remote that to reach them required from two to three weeks of toiling over rocky trails and through morasses. Since the ordinary glycerinized lymph would not remain potent off the ice for more than ten days at the longest, no vaccination seemed possible. We tried to get ordinary lymph to these communities, but it had lost its potency and our time was wasted. Vaccine in powdered form was tried, and also the so-called dry points, but the percentage of success was so small and the danger of infection so great that their use was abandoned.

Unless everybody could be vaccinated, the danger of infection always lurked in the background. It was important to reach to the uttermost parts of the Islands. Since I could not improve the transportation, the length of time for preserving the potency of the lymph had to be extended. I devised a small portable ice box which nearly doubled the period during which the vaccine could be kept potent after it had left the laboratory.

A tight box, filled with ice, was placed inside a larger box, so that the airspace between the two would serve as insulation. The virus was put in small opaque receptacles and laid upon the ice. The whole was then locked and sent to the district medical inspector who had a duplicate key. Sometimes the boxes went by government launch or by bancas, sometimes by carretelas or carabao carts. Where there were no roads into the wilderness, the carts were mounted on skids so they would slide over the mud, and the carabao would follow the streams, sometimes half swimming. Whenever the animals grew hot and tired, they would lie down and wallow, but somehow or other they would manage to get through. Even occasionally the little ice boxes reached their destinations on the backs of runners.

The empty boxes were returned by the same devious routes to the Bureau of Health; there was a continuous stream of them going in and out of the central office.

With all our efforts it was impossible to reach some of those who, through no fault of their own, were maintaining the seedbed of the disease. When I was home on vacation in 1908 I spent an evening at Menlo Park and submitted the question to Edison. He already had wealth to spare and was planning to devote the rest of his life to inventions which would be valuable to the world though they might produce no money. In a small black book were entered just such problems. He had already experimented with a box which would give out carbon dioxide, but the little escape faucet kept freezing and defeating its own purposes. He was so interested in what I told him that he said he would set to work again to try to overcome this difficulty.

But Edison never solved the problem. An even better solution was discovered in Java by the Dutch, who are a very resourceful people. They utilized the knowledge that the strength of a virus may often be stepped up by inoculating from one type of animal to another. They introduced human seed vaccine into a rabbit, rabbit vaccine into a calf, and calf vaccine into a carabao. The resulting serum was emulsified with two parts glycerin, and then sent out in glass tubes enclosed for safety in bamboo containers. This vaccine, which will last more than a month in tropical heat, is now saving thousands of lives in the East. In 1915 the Indian government was about to erect vaccine plants at great cost in the mountains, because vaccine could not be manufactured during the hot season in the lowlands. I had just learned of the Dutch discovery, and suggested that use be made of it. By adopting the Dutch method India was saved the expenditure of thousands of rupees.

We had developed a system of making our vaccine which was efficient and cheap. We would buy carabao calves, shave a place two feet square on each one, and with a knife dipped in cowpox vaccine make stripes an inch apart, crossing them with other stripes until the bare space looked like a gridiron. On this surface vesicles would appear in great numbers. Out of one calf we would secure about three hundred cubic centimeters, or enough to vaccinate a thousand people. As soon as the calves had recovered from cowpox we would sell them back for what we had paid for them.

A complete vaccination of the Philippines could not be accomplished in one year or even two. We worked as fast as we could, taking first those districts where the scourge was worst. I remember in December, 1910, the *Basilan* was returning to Culion with a full complement of lepers. It was obvious that we should arrive too late in the evening to land. I knew I was somewhere in the vicinity of Caluya, a small isolated island I had never visited. Since I did not wish to waste six hours riding at anchor in Culion Harbor, I suggested to the captain, "Let's put in at Caluya. I'd like to have a look at it."

Accordingly, the *Basilan* lay to off the beach and a boat was lowered. The first thing I noticed as we approached the shore was that the usual welcoming throng had not come pouring down to meet us. In fact, the beach was deserted. I walked into the town. It, too, was silent and lifeless; not a human being was in sight. I peered into the dim interior of the nearest nipa hut. The air was fetid with the poisonous discharges of smallpox pustules. Eight fevered bodies were tossing restlessly. I went to the next hut, and there were seven more. Some were in the early stages of pains and fever, their faces covered with hard red pimples not yet broken; some were already approaching death.

From the third hut I extracted a Filipino youth who, although terror-stricken, showed no signs of the disease. In the ten houses I inspected I found only one other Caluyan untouched. Each had a perfect vaccination scar. "How did it happen that you two were vaccinated and not the others?" I asked.

"Last year we were visiting in Calapan when the vaccinators came and we were vaccinated, too."

Out of the thousand inhabitants of Caluya, five hundred had died. The epidemic had started with the arrival of an infected person from Antique. An old woman, in the attempt to prevent the spread of the disease, had harked back to the Eighteenth Century, taken the contents of a pustule from the smallpox case shortly before death, and inoculated a number of the inhabitants. In a little over two weeks the epidemic had followed. The population of the islands in the group totaled two thousand. One thousand already had the disease before my vaccinators, for whom I sent immediately, could arrive. Of the remaining thousand, eight hundred were vaccinated, and of these not one contracted smallpox with a successful vaccination two weeks old. Two hundred had fled in terror of the disease and we could not find them.

The Filipinos in the outlying islands, in their ignorance, were apt to be afraid of vaccination until they became accustomed to it. There were always evaders; even on shipboard where we rigorously enforced vaccination we had to watch carefully. I happened to be out on business in the harbor one day and passed by a ship on which the crew was being vaccinated. One Chinese after another was swarming down a line into a lighter tied to the stern. After my vaccinators were satisfied that everyone on the ship had been accounted for, I ordered one of the crew to cast off the lighter. When we boarded it, I never saw a more astonished lot of coolies. They chattered and gibbered in dismay at having been caught as we lined them up and ordered them to bare their arms.

Legally I had the right to have anybody vaccinated; if necessary I could call on the police for assistance. But I preferred to use other means if possible. The Filipinos seldom made any protest after the first few years. Most of the objectors were unvaccinated Americans, among whom the mortality was twice as high as among Filipinos. When any of my vaccinators encountered one of these conscientious objectors, he had instructions to send him straight to me.

One noon hour I was sitting all alone in my office, and a great enormous American blacksmith entered. "You're the guy who's goin' to vaccinate me, are you?" he began truculently.

"No, I'm not," I answered. "I don't want to vaccinate you if you don't want me to. My duty is to tell you what risks you are running. This contagion is so widespread that I don't know any unvaccinated person who hasn't caught the disease. A health officer's joys are few. It gives me pleasure to attend the funeral of someone who has died of smallpox because he was not vaccinated. Only last week I went to one of those funerals. All I'm going to do is tell you that you're running a terrific risk, but if you don't want to be vaccinated, it suits me perfectly. I'll announce in the afternoon papers that you are an anti-vaccinationist. When you come down with smallpox, I'll have that item printed also, and I'll do the same with your death notice. You know, of course, that you have less than a fifty-fifty chance to pull through. But I'm delighted that you are offering yourself as a human experiment."

"Aw, come on, vaccinate me," was his only retort to this harangue. Like a well-disciplined dog he followed me to the special little vaccination office maintained to accommodate any who came to be vaccinated.

No force, no persuasion, no wiles, were necessary on the German Island of Yap. I observed when I went there in 1911 that vaccination day was a holiday. Native runners were sent out in advance to advise the communities that at a certain time the doctor would arrive prepared to vaccinate all who might desire it. The entire village would appear en masse to avail themselves of this wonderful opportunity to be ornamented with the scars of which they were so proud. Vaccination was a rare treat because the Yaps were accustomed to inflict wounds upon themselves and to keep them open by frequent scratching, or by rubbing with sand, bamboo, or shells. As soon as a scab formed from the vaccination they would scratch it off, so as to make the resulting scar as large and round and white and beautiful as possible. The doctor in charge told me that natives frequently asked to borrow vaccine and a lancet with the idea of vaccinating themselves and adjusting the size of the scarification to their own fancy.

In Mindanao, which was under military rule, and where the influence of the Bureau of Health was nebulous, the Army doctors as a matter of routine vaccinated the troops, and for protection also vaccinated the Moros in the vicinity of the military posts. In the course of time it became evident to the Moros of the back country that their brethren who had been vaccinated did not get smallpox.

One day about three hundred Moros, all armed with krisses, appeared with a flag of truce outside one of the Army camps. "We have come to be vaccinated," their *datto* announced.

The post surgeon met the *datto* in a field nearby and said, "I'm very sorry, but I can't vaccinate you. I haven't any vaccine."

The *datto* replied in a matter-of-fact way, "We came to be vaccinated, not to listen to any foolishness."

The surgeon caught the glint and heard the whisper of drawn krisses. He thought quickly. "Without doubt you're in urgent need of vaccination," he agreed. "I'll see that you are accommodated at once."

He retired, therefore, to his office, and returned shortly with a bottle of distilled water. With a scarifier he carefully scratched each arm and applied the sterile water.

When he had finished the last brown arm, he said to the *datto*, "One time is not enough. There will be no scar from this. You must come back again on the tenth day."

The satisfied savages returned to the jungle and the doctor hurried to the telegraph operator. His message to me requested a large supply of vaccine, which I despatched to him at once. It arrived in time, and at the end of the ten days the Moros all reappeared. This time they were effectively vaccinated.

Our vaccination record in the Philippines was unique both in its wholesale nature and in the total lack of injurious after-effects from infection. In the course of a few years we performed twelve million vaccinations; practically no cases of smallpox occurred among the properly vaccinated, no one died as a result of vaccination, and not one arm or leg was lost. This was absolutely unprecedented; even in Germany, where the most modern sanitary practices prevailed, out of every million vaccinations several people died or lost arms or legs because of infection in the wound. I had conceived the notion that, if the scarification were not dressed but allowed to dry, tetanus germs would be less likely to gain a foothold. Much to our gratification it turned out that, in trying to avoid tetanus, we avoided nearly all infection. Of the hundreds of nurses who served in our hospitals, only one contracted smallpox. She had been vaccinated, but, since she did not believe in the practice, she had rubbed the virus off with alcohol.

In time our system worked with a high degree of efficiency. The death rate was reduced from forty thousand annually to seven hundred, and the fatalities occurred in districts too remote for us to reach or among unvaccinated children. Childhood furnished the smallpox reservoir. The Filipinos who reached the adult stage had either had it or were immunized. There always remained a few who took to the hills, climbed trees, or hid in cellars to evade the vaccinators, and those kept small foci of infection perpetuated. If everybody in the Islands had been vaccinated there would have been no smallpox. In Manila, where we had complete control, there was not one death from the disease in the seven years prior to 1914, where before there had been thousands.

One of the greatest catastrophes in modern times began in the Philippines in 1918 when fifty thousand people, most of them children, lost their lives from smallpox, and the total eventually reached almost a hundred thousand.

I had been away from the Islands for three years, traveling from one out of the way place to another, and had just arrived in the United States. I was on the train from New York to Boston and from the window saw signs which in effect asked, "People of Massachusetts, how much longer will you stand for this frightful practice of vaccination? The Philippine Islands, which have been cited and vaunted so much as having been freed from smallpox, now have one hundred thousand deaths. What better evidence do you want of the valuelessness of vaccination?"

Soon afterward I was recalled to the Philippines as one of General Wood's advisers under a return of the old régime. He, as an administrator, was appalled and worried by the smallpox situation; as a physician he was intensely interested in the causes of this recrudescence of an infection once stamped out. He joined me in my search. We started with the children. We looked up their health records, which certified they had all been vaccinated. We then inspected the Health Service at Manila and found the vaccine had been manufactured and sent out regularly. To make a final check we went to the schools. In classroom after classroom we found to our indignation that, in spite of the records, the children had not been vaccinated. Naturally we wanted to fix responsibility. We discovered that local health officers had consistently falsified their reports. In some instances many more vaccinations had been reported by them than would have been possible with the quantity of vaccine sent to the vaccinators. In other cases, rather than do their jobs they had thrown the vaccine into the waste paper baskets where we found it.

Thus a huge unvaccinated population had come into being, and it had only been necessary to blow upon the ever present spark to start the conflagration. The bellows had been used; the spark had kindled into flame. Century-long exposure to the disease had bred no immunity. The Filipinos had died like flies, and the heat of the conflagration was so intense as to affect those who were only semi-fireproofed by vaccinations of too long standing.

Between 1918 and 1920 the Islands had lost twice as many lives from smallpox as the United States had lost from casualties in the World War. The death toll could have been avoided. The figures showed conclusively that ninety-three percent of the deaths had occurred among the unvaccinated. I described to Wood my previous methods which had proved so successful. He put the same regulations into effect and the Islands were once more freed of the disease.

The problem of eradicating smallpox from the Philippines was no different from that anywhere else; it merely involved the thorough and repeated vaccination of everybody, without exception. Unless local sanitary officials in every country can be made to realize that infants must be vaccinated shortly after birth, that unprotected transients must submit to the operation, and that everybody must be periodically revaccinated, smallpox will continue to prevail.

If the so-called special visitations of Providence for the purpose of convincing people of their errors, could be logically considered in the category of sanitary measures, then the awakening of a sanitary sense of the people caused by a virulent epidemic is productive of good. If the tenets of the believers in New Thought and Christian Science were true, this class of people would never have smallpox. For surely no bigotry could be more pronounced than that manifested by the anti-vaccinationists of the Philippines. Fortunately these fanatics, although vociferous, were small in numbers and not influential in the Legislature, and the unvaccinated among them contracted smallpox so regularly that they were no problem.

It seems almost incredible that, in spite of the absolute proof that effective vaccination makes smallpox impossible, there should still be dissenters. Daniel Webster, in one of his less inspired moments, said, "Compulsory vaccination is an outrage and a gross interference with the liberty of the people in a land of freedom." He failed to realize that freedom must not be granted to those who have proved themselves unworthy of it by endangering others. The construction of fire hazards is not permitted; why should anti-vaccinationists be allowed to generate sparks which threaten the lives of the public? Even now, in these supposedly enlightened days, the ill-founded claims that vaccination produces harmful effects during menstruation, pregnancy, lactation, and early infancy are too frequently respected, even by the advocates of vaccination.

In the United States and England societies have been founded of those whose one idea seems to be that all the ills of the world are due to vaccination. Strange to say, occasionally the prime movers in these anti-vaccination societies are physicians, although it is difficult to understand how any observing medical man could question experience and the evidence of science so far as to doubt the thoroughly established fact that vaccination prevents smallpox.

Simon Louis Katzoff, to quote only one out of many, asks in *Physical Culture:*

"How long are the poisoned pus peddlers to be allowed to run wild and fatten their purses and the insane asylums, hospitals, and graveyards? Priestly despotism is bad, but medical despotism is intolerable.

"Smallpox is a filth illness which follows closely upon flagrant violations of the laws of hygiene and health. No person is susceptible to smallpox or any other filth disease so long as he is in a state of health. . . . Compulsory vaccination ranks with human slavery and religious persecution, and is one of the most flagrant infringements upon the rights of the human race. The more vaccination is practiced to the neglect of sanitation, the more smallpox flourishes, but when sanitation is practiced and vaccination neglected smallpox disappears. Vaccination will be neglected and smallpox will disappear when medical superstitions and medical intolerance have disappeared."

In Denver, Colorado, chiropractors loudly proclaimed the uselessness of vaccination as a protection against smallpox, and for a time succeeded in winning a large section of the public to their point of view. But just as surely as a dry shaving will burn when a match is applied, just so will the unprotected contract smallpox when exposed to the contagion. As time went on, it became increasingly apparent that the unprotected were furnishing all the victims while the properly vaccinated were escaping. Finally the unvaccinated chiropractors began to contract the disease. One of them who fled not only himself died, but started smallpox in faraway Arkansas which had previously been free.

I have always felt strongly on the question of vaccination, because smallpox is a disease we ought not to have. On almost every one of my world trips I used to meet anti-vaccinationists. I remember in particular one man who was traveling with his beautiful daughter. He was rabidly against vaccination. When she contracted smallpox and died in Singapore, I never saw a man burdened with greater remorse. His lesson was a bitter one. He said to me, "I alone am to blame. I pitted my puny opinion against the judgment of the medical world, and this is what has happened."

Anti-vaccinationists should be attacked everywhere as a menace to the welfare of mankind. The disfigurement, blindness, and death for which they are responsible should be brought home to them. Their false doctrines are too costly and should not be allowed to spread.

There are very few anti-vaccinationists now in the Philippines. Most of them have died of smallpox.

CHAPTER 13.　　ALAS AND A LACK

IN 1908 I was delegated to attend an international convention on tuberculosis at Washington, and it was decided that Dr. Francisco Calderon, a prominent Filipino physician, should accompany me. Since he was being groomed for an important administrative position, it was judged desirable for him to see how affairs were conducted in the United States and, incidentally, what was being done for Filipinos in American universities. After leaving Washington we were to circle the globe, inspecting progress in the treatment of tuberculosis in Europe on our way. I started for Hawaii a month ahead so that I could visit the leper colony at Molokai. Calderon joined me at Honolulu and together we set sail for San Francisco.

I had not been in the United States for five years, and when we reached San Francisco I was so busy talking with friends who had come to the boat to greet me that, for the moment, I forgot all about Calderon and his inability to speak English. When I looked for him he was not to be found. Finally I located him in a Customs enclosure.

"*Que pasa?*" I asked.

He shrugged his shoulders and professed entire ignorance. A Customs inspector interrupted, "He's been trying to smuggle cigarettes. He had ten thousand which he didn't declare. That's smuggling on a large scale."

I pointed out to the inspector that ten thousand cigarettes were not so many under the circumstances. Dr. Calderon was a Filipino, and everybody in his country smoked all day and half the night. He would be uncomfortable without his own brand, and was merely taking a supply with him to last during our world trip. Moreover, he was an official representative to an international meeting to which he had been invited by the United States and, as such, entitled to diplomatic immunity.

"He can't do anything like that," insisted the obdurate inspector.

"Well, if you won't let him off, I'll have to go down and interview the Collector of the Port, who's an old friend of mine," I replied. When I reached his office, he had gone to lunch, and I had to wait until two o'clock before he returned. I told him the story and, although he demurred at first, finally, on my statement that Calderon was a prominent Filipino on a diplomatic mission, he gave me an order for release. I returned to the pier, exhibited the document, and saw Calderon restored to freedom.

Since my own baggage had not yet been inspected, I went off to attend to it. But when I returned I found no Calderon. I discovered him again under guard.

"What's the matter now?" I demanded.

"I don't know," he lamented. "This is a terrible country."

I sought the inspector and asked, "What's my friend done now?"

The inspector, who had been somewhat annoyed over Calderon's release, exclaimed triumphantly, "He is a smuggler. You got him out of the cigarettes, but let's see you get him out of this. You said he was a Filipino. Then what's he doing with this big sealskin robe? How could a fellow from a hot place like the Philippines have any use for such a thing? You can't tell me he isn't trying to smuggle it into the country."

I knew better than to argue; I hailed a taxi and returned once more to the office of the Collector of the Port. After I had explained the nature of the new contretemps he said, "I'm afraid I can't help you this time. The inspector is perfectly right. We can't overlook such a serious offense."

"You'll cause a lot of trouble," I interposed. "This man is a guest of the nation. I assure you he has merely borrowed the robe from a friend in Shanghai because he's afraid it's going to be cold in Siberia."

After much persuasion and the assurance that the robe was not to remain in the United States, the Collector of the Port reluctantly agreed to sign a second order for Calderon's release. This time I took no chances, but watched over him as though I were his keeper.

The train for the East left at seven o'clock, and once we were well under way I went forward to the club car, leaving my colleague to amuse himself in the Pullman. I had not been there long when the porter came rushing in after me. "You'll have to come back to your friend right away."

"What's the matter?" I queried.

"He's undressing in the aisle. We can't allow it."

I returned and admonished Calderon. "Look here, this sort of thing isn't done in America. You'll have to undress in your berth."

"How could anybody undress in that little hole?" he protested.

I admitted the art of Pullman travel was a difficult one to master, but I explained its technique as best I could.

"But how do you get your trousers off? There's no place to sit down except in the aisle."

"You get in that berth," I commanded. "I'll see you in the morning."

I went back once more to the club car, but I had not finished my cigar before the porter sought me out again. "What's the matter this time?"

"That man is sitting in the observation car in his pajamas."

"Well, they all do that in his country," I explained. "It's September, and it's hot, and he probably wants to cool off."

"But he can't do it. You'll have to get him back in his bunk. He doesn't understand me."

I went to the observation car and found Calderon contentedly smoking away on his smuggled cigarettes.

"You can't sit here in your pajamas," I began firmly.

"What kind of country is this?" he demanded indignantly. "I've been lying in that infernal bunk where it's hotter than at home, and it's very pleasant here."

I eventually persuaded him to conform to American notions of propriety and return to his bunk.

Until we reached New York everything went smoothly. There we registered at one of the large hotels and started for the elevator, Calderon following behind me—an Oriental always walks two paces in the rear. The door slid shut and, before I realized he was not with me, the elevator was on its way to the twelfth floor. I waited there for some time, but he did not appear. With visions of his being lost in a city where things moved far too rapidly for him, I returned to the ground floor.

Calderon was nowhere in sight. I asked the starter whether he had seen anybody answering Calderon's description.

"Oh, yes," he assured me. "He's just gone up."

"Then I'll go up again, but if he comes down while I'm gone you keep him here until I get back."

I returned to the twelfth floor, but he was not there.

When I once more emerged into the lobby, I burst upon a tremendous scuffle. Calderon was loudly shouting as he struggled with the starter, "He's trying to arrest me!" He had mistaken the uniform for that of the police. I placated the starter, explained to Calderon, and, taking him by the arm, conducted him to his room.

This was by no means the end of my troubles. October came, and the days grew fairly cool. When Calderon donned his bright yellow overcoat he attracted attention wherever we went. A group of small boys would often follow us, shouting derisively, "Look at de guy in de yella coat!"

I spent half my time plucking Calderon bodily from in front of automobiles and street cars, interpreting for him, and trying to find the kind of food which he found palatable. I was almost a nervous wreck before I located a Filipino to look after his wants. Thereafter I could leave Calderon happy and contented in good hands while I went about more important business.

Calderon had received an invitation to go to the Lake Mohonk Conference, which was concerned with helping the Indians and other dependent peoples of the United States. He thought this might afford an opportunity to obtain additional funds for his Gota de Leche Society in the Philippines which had for its object the distribution of milk to poor children. Calderon, who was an extremely well educated and intelligent man, wrote an excellent address in Spanish, which his Filipino guide then translated into English. It was still effective, because the Spanish idiom is beautiful even in translation. He practised his speech daily and, although he scarcely knew the meaning of the words, he could repeat them perfectly in English. He made such an impression that a considerable sum was voluntarily contributed to the Gota de Leche, even though, as a rule, money was not solicited at these conferences.

Calderon's success had been so great that I suggested we interview Nathan Straus, who had done so much for the cause of pasteurized milk in America and Europe, and see whether we could interest him in donating a pasteurization plant for Manila. We were received by both Mr. and Mrs. Straus. The former was not impressed with our story, but his wife showed great interest. When he objected that he had put in all the milk plants that he cared to, she reminded him that this was an American responsibility, and he ultimately agreed to have one which happened not to be in use shipped to the Islands.

Calderon had become so amusing in his idiosyncrasies that I wanted to continue the fun. Accordingly, when we embarked for Hamburg in December, I placed over the door of his stateroom a little sign which read, "Professor of Music." Thereafter he was constantly being invited to play and sing, particularly by the ladies, who took a tremendous fancy to him. He was totally unable to understand his popularity. He refused each frequent request to perform, and I invariably explained he was too shy to make a public appearance.

As we drew nearer and nearer to Hamburg, I noticed that he was becoming miraculously stouter and stouter. I finally grew alarmed and said, "How is this? Your trousers are so tight I'm afraid they'll burst."

The explanation was simple. He had bought a dozen suits of long underwear, and as the days grew colder had added the suits one by one until he was wearing four, and looked exactly like a stuffed porpoise.

In spite of his underwear and the robe, he was shivering when we reached the Customs Office on the Russian frontier. It was bitter cold. Just as the train was about to leave, two American ladies appeared, much distressed because they had no reservations.

"We'll offer them our compartment," I said.

There was no place for us except third class, and we had had no breakfast. Russian was not included in my linguistic equipment, but I had a French time-table, and I believed that by comparing this with the time of arrival at stations, I could pick out a dining place. But the train did not keep its schedule, so that I soon lost track of where we were. At every stop I rushed out to try my languages, one after another, but the big, whiskered Russians shook their heads in bewilderment. By the time I had finished asking in six languages how long the train was going to stop, it was usually pulling out again.

The thermometer was far below zero, and still we had had nothing to eat. Poor Calderon was nearly congealed; I have never seen anybody so cold in my life. I took his pulse and found it so weak I was afraid he would literally freeze to death. When we reached Warsaw I was trying to figure out whether he could be buried there, and what my duties were to a friend under such circumstances.

About seven in the evening an ancient Jew entered the compartment, and I immediately addressed him joyfully in Yiddish. He was the first person during that long, miserable day who had been able to understand a word of what I had said. He informed me the train would stop about ten at an eating place, and I promised him anything he wanted for supper if he would lead us to food. Three hours later he produced steaming borsch, black bread, and tea. Calderon's face began to resume its natural color, and he was soon able once more to articulate.

The next morning we were at St. Petersburg. The great cold of Russia was naturally uppermost in Calderon's mind, and when he discovered a French-speaking staff at the hotel, he had listened morbidly to their harrowing tales of unfortunates who had lost limbs or had been frozen to death. I asked him whether he cared to walk along with me to call on the American Ambassador, and explained that the exercise would keep us warmer than if we hired a sleigh.

According to his usual habit, Calderon kept trailing behind. It grew colder and colder; his hands were practically ankylosed. I had to do something to make him move faster and stir up his circulation. "If you don't hurry up, you'll lose an ear," I warned him. He kept in step with me for a few moments, and then began to dawdle again at his usual gait.

Finally I turned around. An expression of simulated horror came over my face. "It's too late! You've lost an ear!"

He clapped his hand to his head, but it was so cold he could feel nothing. "What am I going to do without an ear?" he wailed.

"If you don't hurry, you'll lose the other one," I admonished him pitilessly.

From that time on it was I who had difficulty in keeping up with Calderon. As we drew near the Embassy he became worried about his appearance. "If you keep your head away from the Ambassador, he won't notice it," I comforted him. "And we'll only be there a short time—it won't warm up enough to bleed."

All through the interview he kept his head carefully averted, and on leaving pulled his coat collar up over his head. As soon as we returned to the hotel he rushed to the mirror. He was so relieved to find his ear intact, that he forgave me on the spot for the trick I had played upon him.

Soon afterwards, homeward bound on the Trans-Siberian, we arrived at the end of the line at Mukden. In order to buy a ticket on the Chinese railway to Peiping I had to have Chinese money, but it was then three o'clock in the morning. I found a nook slightly sheltered from the wind where I deposited our many pieces of baggage with Calderon to watch over them. Because trunks had to pay first class postage rates, we had lightened ours by putting everything possible in bags which could be kept in our compartment.

I started out to find a place to change my twenty-dollar gold pieces, and hurried along the dark streets until I saw a light over the entrance to a gambling place. Much time was taken up in haggling over a satisfactory rate of exchange, but I was ultimately content and started to retrace my steps toward the station. As I drew near I could see Calderon fast asleep, and a big Chinese in the very act of picking up one of the trunks and hoisting it on his shoulder. I yelled and sprinted after him over the frozen rice paddies. Before I could overtake him he dropped the trunk but kept on running. Without its weight he gathered speed, and his pigtail stood out behind him. I had no intention of carrying the trunk back. I caught hold of his pigtail, slowed him down, turned him around, marched him back to the trunk, made him pick it up, and we returned together.

This was the last of my adventures with Dr. Calderon. In spite of not feeling at home in a strange environment, throughout our trip he had acquired an amazing amount of scientific information, which he had assimilated thoroughly. He became Dean of the Government Medical School in Manila and later President of the University of the Philippines.

ALAS AND A LACK

The problem of tuberculosis had its peculiar and complicating features in the Philippines. The dietary was unsuitable for its cure; but, in addition, the people had the insanitary habit of eating with the fingers, a lack of proper exercise, superstitions concerning the contraction of the disease, and an almost unshakable fear of night air as a poisonous thing. They usually slept closely together in groups on the floor. Betel nut chewing made the custom of expectorating in public and private universal and practically incurable. Legislate as we might, the filthy habit of spitting still continued, even among the more intelligent. Added to this was their utter resignation to the disease as a thing inevitable.

Not only did we have the ordinary preventive and curative measures against tuberculosis to organize and enforce, but we had to devise ways of cooking and preparing native products so that they would be both nourishing and acceptable to the masses. But it is often easier to be bad than good, and, similarly, easier to be insanitary than sanitary, and the East likes best the easiest way. We began an active educational campaign for the prophylaxis and treatment of the disease. But curing the people of their superstitions was as great a task as converting them to a new religion; tuberculosis had long been regarded by the public as necessarily fatal, and it was difficult to convince the afflicted that it often yielded to the simplest hygienic measures; they wanted a sign before they would believe.

In the Philippines more people died of tuberculosis than of any other disease, and there was hardly a family that had not lost at least one member. One-sixth of the deaths were directly attributable to it; only Calcutta approached Manila in its mortality rate from this cause.

The tubercle bacillus, which was discovered by Koch in 1882, is exceptionally hardy. If not exposed to sunlight, which kills it in a few hours, it may live for six months. The defensive forces make every effort to kill the tubercle when it gets into the body, but can only succeed when the blood is rich and healthy. The frail physiques of Filipinos make them particularly susceptible.

For thousands of years doctors have tried to find a remedy that would cure tuberculosis, but so far have had to fall back on nature. Sunshine and fresh air are the enemies of disease the world over. Formerly it was the practice to recommend a change in climate, but experience has amply demonstrated that treatment is more dependent on proper nutrition and rest than on meteorological conditions. The benefits of favorable climatic environment are oftentimes more than offset by the inconveniences of travel, loneliness, and homesickness, and the necessary status of patients among strangers.

However, proper hygiene and diet, the attention to the little things peculiar to each individual case, together with appropriate medication for special conditions as they arise, can best be supervised in a sanitarium. One of the principal objects of such an institution is to teach the patients to help themselves and not be a danger to others. The influence exerted by those who have recovered is the greatest power in the educational crusade against this disease. One enthusiastic patient returned cured is worth more than all the circulars and literature that could be produced on the subject.

No disease makes such a drain on the resources of families, for its long, insidious course prevents its unfortunate victims from earning their living, thus oftentimes enforcing a condition of debt and actual want. I considered that the government should take up the burden of providing a tuberculosis dispensary and a hospital for chronic cases at Manila and a sanitarium at Baguio. Even if the great misery, suffering, and despair of stricken victims, of relatives and friends and those dependent upon them, were to be ignored altogether, and the question considered from its financial aspect alone, it would be, I thought, a matter of wise, public policy to relieve, in part at least, this drain on the productive capacity of the country, which was measured in millions every year.

Dr. Calderon and I returned from our trip with a good knowledge of what the rest of the world was doing. But I realized that the hope of freeing the Philippines was in large measure dependent upon raising the economic standards. Until the Filipinos could obtain better food and make more general use of milk they were tremendously handicapped.

This was excellently illustrated by the situation in Europe where before the War the tuberculosis rate in Austria and Germany compared favorably with that of Great Britain and America. As the War progressed, tuberculosis began to increase. In some sections it ran as high as in the past. But after the War, even though overcrowding was universal, even though there was no money, the tuberculosis rate at once climbed down because the Austrians and Germans were again getting the fats and other food essentials of which they had so long been deprived.

Nature evidently intends that every child born should take part in the great drama of life and live until all the purposes which have called it into existence have been satisfied. So determined is she that her plans be successful that she has apparently established a law fixing a direct ratio between the birth rate and the infant mortality rate.

A high death rate among infants, unless brought about by epidemic diseases or other special causes, is normally offset by a higher birth rate. Nevertheless, it is the duty and desire of the health officer to save as many of them as he can. No one wants the children to live more than the health officer, because the bearing of healthy children is a blessing to womankind and to the world at large, while the bearing of sickly children soon to die is a misfortune to humanity. The tiny graves in the cemetery are seen by many, but few hear of the efforts made by self-sacrificing physicians and faithful workers in the children's cause to prevent these graves.

The death rate among young Filipino children was appallingly high. In Manila every other baby died before its first birthday. General debility was a common condition among children. The bodies that these babies inherited from weak parents could not withstand the germs of disease. Another cause was the obstetrical practices which prevailed. If a woman had too small a pelvis to give birth easily, not infrequently a rope was wound around her waist with a man pulling at each end to force the birth. Many children also had died of tetanus neonatorum, because the midwives, according to an ancient and common Oriental custom, had dressed the cord with manure.

The midwives were an organized but untrained and unlicensed group. By the exercise of much diplomacy we took the leaders among these old women into camp, teaching them more scientific and humane methods. In a great campaign of education we issued free packets by the hundreds of thousands for dressing cords, and finally they were used. When the midwives had been converted, midwifery schools were started over the Islands, and the decree went out that before any woman should practice obstetrics she must procure a license.

But improper nutrition was the major cause of the high infant mortality. The struggle for more adequate food has been long and still continues. The use of milk on a large scale was practically unknown in the Philippines, as well as in many other tropical countries. The poverty of the people made properly marketed cows' milk, either fresh or canned, impossible to obtain except by charity. Ordinary cows' milk was extremely expensive, because cows did not do well in the Islands. The native grasses had little spines which, when eaten, caused tiny wounds in the intestinal tract. When these healed over they left scar tissue which ultimately caused such contraction that the natural glands were destroyed and the cow could not absorb what she ate. She literally starved to death. In my early enthusiasm, I tried to start a herd of a hundred and fifty, but all died.

Goats were common and flourished, but the Philippine variety gave very little milk. It occurred to me that if we could cross an Island goat, which could stand the climate, with a Maltese goat, which lactated generously, we might get a satisfactory hybrid. The agricultural department took this up and a breed of goats was produced which seemed to fill the requirements. I believed we could use the slogan, "a goat in every family," and have another cheap method of securing milk, but the Filipinos did not take to the idea.

Whatever milk the poorer classes used came almost exclusively from the caraballa, or female water buffalo, which is, by nature, a dirty animal and doubtless contributed its full share to the sum of impurities that vitiated the infants' milk.

The Filipinos have a degree of understanding with the carabao which the white people have never seemed able to attain. When Manila was first occupied by American troops, a Major, in his delight at getting ashore, went for a long walk on the outskirts of the city. While crossing a field he was observed by a carabao, which promptly charged him. There happened to be a tree in the middle of the field, which he reached with three leaps and a bound. It was then about five in the afternoon. He lifted his voice in plaintive appeal but nobody answered. He would remain quiet for a few moments and then cautiously begin to descend, but each time a warning, "pff-shshsh-oo-oooo" would send him hurriedly back to his perch. Hour after hour the Major sat in a crotch of the tree, and hour after hour the carabao waited untiringly below.

The long night passed. Finally, at about six in the morning, a four-year-old child toddled over the field and led the carabao unprotestingly away by its nose rope. The brave Major then made good his escape.

The Major had probably been wise in his policy of watchful waiting, because many people have been gored and killed by infuriated carabao. The animal has no sweat glands except in his nose, and if he does not have an opportunity to soak himself once a day in water, or at least in mud, he will go *loco*. Though ordinarily slow and deliberate, under such conditions he will attack anything on sight, preferably a white person. At all times he loves mud and filth, and if, while dragging his cart or sledge, he comes to a mud puddle, he will promptly lie down, and only under the most urgent suasion will he move on.

The scarcity of milk was accentuated by the rinderpest epizootic which, in its slow girdling of the world, had finally reached the Philippines. It carried away from seventy-five to eighty percent of the carabaos—hundreds of thousands of animals that were indispensable in cultivating, reaping, hauling, and disposing of the agricultural products upon which the prosperity of the Islands was totally dependent.

Rinderpest is a dysentery in cattle which has a ninety percent mortality rate. I have gone through fields where hundreds and hundreds of these dead animals were lying. At that time we could do nothing for them except keep a strict guard at the quarantine stations and try to prevent the infected animals from rubbing noses with those as yet untouched. So many cattle perished that for years meat had to be imported from Australia, and milk became almost an unknown quantity. Finally, an army veterinarian named Kelser developed a vaccine which made cattle immune to rinderpest, but the Filipino owners were suspicious of it, and the veterinary corps were not always considerate of their sentiments and prejudices. It was extremely pathetic when the only animal upon which a family depended for the necessary work of the rice field succumbed to the disease. No money with which to indemnify the owners was available until the United States Congress appropriated a million dollars, *the only money ever contributed to the Philippines.*

Even when the caraballa had recovered in numbers, difficulties arose about the nature of the milk, which contained twice as much butter fat as ordinary cows' milk. It could be diluted in half and still have the proper amount of fat, but such dilution made the carbohydrate content entirely out of proportion. To remedy this, the dealers in caraballa milk tried all sorts of experiments, hoping to make the product correspond to cows' milk—rice, starch, and other substances, many of which produced weird looking mixtures and bacterial counts that would have staggered a statistician.

Regulating the trade in caraballa milk was complicated because there were no big producers, and keeping watch over every caraballa owner was an obvious impossibility. We tried at one time posting inspectors on the roads, but there were so many tracks and trails by which milk could enter Manila that the attempt proved a failure. As always, our recourse was education. Nurses went from home to home to talk to the housewives.

Ultimately, several substitutes for fresh cows' milk were discovered. The Swiss developed a method of preparing natural milk with no preservative and not heated enough to coagulate the casein. It kept well, would not transmit disease, and could not be infected so long as the tin was unopened. It could be bought for eleven cents a quart at the grocery store, and in time it came to be generally used throughout the East.

Another discovery, made at the Peiping Hospital, was that a substitute for milk itself could be manufactured from the soya bean. With the addition of cod-liver oil and calcium it closely resembled natural milk. A number of children were fed only on this food from the time they were three weeks old, were examined regularly, and proved to be healthy and normal in every way. I was convinced that the "eat only what you crave" idea was nonsense when I saw how children who had never had any other food loved this soya bean milk, because to an adult it was one of the worst-tasting decoctions that could be imagined.

A Filipina college graduate in chemistry from Columbia University then made her contribution. She found that extract of banana added to the soya bean mixture made it taste like fresh milk. The Filipina housewife can now make this milk in her own kitchen, using a little handpress for the bean and adding the other ingredients according to the prescribed directions.

The soya bean has proved of inestimable value to the East and promises to enlarge the dietary. I once attended a delicious full course lunch in the Bureau of Science Laboratory in Manila where everything from soup through steak to cake was made from this bean.

Another food deficiency was responsible for one of the most debilitating and crippling diseases of the Orient. Beriberi is as needless as smallpox and a disease about which I feel as strongly. Each year it takes a toll of over a hundred thousand lives. In the War of 1895 between Japan and China nearly half the Japanese troops had it; in the Russo-Japanese War of 1904–05 eighty-five thousand cases were reported. It was estimated that in the Philippines at least five thousand died and twenty-five thousand were made ill from it annually.

Among the poorer classes beriberi was particularly prevalent; people for whom the government was directly responsible suffered badly. Bilibid Prison was filled with it. On more than one of my leper collecting trips the captain of the *Basilan* pointed out a lighthouse where there was no light, and on investigation we would discover keeper and assistants dead of beriberi. Or more often the American flag would be flying upside down as a signal of distress. In almost every instance we would find the crew, although still able perhaps to tend the lamps, seriously ill.

Beriberi caused a multiple neuritis affecting both the motor and the sensory nerves. The extremely painful inflammation brought about a partial and even complete loss of the use of the muscles supplied by these nerves, and particularly affected the heart. One of the most apparent manifestations was the dropsical appearance. The patient ultimately became bedridden, and large numbers died from heart failure. I remember the impression made upon me by the huge hospital for beriberi incurables at Singapore, where these poor people were crawling around on their hands, dragging their paralyzed legs behind them. The disease was too far advanced for a cure; it might easily have been prevented.

Many causes were assigned for beriberi, such as overcrowding and poor ventilation. The French clung to the theory that it was infectious long after it had been proved otherwise. Many claimed it was due to bacteria on rice which produced a toxic condition. The discovery of the true source came with the opening up of huge rubber plantations in the Straits Settlements and Malay States. Chinese and Indian laborers were imported, and promptly developed beriberi. The British government employed two scientists, Henry W. Fraser and A. T. Stanton, to work on this problem. They arrived at the startling conclusion that this horrible affliction was due to a food deficiency; that beriberi was a disease brought about by the absence of certain chemical constituents essential to the nourishment of the human body. They gradually found out that Vitamin B was missing from rice which had been polished; the outer surface of the rice grain containing substances essential to nourish the body had been ground away. Those who ate unpolished rice did not get beriberi. Europeans and Americans did not have it because they received Vitamin B from other foods which Orientals ordinarily did not eat.

After trying out their theory on chickens, Fraser and Stanton tested it on inmates of the insane asylum at Kuala Lumpur. The results were the same. Those who ate polished rice came down with beriberi; those fed only unpolished rice remained healthy. They then tried a further experiment. The government was building a railway in Malaya, and three hundred of the workers joined in the test. Half were put on a diet of unpolished rice; half on polished. The latter group came down with beriberi. Then the diets were reversed. The sick group recovered and the well group came down with the disease. It warranted the deduction that a diet which included Vitamin B was a preventive for beriberi.

After the British had made the discovery, it developed that Professor C. Eijkman in Java had caused beriberi in chickens but had never applied the same test to humans as the British had done.

Fraser and Stanton determined further how to tell whether rice was polished to the danger point. If when stained with methylene blue or iodine the grains took a deep color, then the rice was deficient in Vitamin B, and, therefore, beriberi might result. If the grains stained slightly, the rice was safe to use. This test was extremely valuable, because it was so difficult to judge with the naked eye how much of the coating had been removed from the kernel. A more exact index was to determine the amount of phosphorus pentoxide. If it contained four-tenths of one percent or more it was safe; if less, it might cause beriberi.

At the first meeting of the Far Eastern Association of Tropical Medicine at Manila, in 1908, the two British scientists read the story of their epoch-making discovery. I decided to try it out at once among those for whom I was directly responsible. Before the Fraser and Stanton report, we had striven in vain to wipe out beriberi entirely at Culion. By adding to the rice more meat and mongos (beans resembling lentils), the number of cases could be reduced, but many of the inmates preferred to deny themselves food rather than eat mongos, so that we had starvation as well as improper diet to deal with. At the beginning of 1910 the use of unpolished rice was made compulsory, and beriberi stopped immediately.

With this evidence Forbes issued an order that only unpolished rice should be used in all government institutions. But soon commissary officers, prison wardens, and others directly charged with carrying out the order began to be besieged with complaints, and it was but natural that they should take a course of least resistance and recommend that the use of unpolished rice be discontinued. It was asserted that a penurious government was attempting to cheapen the diet at the expense of inmates and employees, who, consequently, often refused to eat it. However, we insisted upon strict obedience, and when its use finally became general, the results were startling. The thousand deaths from beriberi in government institutions that formerly occurred annually ceased altogether.

During the autumn of 1911 a great shortage of rice occurred throughout the Orient, and certain grain interests attempted to corner the world market. The price soared one hundred percent. In some instances to protect its people from extortionate prices, the Philippine government also plunged, and bought and bought until it had broken the corner as far as the Islands were concerned. In a short time it had the cost to more normal figures, but in so doing had been forced to buy great quantities of polished rice. So much was on hand that large issues were made to Culion in November, 1911, and continued until February, 1912. I was away at the time or I should have protested.

During January cases of beriberi broke out among the inmates, and the general mortality rate rose rapidly. As many as fifty deaths a month were occurring. Immediately upon my return in February, I ordered rice polishings, which contained the essential Vitamin B, fed with the rice, and soon beriberi disappeared again.

We could control inmates of government institutions; one year after Forbes' decree beriberi had disappeared from the prisons, the lights burned steady and true along the coast, and the United States Army Scouts marched with firm step. We then turned our attention to teaching the general public to eat the more healthful rice. But the Filipino, like all other Orientals, is very fond of his polished rice. Any time the Filipina housewives decided to wipe out beriberi from the Islands they could do so. But even to this day they have not been convinced.

The solution of the beriberi etiology unexpectedly shed much light on one of the important causes of infant mortality. In Manila the death rate curiously was much higher among breast-fed children than among those fed from a bottle. The exact reverse is true in America and Europe. Since the staple article of diet among the masses was polished rice and fish, neither of which contained the requisite nutriment for mothers' milk, the breast-fed child was not properly nourished and became irritable and fretful, cried, failed to sleep, and did not gain weight. Ultimately it became paralyzed. This condition was called *taon*, and was thought to be due to a toxin in the mother's milk.

Major Weston P. Chamberlain and Captain Edward B. Vedder of the United States Army Board began a series of experiments with *tiqui-tiqui*, or rice polishings, and made an extract from these. Vedder had noticed that the Filipino cocks grew strong and sturdy if given *tiqui-tiqui*. He knew that polyneuritis among chickens and beriberi among humans were due to the same causes. If, then, *tiqui-tiqui* were good for roosters, it might also be good for babies. The two Army doctors sought out babies on which to try their extract. This was not easy, because parents whose children had *taon* were usually poor and ignorant, and their ignorance made them distrustful.

No one who did not see the effects of administering *tiqui-tiqui* extract to these children could believe the quick results which followed. A child who for days had slept no more than a few hours, who had been whining and crying constantly, would fall into a quiet sleep. In a day or two its weight would begin to increase, and the paralysis to leave its limbs. It was just like a miracle.

Nevertheless, we were dealing with a symptom and not getting at the cause of the disease. Another paper outlining progress on beriberi was read in 1911 at the Hongkong meeting of the Far Eastern Association of Tropical Medicine. Among the most convincing proofs were that the Hongkong jails, formerly riddled with beriberi, had been freed of the disease, and the entire native army in Java had been cured. The Association adopted a resolution that all governments with Eastern possessions should be petitioned to have white rice barred and only unpolished rice used.

The next day the French delegates moved to reconsider, asserting they would like to present certain facts. At Saigon, in Indo-China, there was a monastery and a nunnery. Both monks and nuns ate the same diet of unpolished rice. If we could explain to their satisfaction why the women always had beriberi and the men never, they would be glad to join us in signing the petition. We had no answer at the time. It remained for a Netherlander, Kuenen, years later, to discover that if rice were thoroughly washed, the protective substance was removed as effectively as though it had been polished. In Saigon the dirty men had not washed their rice, while the cleanly women had rinsed theirs thoroughly. The campaign against beriberi was held up for years because of French dubiety.

I realized that solution of the beriberi problem would be of tremendous humanitarian and economic advantage and be one of the great forward steps of modern times. A simple method of protecting the poor against themselves would be to tax white rice. This would work no hardship on them, because the price of unpolished rice would not be raised. But harmful polished rice, even at a few cents' higher price, would be put out of their reach. On the other hand, those able to afford the polished rice would not be hurt by it because their living scale would allow them to include a more varied diet.

In spite of much opposition, I managed to get a bill to tax white rice passed by one House of the Philippine Legislature, but adjournment took place before the other House could consider it. Later, owing to the unsettled condition of the rice market, the Legislature was not disposed to take any action.

For years I have peddled my tax idea around the world. Over and over again I have pointed out that its action would be automatic, because people would buy the cheaper unpolished rice and beriberi would disappear. The War interfered with my plans. Afterwards I interested Sir William Osler, then Professor of Medicine at Oxford, and Viscount Bryce, who agreed to use their influence with the British government to impose such a tax. But before they could take any action, both of them died. Though progress has been slow, I continue to peddle the idea.

It is perfectly amazing that, in face of the miraculous results from so simple a dietary reform, incredulity, with its attendant sacrifice of life and health, should still persist. But I am convinced that if somebody could prove today that cancer was caused by the eating of white bread, twenty-five years from now most people would still be eating white bread.

CHAPTER 14. THE HOUSE OF PAIN

HUNDREDS of thousands of lepers still exist throughout the world as social pariahs, thrust out of society because they have, through no fault of their own, contracted a repulsive disease. Far beyond their physical suffering is their terrible mental anguish. No criminal condemned to solitary confinement is confronted with such torture and loneliness. Shunned by friends and acquaintances, who are in terror of even coming within speaking distance, the unfortunate victims soon find themselves alone in a world in which they have no part. The few who come in contact with lepers instinctively draw back from them, so that normal social relationship dies at birth. Patients, when avoided by everybody, sit idle and brood; a human being devoid of hope is the most terrible object in the world.

The treatment of cases of leprosy today is sometimes as inhuman as in former times. In India a leper is often cast out by his own relatives, and has to go to the government for relief. The Karo-Bataks of the East Coast of Sumatra expel a leper from their villages, and at night surround and set fire to his hut, burning him alive. The Yakuts of Siberia, in their great terror of leprosy, force the leper to leave the community, and he must henceforth live alone unless he finds some other leper to keep him company.

Even in the United States lepers have not always been treated kindly. The people of a West Virginia town, when they once found a leper, placed him in a box car and nailed the door shut. The train departed. It was the middle of winter, and before the door was finally opened, the man had starved and frozen to death.

Leprosy is the most ancient and exclusively human of diseases. It has followed man in all his migrations. The ancient records are not precise, and it is impossible to say with certainty that Egyptian papyrus, or Sanskrit *Rig-Veda*, or Chinese parchment, or Jewish *Old Testament* referred definitely to what we know as leprosy. Syphilis and yaws and various skin ailments have clinical symptoms often readily confused with it. One of the oldest works in Chinese medicine, called *Su-yen*, 400 B. C., described a disease which certainly had the characteristics of leprosy. Tradition ascribes an existence of more than two thousand years to leprosy in China. It is claimed that Buddhist priests used to frighten people into conversion by threatening them with the disease should they close their ears to the holy teachings. For centuries overpopulation and misery have sent the Chinese out into all parts of the world, and they have carried leprosy with them.

Leprosy among the Jews is undoubtedly very old, although from the description in *Leviticus* (14, 4–8), many different forms of disease appear to have been included with leprosy. Moses, one of the first great sanitarians, laid down a system of regulations for those having leprosy, threatening the Jews with the wrath of Yahweh if they disobeyed. At intervals of seven days the isolated ones were examined by the priests, who attempted to cleanse them by the following ritual:

4. Then shall the priest command to take for him that is to be cleansed two birds alive and clean, and cedar wood, and scarlet, and hyssop.

5. And the priest shall command that one of the birds be killed in an earthen vessel over running water.

6. As for the living bird, he shall take it, and the cedar wood, and the scarlet, and the hyssop, and shall dip them and the living bird in the blood of the bird that was killed over the running water.

7. And he shall sprinkle upon him that is to be cleansed from the leprosy seven times, and shall pronounce him clean, and shall let the living bird loose into the open field.

8. And he that is to be cleansed shall wash his clothes, and shave off all his hair, and wash himself in water, that he may be clean; and after that he shall come into the camp, and shall tarry abroad out of his tent seven days.

If after the alternate periods of examination and isolation the lesions persisted, the accused was declared leprous. He had to go out with clothes torn and dirtied, bareheaded, with his face covered, and hair uncut, crying to all he should meet *"Tame! Tame!"* "Unclean! Unclean!"

The origins of leprosy are hidden in the mists of antiquity. But the routes of travel, for trade or for conquest, have been the paths of disease as well. The Phoenicians may have bartered leprosy for sandalwood and spices; the Achaians crossed the wine-dark sea for Helen, but their slaves may have brought leprosy back to the shores of Greece; leprosy is supposed to have followed the armies, and was brought by Pompey's legions from the conquest of the East; and the Soldiers of the Cross who set forth to rescue the Holy Sepulchre, staggered back bearing the cross of leprosy to the Christian world.

By the middle of the Twelfth Century leprosy was in Scotland, Norway, the Shetland Islands, Holland, Denmark, Sweden, and parts of Russia. There were many leprosaria in England—seven in London alone, among them St. Giles, founded in 1101. In Scotland the leper houses were called spetels, and the disease to the Scots was the mickle ail.

There is great controversy and doubt as to how many leprosaria existed in Europe in the Middle Ages. One reading of Mathew Paris gives nineteen thousand in 1244, but this is vehemently disputed. Certainly there were many thousands. Mézeray, the French historian, says that in the time of Philip Augustus, 1223, there was no city or town which was not obliged to build a hospital for lepers, solid and durable. Louis VIII in 1226 left legacies to two thousand leper houses. In Spain the first leprosarium was founded by Ruy Bivar, the Cid. In 1284 sequestration was required by Sancho IV of Castile. The Castilian monarchs had a special interest in the disease, because more than once a leper had sat on the royal throne.

Some contend that in the Fourteenth Century the religious orders began to found hospitals for the lepers, known as Hospitals of the Holy God, but more popularly as lazarettos, in honor of St. Lazarus, the Bible beggar, while others say the name derives from the island of St. Lazarus in Venice, which was the site of one of the first leprosaria.

The leprosaria in the Middle Ages were directed by the ecclesiastics of some nearby monastery. They were endowed in different ways. Many of the rich lepers had to take at least a part of their patrimony with them. The service of the houses was done by Brothers or Sisters, clothed in the leper livery, and wearing on their sleeves a piece of red cloth, so that they might be recognized when they walked abroad.

In general the leprosaria were for the rich. The poor, if there were no hospice nearby especially dedicated to them, were treated in quite another manner. A complaint was lodged against anyone suspected of leprosy, and a hearing held before the ecclesiastical judge. If he were accused and convicted of having the disease, he was cast out of the world. In nearly all countries the ceremony, called the *separatio leprosarum*, was similar and differed little from the offices for the dead. According to the ritual of Paris, the leper knelt before the altar, his face covered with a black veil, and listened devoutly to mass. The officiating priest three times took a spadeful of earth from the cemetery and let it fall on the head of the leper while saying, "My friend, this is a sign that thou art dead to the world, *'Sis mortuus mundo.'* " And in consolation he added, *"Vivus iterum deo."* Thou shalt live again with God.

Then the priest read the following rules which the leper was to observe:

"I forbid you ever again to enter in this church, or the market place, or the mill, or the public fair, or in any company or assemblage of people whatsoever.

Item, I forbid you ever to wash your hands and all necessary things in fountain or in brook or in any water whatsoever. And if you wish to drink, take water with your jug or some other vessel.

Item, I forbid you henceforth to go without the habit of lepers, so that you may be known to others, nor shall you go barefooted except within your own house.

Item, I forbid you to touch anything that you wish to buy in any place whatsoever, but point to it with rod or staff, so that what you wish may be known.

Item, I forbid you, while going through the fields, to reply to anyone who may question you, except first, for fear you might infect someone, you step off the road to leeward. And also henceforth you shall not go by the highway for fear that you meet someone.

Item, I forbid you, if necessity requires that you take a path through the field, to touch the hedges or bushes on either side, except before this you have put on your gloves.

Item, I forbid you to touch little children, or any young people whatsoever.

Item, I forbid you henceforth to eat or drink with companions, save they be lepers."

The leper then put on the leper garb of black with a veil over his mouth, and received from the priest the cliquettes with which he must warn of his approach. The priest finally took leave of him in these words, "Thou shalt not be disconsolate for being sequestered from all others, for thou shalt have thy part and portion of all the prayers of Holy Mother Church, as if in person thou wert daily attending divine service with the others. Only take care, and have patience. May God be with thee."

In some districts the leper at the close of the ceremony was made to descend into an open grave in the cemetery and undergo a pretended inhumation, but more often was merely led outside the church and in procession conducted to his cabin in the fields. Before his door was planted a cross on which the priest hung a box for alms.

The leper houses of wood, surrounded by palisades, were invariably located outside the villages in the country, but usually in close proximity to a traveled highway, so that begging might be fruitful. At a leper's death, his household utensils were broken if of earthenware, burned if of wood, and passed through fire if of metal. The corpse was buried under the cottage and, in certain regions, a cartload of lime was thrown into the grave.

At a later period lepers were very rarely kept strictly to their houses, in accordance with the prohibitions given by the priest. Privileges were often accorded them which would seem to fit in poorly with the theory that the Middle Ages were cognizant of the extremely contagious nature of the malady. They had the right to circulate in the environs of the town, provided they did not pass a certain road, square, bridge, or river. On certain days and hours of the day they might enter the city, although they could not eat there nor frequent taverns. But they had to beg, and a begging space was usually carefully specified. Often a well person would be there to receive alms for them. They also had to buy provisions, and attended church, where a special place was assigned them, since they were not admitted to the common confessional.

Usually at Easter the lepers would go "out of their tombs like Christ himself" and enter for several days in the cities or villages to participate in this universal Christian festival.

On the other hand, lepers might be subjected to extreme severity. At Vicenza anyone who found a leper wandering in the city or its environs had a right to hunt him out with a whip, even though he were ringing his "leprous bell."

The treatment of lepers was a curious compound of horror and compassion, in which, as the years went by, the latter gradually gained the ascendency. The diseased ones became something sacred; in France they were called *les malades de Dieu, les chers pauvres de Dieu,* or *les bonnes gens.* Anyone who helped them reached the heights of sacrifice, and thereby attained the greatest honor. Hans Holbein painted a picture in 1516 of Elizabeth of Hungary, patron saint of queens, succoring a group of lepers. Albrecht Dürer also treated the subject by painting the limbs of the lepers as crippled or amputated, and the skin covered with blotches like those of a leopard. It is obvious that the horror rather than the accurate portrayal of the disease was the artists' aim; they desired to express the heroism of those who helped lepers. Matilda, wife of Henry I of England, Countess Sybil of Flanders, Rochilde of Hainaullt, and St. Catherine of Siena were among the great personages who believed they were honoring themselves by caring for lepers.

And Ambroise Paré, physician to Henry II of France, and often regarded as the father of modern surgery, at the end of his discourse on leprosy gives the advice that, when the lepers are separated from the world:

> "one face them as kindly and gently as possible, having in mind they are like to ourselves, and, should it please God, we might be touched with the same malady . . . And it is necessary to admonish them that although they are separated from the world, yet at all times they are loved by God while bearing patiently their cross."

At the time throughout Europe it was a consistent policy to stamp out the disease by isolation in colonies or hospitals. Even a healthy person who had been known to have been touched by a leper might be banished from society. Probably such measures had a most important influence in preventing the spread of the malady. The leper house period in England lasted roughly from the Eleventh through the Fourteenth Century. The disease died down in Europe much in the order in which the countries had been attacked. One of its most remarkable features was its rapid decline in the Fourteenth and Fifteenth Centuries.

Nobody knows why leprosy occurs in one place and not in another. As Frank Oldrieve, Secretary of the British Empire Leprosy Relief Association, expressed it, "There is a caprice of distribution which it is difficult to explain, and it does not seem to depend directly on climate, geological formation, or such-like physical conditions; for leprosy is found in mountainous districts, on the plains, on the coast, in the interior, in all varieties of climate, and on all kinds of geological strata."

Leprosy never breaks fresh ground unless it has been introduced from without by a leper; and a sure and safe way of stamping it out is by isolation. For example, lepers were unknown in Hawaii until 1859, but thirty-two years later one out of thirty of the population was leprous. A Chinese introduced the disease into New Caledonia in 1865, and four thousand cases grew up in twenty-three years. The first instance in the Loyalty Islands was in 1882, and on one tiny islet six years later there were seventy cases.

It is generally assumed that a sufficient concentration of cases in any small area will soon result in the appearance of other cases among persons who frequently come in contact with them. This is strikingly illustrated in the Island of Nauru in the central Pacific Ocean, south of the Equator. Although only about twelve miles in circumference it supports a population of about twenty-five hundred. In 1920 there were four cases of leprosy on the island, in 1921 sixty, and in 1927 three hundred and thirty-seven, or about one in seven of the population.

More than three million lepers are supposed to exist in the world, the great strongholds being India, China, and Japan. India has a million or more cases, and China is in much the same position. There are forty thousand in Burma alone. South America has had large invasions; Colombia is said to have over one hundred thousand lepers.

Also the islands of Ceylon, Java, Hawaii, and many islands in the West Indies have suffered terribly. In Korea, curiously, the disease is confined to the southern half of the peninsula.

Leprosy occurs now in Europe only in sporadic form; a few centers remain in Italy, Finland, Russia, Norway, and Sweden, but they are diminishing rapidly. About sixty years ago the disease in Norway was declining, but then it began to spread once more. It also reappeared in Holland after a long absence. Although there are many persons in England today afflicted, there have been no indigenous cases for the past fifty years.

The weight of authority would seem to indicate that leprosy did not exist on the Western Hemisphere before the coming of the Spaniards, but afterwards it spread throughout South America, and was augmented by the traffic in slaves, among whom were lepers. Cortez erected the first hospital of San Lazaro in Mexico. In 1573 the first white man of prominence was declared a leper in Cartagena, Colombia, then the center of the slave trade, and still a focus of leprosy.

Leprosy was brought to the United States with the slave traffic, the French settlers of Louisiana, and worldwide immigration. The disease now spreads in but four of the states—Florida, Louisiana, Texas, and California, although at one time it could be contracted in Minnesota. If the same incidence prevailed in this country as in the Netherlands East Indies, where the rate sometimes runs as high as ten cases per thousand, we would have over a million lepers instead of a few hundred.

New York State proceeds on the theory that cases of leprosy introduced within its borders are no danger to others, and is loath to segregate, especially if there is any objection on the part of the patient or his friends. In New York City there are dozens of lepers, but no one contracts the disease from them. Massachusetts had a leper settlement on Penikese Island near Buzzards Bay, of which the normal capacity was nineteen. All but one of these were of foreign birth or parentage.

A very interesting story is told in connection with the entrance of leprosy into the Philippines. One of my predecessors, Major E. C. Carter, had put in print a story to the effect that the Japanese, annoyed by the efforts of the Spanish Catholic Church to implant Christianity in Japan, had, in retaliation, loaded one hundred and thirty-four lepers on a ship and despatched them to Manila, saying, "If it is converts you want, begin with these."

Japan resented Major Carter's statement so deeply that the United States was requested to make a public withdrawal and an apology for this alleged outlandish charge. It devolved upon me to make a defense. Accordingly, I had the royal documents at Seville searched. In Section V, drawer II, bundle XXIII, it was recorded that Philip IV, King of Spain, acknowledged the receipt of a communication from the Captain General of the Philippine Islands, on June 8, 1632, in which His Majesty had been informed that one hundred and thirty-four "converted Christians" who had been sent over by the Emperor of Japan, had arrived in Manila Bay. The Most Christian King had directed that the "converted Christians" be welcomed with a parade, and that, in addition to the five hundred reales already set aside for their reception, two hundred more be expended for their maintenance. In that same year one hundred and thirty of them were admitted to San Lazaro Hospital.

These facts were submitted to the Japanese government, which then reported they had already confirmed the story from their own records and withdrew the demand for retraction. They were, however, of the opinion that these lepers had been deported from Japan for sanitary reasons, but admitted cautiously that there might have been some lepers among the Japanese Christians who were banished when the feudal system had become dominant in the Empire.

By royal decree promulgated in 1830, leper settlements were established at Manila, Cebu, and Nueva Caceres, in which some four hundred lepers lived. Only those were gathered up who were in such advanced stages of the disease as to be loathsome to the public or objects of charity. Even though not allowed to live in the same houses as the healthy, frequently they were permitted to mingle freely with the people in the markets and other places. Friday under Spanish rule was lepers' day, when the afflicted walked the streets seeking charity. If alms were not forthcoming, they would squat patiently in groups in front of a residence or alongside a ship. No effective guard was maintained at Cebu, where at one time whole parties of lepers left the hospital and settled down in nearby towns. San Nicolas and Opon, which are now foci of leprosy, were in all probability two of the points to which they fled. Supposedly due to this early laxness, two-thirds of the Philippine lepers now come from Cebu, which has only a seventh of the population.

When the United States Army arrived in the Philippines thousands of lepers were at large. Some were eking out a miserable existence on isolated sandspits, others begging in the market place, and still others trying to earn a pitiful living. Their labors, which of necessity had to be those requiring little strength, sometimes, most unfortunately, had included making cheese or handling foodstuffs in grocery stores. The spread of the disease had been practically unchecked. The attitude of the Filipino public had fluctuated between a great horror of it, amounting almost to panic, and the greatest callousness.

The San Lazaro Hospital for lepers at Manila is an old stone building constructed by the Franciscans in 1784. It was maintained by the income from the district of San Lazaro outside the walls, granted the Fathers for this purpose. At the time I took control, the Hospital contained two hundred and forty-three lepers.

Here, as in so many other instances in the Philippines, success in dealing with the leprosy problem could be obtained only through a program of educating the public. The people had to be taught not to shun the leper, but leprosy, and that the leper who concealed his disease was a constant deadly menace to the community in which he lived.

Leprosy is one of the most repulsive ailments that afflicts man. Of the two main types, one, the neural or anesthetic, exhibits little outward evidence, and the other, the cutaneous or hypertrophic, is marked by lesions which form on the surface tissues. The two types often occur together. In neither are the lesions confined to a single tissue.

The first signs of leprosy are often indicated by an enlargement of the lobe of the ear, or an infiltration or ulcer of the septum of the nose. Then erythematous, or red spots commonly appear, on which all sorts of ointment are apt to be tried, none of which is efficacious. When I have described these symptoms at lectures, I have often noticed how here and there a member of the audience would feel his ear. Occasionally after one of these addresses I have had someone come knocking at my hotel door late at night, saying "Doctor, I seem to have a nodule in my ear. I want to have an examination to see whether I have leprosy."

Leprosy begins insidiously, progresses slowly, and may last for twenty or thirty years. Aretaeus, a Greek physician of Cappadocia who came to Rome in the First Century A. D., wrote an account of the disease which holds true today:

"Shining tubercles of different size, dusky red or livid in color, on face, ears and extremities, together with a thickened and rugous state of the skin, a diminution or total loss of its sensibility, and a falling off of all the hair except that of the scalp. The alae of the nose become swollen, the nostrils dilate, the lips are tumid; the external ears, especially the lobes, are enlarged and thickened and beset with tubercles; the skin of the cheek and of the forehead grows thick and tumid and forms large and prominent rugae, especially over the eyes; the hair of the eyebrows, beard, pubes, and axillae falls off; the voice becomes hoarse and obscure, and the sensibility of the parts affected is obtuse or totally abolished, so that pinching or puncturing gives no uneasiness. This disfiguration of the countenance suggests the idea of the features of a satyr, or wild beast, hence the disease is, by some, called satyriasis, or by others leontiasis. As the malady proceeds, the tubercles crack and ultimately ulcerate. Ulcerations also appear in the throat and nose, which sometimes destroy the palate and septum, the nose falls, and the breath is intolerably offensive; the fingers and toes gangrene, and separate joint after joint."

The ancient world often mistook other diseases for leprosy. There is an innocent skin disease, characterized by white spots which changes the epidermis and turns the individual affected into the Biblical whited sepulchre. The lesions of yaws and syphilis may resemble leprosy; lupus vulgaris, or tuberculosis of the skin, may be as disfiguring as leprosy, but can usually be cured by proper treatment. Once at Oris in Samar I found awaiting me in a leper compound at the edge of town a hundred of the most mutilated, repulsive individuals I had ever seen. For years these tragic figures had endured the stigma and mental anguish inseparable from leprosy, but not one of them was a leper. A temporary hospital was opened, the cases were successfully treated, and the patients were released.

The manifestations of leprosy differ widely throughout the world. The incidence in the Philippines is relatively high but the type is mild compared with certain other countries. India has the more serious nerve type, and the tuberculoid form is predominant in South Africa. In the Philippines about one-quarter of the cases are purely cutaneous, without much nerve involvement. In such instances, the disease first appears with a small round patch on the skin, white or red, or whitish and scaly in the center with a red margin. No pain and no itch are experienced, the principal symptom being the lessened sensitivity to feeling. After the disease has lasted a few years the nerves usually become involved, and, ultimately, in those who live long enough for the skin manifestations to disappear, only neural manifestations remain.

Americans are not immune to leprosy in the Philippines; as far as can be determined the incidence among those who live in the lower social strata is as high as among Filipinos.

Anesthesia among lepers is extremely common. One of the earliest authentic accounts of the anesthetic features of leprosy occurs in the chronicles of William of Tyre. He tells how it was discovered that Baldwin, son of Amory, the King of Jerusalem, was a leper:

"One day the future king was playing with his comrades and in the course of the game the hands and arms of all were scratched. The other children uttered cries, but Baldwin made no complaint. His tutor remarked upon it. At first he believed that the child, through valiance and bravery, was hiding his pain, but Baldwin, questioned, affirmed that he felt none whatsoever in the region of the scratches. His arm and hand had gone to sleep, and even when his tutor bit him, he did not feel the bite."

I have often seen a lighted cigarette burning into the fingers of a leper without his being at all aware of it. Even the odor of burning flesh did not attract his attention, because the sense of smell was also gone.

Anesthetic leprosy attacks the trophic nerves, which carry impulses throughout the body, causing the blood to bring essential elements to damaged tissue. Ordinarily, if the fingers of a well person are merely drawn across a piece of paper, a few surface cells of the skin are rubbed off. But nature telegraphs by means of these trophic nerves to headquarters that tissue has been removed, and at once the blood supply opens, the repair is made, and the hand heals. But this telegraph system in lepers is completely out of order. Nature is not aware that any cells have been removed, and the result is they are not replaced, but are gone forever. Lepers frequently have worn their hands down until they are no more than bats.

Wounds in anesthetic cases heal with great difficulty. A slight injury, such as caused by running a thorn in the foot, often starts an unhealable ulcer that produces a deep hole and discharges foul pus. We keep such wounds dressed and try to make them bleed, but the ulcers often become so bad that the bone is exposed and the feet often have to be amputated. A characteristic lesion is interosseous atrophy, where the tissue between the bones at the back of the hand is absorbed.

The anesthesia is not accompanied by paralysis, because the motor nerves are not affected and still retain their functions. The nerves of the eye are sometimes attacked, often resulting in frightful suffering from iritis. The larynx may be affected and the voice becomes hoarse.

Leprosy is horrible to live with and difficult to die with. Death seldom comes unless from some other cause. The average life of a leper is probably about ten years after the disease first becomes apparent. At Culion a pathological survey of the causes of death showed that twenty-four percent died of tuberculosis and sixteen percent of nephritis. The mortality at the colony was high, but it was believed to be materially lower than it would have been among these people in their homes. Many of them had been beggars and wholly dependent upon public charity for their living. The great majority of cases during the early years were so far advanced when admitted that they were practically beyond human aid.

There are usually two male for one female leper. Why this is so no one has been able to tell. When I visited any leper colony for the first time I used to ask, "How many men have you?"

"We have two hundred."

"Then you have one hundred women."

The invariable reply was, "Yes."

Gerhard Armauer Hansen, a Norwegian doctor of Bergen, in the early 1870's first proved leprosy due to a bacillus. This microbe, which usually grows in bundles of rectilinear sticks resembling the Chinese puzzle, is too small to be seen with the naked eye. Whenever this bacillus can be demonstrated in the tissues, it may be stated beyond

223

question that leprosy is present. Scientists have tried to advance the study of leprosy by attempting to transmit it to guinea pigs, Japanese dancing mice, rats, and monkeys, but without success because no animal contracts it. They have also attempted to isolate and cultivate the lepra bacillus in the test tube. Many have claimed to have succeeded, but their claims so far are open to question because the experiment could not be satisfactorily repeated by others.

In acute leprosy, accompanied by fever, bacilli abound in the rash which covers the body, and it is quite easy to recover them from the scales constantly being shed and from the serum that oozes from abraded surfaces of the epithelium. Such cases are assumed to be extremely dangerous. From the mucous membrane of the nose thousands of bacilli are discharged from lepers who at the time show no cosmetic or anesthetic evidence of the disease.

The nose still continues to be the site where mycobacteria of leprosy can be detected with the greatest frequency and certainty. A scraping from the septum mixed with the serum drawn from the scarification remains a standard test.

Falsehood is a hare and truth is a tortoise which travels slow to its destination. I have been severely criticized for allegedly having stated that the lepra bacilli were found in secretions of the nose. I have denied this again and again and again. But the statement, "Heiser is entirely mistaken in his nasal secretion theory," continues to crop up. I had never made mention of any nasal discharges; I had said only that a scraping from the septum of the nose would show the existence of leprosy more frequently than other tests.

To recover the bacilli in the neural form would necessitate cutting into the nerve trunk to scrape off the sheathe, but this painful process is unnecessary because the clinical signs of anesthesia are unmistakable.

We have learned how leprosy affects the body but not why. As in tuberculosis, we still lack the knowledge to attack the disease by breaking a link in the chain of transmission. Nobody knows how leprosy is contracted, except that it apparently requires prolonged intimate contact. Because the incubation period is unknown also, one of the disquieting features of handling lepers is the long period which may elapse before the disease manifests itself. The shortest known time is about two years, and in some cases it has been over twenty. This makes it extremely difficult to obtain any positive proof as to the exact time at which the disease was acquired.

Some people have believed that mosquitoes were responsible for the transmission of leprosy. But lepra bacilli are found only in the intestinal contents and do not reach the proboscis of the mosquito, which is inserted directly into a blood vessel of its human victim. The evidence against flies is greater; their feet could easily carry bacilli from the sick to the well and it has been proved that flies retain the bacilli in their intestinal tracts for several days after feeding upon leprous material.

Something more than ordinary contact is apparently necessary before transmission can take place. What this is we do not know. But it is also true that leprosy does not occur in areas in which there is no leper. This fundamental fact was the foundation stone on which I built my policy.

The segregation of lepers has been subjected to much criticism in the past. Many have held that attempts at rigid isolation have generally defeated their own ends because victims of the disease were driven into hiding, whereas if treatment were offered and assurance given that there would be no forcible detention, lepers would voluntarily apply for medical attention and thus open cases could be rendered much less communicable. However widely eminent medical men may differ upon this question, the incontrovertible fact remains that every leper who is capable of giving off lepra bacilli is at least one center of infection if the bacilli can find suitable soil in which to lodge.

The real gains against leprosy are due to the disinterested cooperation of physicians, research workers, and sanitarians who have shared their knowledge and experience and helped governments and institutions to organize systematic measures of isolation and treatment. Their aim has not merely been to relieve the afflicted but to protect whole populations. These modern crusaders will not be content until leprosy has been banished from the world. The recent trend has been for more and more countries to recognize their responsibilities and earnestly to try to control the disease and give the lepers adequate care.

The United States has a creditable record in taking care of leprosy at home and in its dependencies. When I made my first trip around the world in 1908 I spent a month at Molokai, where Father Damien had labored so long. At that time this place was foremost in the treatment of leprosy. The colony occupied only half the island, but the three hundred and fifty inhabitants were cut off by a precipitous mountain from all communication with the other section.

Leprosy was called *mai pake*, or the Chinese Evil, by the Hawaiians. It had probably been brought out by the coolies imported for work on the sugar plantations. It had spread rapidly in the Islands, due partly to the fact that the Hawaiians do not shrink from those afflicted with the disease. They had tried various remedies of their own, scarifying themselves with pieces of glass, eating the flesh of cats, drinking Pain Killer, and consulting the *Kahuna*, or medicine man.

A place of isolation had first been set aside by Kamehameha, and the United States government had carried on the work. Not only was everything done for the lepers' comfort and for advancing our knowledge of the disease, but many luxuries had been introduced.

The lepers also profited by exercising their franchise. The political parties of Hawaii were about evenly divided, so that the votes of the lepers could almost swing the election. Hence they were cherished solicitously by the leaders of both parties. Native orators harangued the inmates of the colony, but took care to have the platforms erected near the shore and with palm leaf screens to protect themselves from possible contagion. But more substantial bait was required. The fermented taro dish called *poi* was particularly delectable to the Hawaiians. One political aspirant would guarantee, in case he were elected, to provide each leper with one pound of *poi* a day. The other aspirant would then promise two pounds of *poi*. At the time of my visit the bid had been raised, and each leper was entitled by law to seven pounds of *poi* a day, far more than he could possibly eat. The lepers were taking advantage of their strategic position and favoring a law which would give them the right to sell the *poi* which had been thrust upon them and retain the proceeds.

A study of the history of leprosy in Hawaii shows that until isolation was carried out, the number of lepers was constantly on the increase. It may be argued, however, that the Hawaiians are unusually susceptible to leprosy, while the Japanese, who are now numerically predominant, are not. Thus, although the total number of lepers in Hawaii has been reduced, it is not certain whether this reduction may not be due to the lesser susceptibility of the Japanese and other introduced races.

When I became Director of Health of the Philippines I realized that one of my most important duties would be to isolate the lepers whose numbers were estimated anywhere from ten to thirty thousand, although officially a little less than four thousand were recorded. There were twelve hundred new cases developing every year and practically nothing was being done about them.

Segregation is always cruel. We did not want to separate husband and wife or children and parents. But segregation is cruel to relatively few whereas non-segregation threatens an entire people. I believed that isolation not only protected others from contracting leprosy but, furthermore, was the most humane solution for the leper himself. Instead of being shunned and rebuffed by the world, he could have an opportunity to associate with others of his kind in pleasant relationship. In the Philippines the lepers were sensitive and proud and quick to notice any infringement upon their human rights.

Among the Filipinos family ties are unbelievably strong. Every step would have to be taken most tactfully; otherwise the Filipinos would conceal their lepers, or even actively oppose segregation. First, the colony would have to be prepared, and, then, the Islanders would have to be educated to the benefits of the plan.

Almost at the very inception of the civil government, negotiations had been carried on by Worcester which led to the setting aside of Culion Island for a leper colony. Culion is one of the Calamianes group between the Sulu and China Seas, two hundred miles southwest of Manila. It is twenty miles long and twelve miles at its widest point. The population was then about eight hundred; more than half were harmless, wild Tagbuanas, without fixed abode or title to land beyond that of possession. Outside the town of Culion there were only eight small houses.

The Bay of Culion is almost landlocked, and is surrounded with marvelous green hills. Through the water, calm and blue and crystal clear, are plainly visible coral and marine plants of almost every

227

conceivable hue. Across the Bay is the Island of Coron, over which hangs in the early morning a diaphanous blue haze. The rising sun gradually clears the air, only to have the mists gather again as the sun sinks. Coron has long been a lodestone for those who specialize in coral. Beautiful to look at, it is almost impossible to investigate. There are some tiny coves with a little sand in them where a boat can be landed. Otherwise the whole shore is a sheer cliff, usually undercut three to four feet; at low tide a rowboat can glide beneath comfortably.

The greenish-blue surface of Coron is built up of thousands of razor-sharp plates, like meat cleavers, set perpendicularly and so sharp and so close together that the toughest leather is sliced to ribbons after a few steps. Only one man has been able to penetrate any distance. When his shoes were completely shredded, he bound twigs upon his feet, proceeding cautiously for a few paces, and then repairing the damage with more twigs.

Culion was valuable for its forest products and had good fishing grounds. Thus it was a constant temptation for poachers. In addition, the many wild carabao were a lure to sportsmen. We were glad to have these dangerous animals shot, and we would grant special permits to those who wished to try their skill. But so many mighty hunters had come to grief at the horns of the carabao, that it was customary for a small relief expedition to be kept in readiness.

Once the brother of Governor General Harrison, an internationally renowned Nimrod, scorned our warnings, and set forth boldly. When dawn of the next day broke without his having returned, the relief party started out and discovered him, gunless and hatless, in the topmost part of the tallest tree in the vicinity.

At first the plan had been to locate the leper colony outside the old town of Culion at a place called Halsey Harbor. In January, 1903, fifty-nine laborers and two foremen had arrived, constructed a weir to supply fresh fish for the camp, and tried to get the natives to saw planks for a wharf, but this had proved to be beyond their skill. Moreover, siesta hour for the Filipinos had seemed to come the moment the foreman turned his back. Lonesome for their women, and discontented at the working conditions, as soon as they were paid, they had said, "We want to go home." Finally beriberi and malaria had set in, and the site had had to be abandoned for another.

A little over a year later steps had been taken to purchase the village of Culion and transfer its inhabitants to the Island of Busuanga, near Coron. There were a number of good houses, and also an old fort, dating from the time of the Moro raids, where the Filipinos, although outnumbering their assailants twenty to one, had judged it more prudent to hide than to fight.

The problem of Culion was one of the most arduous which faced me when I took office. I became wholly responsible for the undertaking, which proved more difficult than I could ever have anticipated, even in my wildest dreams. The actual building began in 1905. Every imaginable type of social question presented itself. Not only houses and a hospital had to be constructed and separate quarters for the non-lepers built, but streets had to be laid out, wharves constructed, buoys planted, a sewer system installed, amusement halls and a postoffice planned. Arrangements had to be made for public order, for municipal ordinances, for banking, and for disinfecting letters.

We never could be sure of holding labor any length of time. Good mechanics had no desire to undergo the isolation. Some left after a few days' work, and the class that could be induced to go often lacked skill and made blunders which sometimes took months to correct. At one time three hundred workmen laid down their tools and retired to a safe distance at the first report that a shipload of lepers was soon to arrive at the Island.

Delays were constant and inevitable. There was no telegraph, and mail steamers arrived only once every three weeks. Moreover, captains of vessels carrying building materials who were unfamiliar with the port often would anchor far off, and the supplies had to be laboriously landed in small boats. Sometimes a part of a machine would be lost in transit. This island in the China Sea was ten thousand miles from a market; all supplies had to come from the United States. It took four to five months to procure even an odd screw which might be missing.

In May, 1906, we prepared to transfer the three hundred and sixty-five inmates of the San Lazaro Hospital at Cebu to Culion. Often, before and afterwards, we had to contend with fear. A government boat had been set aside for the purpose, but as we were about to sail the entire crew deserted. Only the chief engineer and the skipper, a Maine Yankee named Tom Hillgrove, stuck to the ship. Even after a new crew had, with great pains, been assembled, I had qualms about setting forth over the treacherous waters of the China Sea, because the skipper had fortified himself with such huge quantities of alcohol. But he was so good a navigator that he was equal to all emergencies, and we arrived safely at Culion, where Father Valles, a Jesuit priest, and four Sisters of the order of St. Paul de Chartres were on hand to receive the lepers.

I wanted to popularize Culion so that the lepers who were at large would come there willingly. I had photographs taken of the colony, and even moving picture reels made, a great achievement in those days, showing how attractive it was. I invited leaders of public thought to come to the Island, trusting they would write home about it to their friends. Agents were sent to the various towns to explain the purpose of Culion, and tell the lepers what they would find there, the type of house they would live in, the food they would eat, and the facilities for treatment. The Filipino is cautious, and not many came at first. But those who were persuaded found they were much better off than at home. The first two years we received enough volunteers to tax all our resources.

My plan was to remove lepers first from well isolated islands which had comparatively few victims, so that the spread of the disease could be prevented where it was not firmly entrenched. For the leper collecting trips we chartered the *Basilan* which could accommodate one hundred and fifty. Orders were telegraphed a few days ahead to the local health officials to have the lepers assembled at central points in preparation for my arrival, giving them the date.

In collecting lepers, as in every other activity, expenses had to be watched carefully. The Bureau of Health was prepared to bear all reasonable charges, but it was found necessary to inform the municipal authorities in advance that only a limited amount of money was available. If not so notified they would usually erect expensive quarters instead of the temporary shelters which would adequately serve the purpose.

Many municipalities used to try to evade their responsibilities by presenting for transfer to Culion their insane, blind, cripples, and other incurables who had become public charges, and some were surprised and pained when we rejected them. In the first collections only about half those reported as lepers were authentic cases.

In the early days the very word leprosy struck unreasoning terror into the hearts of those suspected, and a number went into hiding. There was a young leper girl in Cebu whom the local authorities were never able to produce when we arrived. Finally her brother was stricken and taken to Culion. On our next visit she gave herself up voluntarily. When I asked her how she had eluded us so long, she explained that the telegraph operator was her friend, and had informed her in advance when we were due. She would then speed away to a cave back in the hills where she had always had enough food cached to last her until we had gone.

I have never seen remorse that equaled hers. Her heart was broken. I used to talk with her each time I visited Culion, and each time she would say to me, "I thought I was fooling you and all the time the only person I fooled was myself. I infected my brother, and if only I had given myself up it would never have happened."

One of our most prolific sources of information as to evaders was the anonymous communication. If a Filipino wants to secure revenge on an enemy, he spies upon him until he discovers some evidence to report to the authorities. Curiously enough such delations as we received were, in the main, correct. On one occasion we were told that if we were to go to a certain house in the center of Manila, and knock three times, and then again once, a trap door in the ceiling would open, and there we would find a leper. We followed these instructions, and found the leper. Somebody had a grudge against his family, and was trying to get even.

The anonymous letter writer was not always accurate, however. We once received information that the son of a mayor in a small provincial town was ill with leprosy. When we went to the house we found him in bed with all his clothes on. There was nothing wrong with him but malaria and a skin rash. We furnished him quinine and a cake of soap, with the stern advice to use both. He recovered shortly.

The Filipino is also likely to be unscrupulous when he is attempt-

231

ing to secure a political advantage. When I arrived one day at a small town, the mayor reported he had all the local lepers ready in waiting. On the way to the detention building one of the prominent citizens approached me and asked me to help him, saying his daughter, who was perfectly healthy, had been shut up with the lepers. Since this was a very common story, I was not particularly impressed, but told him I would look into it.

I was somewhat surprised to find that he was right. His daughter, a beautiful girl, had been herded into camp with real lepers, although she had not the slightest sign of the disease. I ordered her released and then demanded of the local health officer, "Why did you lock her up?"

"The mayor told me to, and I have to obey his orders."

"But what reason did he have?"

"Her father is a candidate. The present mayor thought he could win the election if he could brand his rival's daughter with the stigma of leprosy."

At the very inception of gathering up the lepers it became our fixed policy not to confine anyone at Culion from whom leprosy bacilli could not be recovered and demonstrated by microscopical examination. Filipinos had so many skin diseases that an occasional mistake might easily have been made in diagnosing non-lepers as lepers. We never placed anyone on the ship until from three to five leprosy experts, acting as a Board, were unanimously satisfied that the man or woman had leprosy. If we erred it was on the side of safety, but, as far as I know, no mistake was ever made. The reason more cases are now being found is that since those days many refinements in diagnosis have been made. The more recent complete knowledge is of great value because the early stages of the disease are the most infective.

For the clinical examination of the anesthetic form the suspect was blindfolded. Then his skin was touched with a cotton swab, a feather, a camel's hair brush, or a paper spill, and he was asked to indicate where he had been touched. The head and the point of a pin were pressed alternately against suspected spots, and the patient was asked which caused the more pain. Test tubes, one filled with hot water and the other with cold, were held against his skin, and he was asked to tell which was warm and which was cold. Finally, a scraping was taken from the septum of the nose with a blunt, narrow-bladed scalpel, and put under the microscope.

The actual work of collecting the lepers and caring for them after they were gathered together presented obstacles, many of which at times seemed insurmountable. Most people have a spontaneous impulse toward charity and a social conscience which impels them to do good, but these emotions are often dissipated in the face of actuality, particularly where the task is loathsome and repellent. When it came to transporting lepers to a seaport, providing their subsistence, aiding them aboard the steamer, making the necessary medical examinations, and attending to their needs, experience again and again demonstrated that only those of my doctors who were possessed of superior courage and capable of supreme self-sacrifice could be induced to continue at the work.

Often lepers had been confined in a barbarous manner by the local officials at the outskirts of towns. Once when we arrived in a province we found them in an abandoned warehouse, where they had been shut up for weeks pending our arrival. Some were literally rotting away. I had several doctors with me, most of them long experienced in work of this kind, but they became so nauseated by the foul stench from the gangrenous, putrescent ulcers that they could hardly bring themselves to handle the patients. One old woman in particular was no more than a mass of decaying flesh, rotten as a corpse long exposed; she looked as though she were going to fall to pieces. It was with the utmost difficulty that I finally summoned the courage to gather her up and carry her on board in a basket.

There was always, of course, the danger of infection. On one occasion cholera broke out on the *Basilan* in the midst of a collection trip in the Southern Islands. I ordered the boat to make for Culion as quickly as possible, but at best it would take several days, and the quarters on board were too small for effective isolation. After we arrived at Culion, I immediately segregated the lepers in groups of ten, so that if one group should become infected, it alone would have to be quarantined. One leprous woman was not only violently insane, but also came down with cholera. She would keep no clothing on and, since she was completely uncontrollable, she was a deadly

233

menace to everyone. It required a physical struggle, but I finally succeeded in pinioning and imprisoning her. In the process she scratched me so deeply in the arm that I still bear the scar. It is extremely unpleasant to be scratched by an insane leper with cholera, and I lost no time in drenching the wound with disinfectant, though I could not be certain that it would prove effective. There is no way to tell who have and who have not immunity to leprosy, but my mind is now at rest, because the twenty years of possible incubation have passed, and I have not yet evidenced any signs of leprosy.

In the light of our present knowledge I believe that isolation is the best course in a country such as the Philippines, but it will take a long time to prove that it can wipe out the disease, because many cases in the incubation period cannot be detected.

By 1908 at least one collection of lepers had been made all over the Archipelago, and a number in many provinces. Four years later every recognized leper was in confinement. Certain elements in many communities were not open to persuasion, and there force was necessary. The obstreperous cases often belonged to the criminal classes, so that sometimes we had to resort to legal compulsion. But most of the patients who were to become the inhabitants of Culion were persuaded rather than compelled to go. Gradually the terror it caused was lost through our educational propaganda, and lepers were lured there by hope of cure.

It must be said to the credit of the Filipinos that the effort to segregate lepers was never seriously opposed. In the majority of cases they cooperated, even though this often involved the lifelong separation of wife from husband, sister from brother, child from parents, and friend from friend. Only in comprehending this can it be realized what forbearance was exercised by the Filipinos.

I can still hear ringing in my ears the cries of anguish of the relatives and friends who used to follow us down to the boat drawn up on the open beach. As we rowed out to the *Basilan,* and the *Basilan* steamed out to the open sea, I could see them standing there, and hear faint echoes of their grief. It was an experience to which I never became hardened. I knew that even as the *Basilan* was hull down on the horizon they would still be there, straining for a last glance at those whom they never expected to see again.

CHAPTER 15. PRISONERS OF HOPE

THE *Basilan* had no sooner landed its first grim cargo at Culion than I realized that my responsibilities toward the lepers whom I had uprooted from their homes had only begun. Transporting them there and providing them with food and lodging was merely a prelude to the real work.

After the novelty of their surroundings had ceased to attract and divert the lepers, they often became homesick, and yearned for their old associations. In every way we tried to make their life as nearly as possible like that of their own villages, always remembering Culion was a town of invalids. We put Tagalog with Tagalog, Ilocano with Ilocano, Visayan with Visayan, Moro with Moro; they would mix during the day but at night liked to be with their own kind.

Little by little we beautified the place with trees, palms, and shrubbery. I designed a semi-open air theatre, with Chinese spirals and other roof decorations, but the workmen were unable to follow my intention so that when finished it resembled no known style of architecture. It served its purpose, however. It was so constructed that those who needed protection could sit under the roof, and the rest in chairs around the outside.

Filipinos are born actors and the lepers took eagerly to dramatics. Besides putting on plays of their own, they enjoyed greatly the films with which generous motion picture companies kept me supplied.

Filipinos are natural musicians also. I have always believed it would be possible to hand fifty band instruments at random to fifty

235

Filipinos and hear sweet music at once. The Filipinos have made music for the entire East. I have heard the rhythm of their Spanish melodies echoing from dance floors and theatres at Calcutta, Bombay, Singapore, and everywhere else in the Orient.

The lepers were no exception. Culion took great pride in its band and practised faithfully. This we encouraged, because the music cheered them enormously. The lepers at San Lazaro at Manila had a particularly good stringed orchestra which used to greet me on every visit. Once after a long absence I was welcomed as warmly as ever but observed with surprise that no music was on hand. "Why don't you play?" I asked.

"We can't."

"Why not?"

In dumb reply they held up their hands; they had literally played their fingers off.

Our first collections of lepers were composed of those who were so ill as to be nearly helpless. The disease had produced such contractions of limbs, destruction of tissues, losses of fingers and toes, impairment of muscular power, and general debility, that only a few could perform the heavy work connected with agriculture, which we hoped would divert them as well as contribute toward their support. Also, many had fever several days during the month, and more were entirely bedfast.

It was not easy to keep the semi-well occupied and distracted. Because of the public's great fear of infection, they could not weave hats of palm or dresses of jusi cloth, carve knickknacks or hammer brass ash trays for general sale. We did not even advocate the manufacture of these handicrafts because the innate Filipino disposition to take life easy, while deplorable for the healthy, is not at all a bad thing for lepers. They did little work other than that entailed by their own domestic requirements.

At first we tried serving cooked food in a cafeteria, but when our Occidental methods of preparation obviously did not please our patrons, we gave them the raw food and let them prepare it to suit their own tastes. Some years later Miss Hartley Embrey, an able food chemist, went to Culion as a volunteer to devise ways of combining proper dietary with Filipino gustatory preferences. The most advanced cases had been collected earlier; the later comers were in the initial stages of the disease, and consequently not so badly incapacitated. Basing his action on Miss Embrey's advice, General Wood arranged for the employment of competent gardeners. Ubi tubers were introduced from the Batanes and leafy vegetables were grown with great success. They started tiny sugar plantations, the output of which was purchased by the government and reissued as food to the lepers.

Cattle raising was started. We also encouraged them to fish, and they paddled little balsas of lashed bamboo to the huge fenced fish traps and to other waters. They did well at fishing, and daily we purchased large quantities. In addition to buying their produce we gave them a gratuity of twenty cents a week, and established a store at which small comforts were sold. In order to avoid all risk of infection outside, special money was used, which circulated only in the colony.

We helped the townspeople to set up an organization with a *presidente*, or mayor, and ten councillors, all of whom they elected themselves. They were allowed to make their own regulations, and punish offenders. The first woman suffrage in the East was established at Culion in 1908. The women were influential in elections, and invariably picked out the best looking man for *presidente*, no matter what his qualifications.

A former sergeant of Constabulary who had developed leprosy was chosen to captain a leper police force of twelve, which grew in size with the expanding colony. We did not attempt to restrict the liberty of the inmates; as far as we were concerned they could escape whenever they were so minded. The idea was that they were to prevent themselves from running away.

Very little went on in the colony that the police and secret service men did not know. Nevertheless, being lepers themselves, it sometimes happened that they were at one with those who grew too lonely. The refugees would make rough rafts of bamboo with sails woven of palms, and hide them away in some safe place. Then, when the occasion was propitious, off they would sail into the China Sea.

Often the lepers came from distant islands, hard to reach with improvised craft, and in the endeavor to gain home an occasional one

237

was shipwrecked and drowned. A few of the deserters leaving Culion escaped, because the Islands are dotted so closely that the voyage from one to another is not far and could be negotiated even with their frail balsas; under favorable weather conditions the crossing to Luzon could be made without excessive risk. The lepers would be missed when they did not show up for their gratuities, and occasionally we could rescue them in a launch. Escapes were comparatively rare and never were a source of great trouble. Even those who reached their homes usually gave themselves up after they had satisfied their nostalgia.

The comparative contentment of the lepers was in great measure due to the Sisters of St. Paul de Chartres, who had dedicated their lives to the care of these unfortunates. Outwardly calm and happy, the Sisters spread an atmosphere of cheer around them that was truly magnificent. Whenever the *Basilan* came into port, they would have to dress the nauseating, disgusting wounds of the newcomers, and each day thereafter throughout every year, this routine had to be repeated with never a break. In emergencies they had to perform amateur surgical operations.

I had always had a notion that cleanliness was an important factor in the prevention of leprosy. If those even in the closest contact kept free of vermin and washed their hands and bodies frequently and thoroughly, I believed they would incur little danger. Although I could not confirm this theory scientifically, I had noted that nurses and attendants who worked at leper colonies and did not keep themselves clean often did contract the disease.

I asked the Sisters to promise me solemnly that when they entered the hospital from their quarters in the clean part of the colony, they would remove their clothes in a room provided for that purpose before walking into the next room, where disinfected clothing would be waiting. When they left, they were to reverse the process, bathing themselves with disinfecting soap, stepping into the clean room, and there putting on their own clothes. Some of these nurses have been at Culion almost thirty years and not one has contracted leprosy. I have always ascribed this to the faithful manner in which they have carried out my initial instructions.

Among the loyal band of nurses Sister Calixte Christen was outstanding. As a young woman she had left Chartres and her family and friends to devote her life to lepers, the most friendless of human beings. With her own gaiety she lightened the burden of the hopeless. She had an extraordinary facility for languages, which she cultivated so that she might bring to each of the patients under her care added cheer. In June, 1926, General Wood and his staff attended the ceremony of presenting her a gold medal, cast especially for the occasion and given in recognition of her remarkable services over this long period of time.

Graduates from Philippine nursing schools are now sharing the burden. Their zeal, both from a scientific and humanitarian point of view, spurs them on to great heights of self-sacrifice.

Individuals who are willing to abandon the pleasures of the world for lepers are rare, but, when found, usually exhibit complete abnegation of self. The American lay brother Dutton, who insisted on remaining at Molokai, was a case in point. No one knew whether he were truly a leper, since he would never allow himself to be examined, merely implying that he was leprous. To the lepers around him he was a friend, reading to them and advising them. He worked toward their interests indefatigably, writing letter after letter to cabinet ministers, politicians, millionaires, and presidents. By his solitary efforts he succeeded in raising moderate sums, which he turned into the common fund for lepers.

The doctors who went to Culion, although again they lacked the religious inspiration of the Sisters, possessed in full measure professional zeal and enough human charity to enable them to stand the loneliness of the life and the particularly trying and disgusting duties. The treatment of the foul-smelling gangrenous ulcers on a single patient often required more time than a major surgical operation.

I remember one occasion and only one when a physician deserted. I had promised him a relief in ten days, but several Filipino doctors had found excuses at the last moment for not sailing, and I was unavoidably detained in the endeavor to find one courageous enough. Nevertheless, I regarded my tardiness as no excuse for abandoning a post of confidence and trust, especially as he had left the hospital full of sick.

239

Life for the staff at Culion was exceedingly monotonous. Few diversions and little humor broke the monotony of the daily round. The coming of visitors was heralded as a great event. One of the doctors, who was something of a wag, was asked to be prepared to entertain a gentleman who was coming to inspect the work, and whose reputation for prohibitionist sentiments was well known. Prohibitionists have always been a temptation to jokesters. The doctor had a boy climb a cocoanut tree, puncture a nut with a hypodermic needle, draw out some of the milk, and replace it with whiskey.

The prohibitionist in due course arrived, and after half a day's inspection in the hot sun, his tongue was hanging out with thirst and his mouth was cotton wool.

"Wouldn't you like to have a drink of cocoanut milk?" asked the doctor. "There is nothing quite so delicious when you are hot and tired."

The visitor welcomed the proposal and the boy was sent up to fetch down the doctored cocoanut. The top was slashed off and the juice poured out before his eyes. After draining the bumper, he smacked his lips and said, "I've never tasted anything so pleasant in my life."

The inspection was finished in a spirit of hilarity.

Each time I paid a visit to Culion there was usually a public reception, complete with banners, a band, and an impressive parade. The duty of presenting petitions weighs heavily upon all Filipinos, no matter how unimportant the subject matter may be. My coming offered an unexampled opportunity to fulfill this obligation. Such petitions I was usually able to handle with a fair degree of diplomacy, but once I found myself obliged to retreat ingloriously from a mass attack of the women of Culion on the question of segregation of the sexes.

We had provided separate sleeping quarters for men and women but did not forbid them to mingle by day. Certain well-meaning persons who had interested themselves in the lepers were horrified. They brought pressure to bear on the government, and the Governor General issued orders. One part of the Island was to be set aside for the women and surrounded with a very high barbed wire fence. It was all finished and prepared for occupation when I arrived on my next trip. But I found that the sequestration had not been carried out in accordance with the decree. "Why hasn't this been done?" I asked the doctor in charge.

"The women simply won't go," he replied. "Short of a couple of regiments of constabulary we can't do anything with them. If you think you can persuade them, you go ahead and try."

"Let's call a meeting," I suggested. I had often addressed them before and anticipated no trouble. When the women were assembled, I climbed up on a soap box and stood under the blazing hot noonday sun, looking down on the bobbing mass of black umbrellas, tipped back to frame the furious faces. I explained to them that separation was believed to be for their own good, and that in any event the instructions of the Governor General must be carried out.

The Filipino women are even better orators than the men. One of them rose and delivered a fervent harangue to the effect that the rest of the world, after having segregated them, had not before seemed to concern itself with their welfare, and why should it take this unpleasant interest in them now? The women of Culion had asked for no protection from the men and did not want any.

Another rebel followed with an even more impassioned address. She worked upon the audience, already aroused, until they began to shout, "Kill him! Kill him!"

The umbrellas shut with a loud concerted swish, and with steel points sparkling, they converged towards my midriff. As the rush began, there flashed through my mind a picture of the ignominious fate which awaited me—punctured to death by umbrellas.

I held up my hand and shouted at the top of my lungs. "Wait a minute! Wait a minute!"

Fortunately one of the leaders heard me, and with a stentorian voice repeated, "Wait a minute! Let him talk! Let's hear what he has to say."

The umbrellas were poised in mid-air, steel points still aimed at me.

"If you feel so strongly about this, I promise you will not be isolated until I have had a talk with the Governor General! I give you my word that no further attempts will be made to carry out the order until after we have had this conference!"

Slowly the points were lowered, and the women disbanded. I was saved. I went to the Governor General as I had promised. "It's no longer the responsibility of the Director of Health to carry out such orders. I've made every reasonable effort, and I'm not going to risk my life again."

He agreed that other means should be found to meet objections. The women continued to live as they had done formerly, but ultimately homes were established for the young girls. The Sisters took charge of them, and saw that the doors were securely locked at night, although a rumor was current that a Sabine raid had once been planned and executed.

We had discouraged marriage because we did not want the lepers to contract lasting relationships which might entail suffering later if one partner should be cured and dismissed from Culion. But when they produced offspring without benefit of clergy, moral necessities obtruded upon medical ones, and our religious advisers insisted they must marry. Our concern before had been to prevent propagation, but now the birth rate began to increase.

Leprosy is most easily contracted in childhood; the earliest age at which it can be detected is about two, although generally it evinces its presence at from three to four years. Possibly the contraction of the disease in infancy is due to the close contact of leprous parents and children. Statistics show that if babies are not removed from their mothers before they are six months old, approximately half of them will become leprous.

That heredity plays little part in the transmission of leprosy has been shown at Molokai, where the children of lepers are removed a few days after birth to beautifully appointed homes in Honolulu, one for boys and another for girls. There they are cared for until they reach the age of twenty-one. During the thirty years this system has been in effect, not one child, according to the report, has ever developed leprosy.

The problem of what should be done with the children born at Culion offered great difficulties. No law existed, as in Hawaii, whereby we could take them from their parents. The duty seemed to devolve upon me of persuading the mothers of Culion to surrender their babies. I used to get them together and harangue them for hours, appealing to their mother love, and explaining how their children would almost certainly contract leprosy unless they were put in a safe home outside the colony. After having my pleas fall on deaf ears time after time, on one occasion my persuasive powers must have become transcendental, because twenty-six mothers, inspired with the spirit of self-denial, offered me their children.

> "He that will not when he may,
> When he will he shall have nay."

"All right," I said. "The boat sails tomorrow morning at eight. Have the children ready."

I ordered the *Basilan* prepared at once. Canvas was stretched around the railings, so that the babies could not fall overboard. I arranged to take six Sisters with me to watch over them and give them proper care on the twenty-four hour trip.

Long before eight o'clock the children arrived at the beach. Everybody was crying; the children were crying, the fathers were crying, the mothers were crying, and the friends were crying in sympathy. Lamentation was loud in the land. I could stand it only so long and then rushed to the bridge and told the Captain to be ready to leave the moment the last child was on board. The hawsers were cast off, the engine room bell jingled, and we slowly pulled out, leaving a weeping band behind us on the shore, and reducing the audible criers to twenty-six.

The *Basilan* puffed placidly over the beautiful calm waters of Culion. The Sisters could be seen moving about efficiently in their starched caps, quieting the children, and feeding them. I viewed the peaceful scene complacently, proud of the way I had managed the whole affair.

But just as we left Coron Passage I felt the first faint suggestion of roughness. The *Basilan* shifted uneasily, rocking gently from side to side and up and down. Then things began to happen that I had not anticipated. The English Channel is a mill pond compared to

243

the China Sea. First one Sister became sick and silently retired, then another followed, and another, until finally I, a bachelor, was left alone on the after deck with twenty-six babies.

The ship began to pitch and the seas grew heavier. Easily identifiable noises came from the cabins, and buckets were in demand. Now and then a wave curled over the deck. The rolls grew more prolonged. The *Basilan* would lurch to one side and babies and water and I would be awash in the scuppers. Each moment I expected to see one of my charges go overboard. Clutch and grab as I might it was impossible for me to contain all twenty-six in one embrace. Back we would go in the scuppers on the other side. During a lull I would get the babies all collected on a high spot, but although I held on to a leg here and an arm there, each roll sent some tumbling.

The loud, incessant, and nerve-wracking wails kept up from nine in the morning until three in the afternoon. Everybody gave me a wide berth. I was all alone with the sea-urchins in this dreary game of pitch and toss.

At last a sailor hove in sight. Filipino men were as good nursery maids as any women. I hailed him.

"I've had no lunch, and I must have a rest. You'll have to take care of these babies for a while."

When my sense of honor drove me back to the nautical nursery, a most amusing sight greeted my eyes. The sailor was seated flat on the deck, a baby on his right arm, a baby on his left arm, a baby under his right knee, a baby under his left knee, a baby hanging on his right ear, a baby hanging on his left ear. He had filled a beer bottle with milk. Whichever child howled loudest would find the neck thrust into its mouth. Until the baby subsided he would keep it there; then he would pull it out and stick it into the mouth of the next yowler.

The weather was so rough on this trip that the usual twenty-four hours lengthened into forty-eight. Since the time of which I am telling was before the days of wireless, I had to wait until we approached Corregidor to announce our arrival. But the instant we were within reach of the signal station, a message was sent summoning doctors, nurses, and ambulances to meet the ship at Manila. As we drew alongside the government pier, I made one of the longest broad jumps in history. Doctors, nurses, and ambulances were there ready to take over, and I streaked for my office. I figured that I had done my share in delivering the babies from the devouring sea.

I was just relaxing before the huge pile of mail which had accumulated in my absence when the telephone rang.

"Hello," I said unsuspectingly.

"This is the hospital. You'll have to come up here right away."

"Why? What's the matter?"

"We can't register those babies of yours until they've been identified. We don't even know their names."

"That's simple," I assured the head nurse. "Each child has a tag around its neck, giving its name, age, and parents' history."

"They may have had tags when they started, but they're ravenously hungry and must have eaten them. They're not here now."

I sighed resignedly and set off for the hospital. Sure enough, the tags were missing.

I picked up a baby, turned her over a few times, and then said, "This is Pepina de la Cruz." I laid her down and picked up the next. "This is Juan Cabonegro," and so I went down the line. After the first five or six identifications, the watching nurses accused me of hocus pocus.

"Come on now, Doctor, you're making up those names."

I assured them I was not, and fortunately was able to prove it. During the voyage I had had plenty of time to become acquainted with the babies and, since I had a numbered list, I scratched the number of each baby on its finger nail—merely as a precaution. Number 1 was Pepina, and Number 2 was Juan, and so on. Long before we reached Manila the names and corresponding numbers were engraved in my memory.

My original intention had been to put the children in an orphanage, but meanwhile they were kept in the hospital, theoretically to recover from the effects of the voyage. A week went by, plaintive appeals from the hospital coming in daily. "Please take these babies away. They're perfectly healthy. They don't belong here, and they're taking up space that we need for the sick and eating us out of house and home."

I was conscience-stricken, but was also in a quandary. If I put my

245

twenty-six charges in the orphanage, I might be exposing four hundred other children to leprosy. The babies were possibly in the incubation stage of the disease, even though they bore no evidence whatsoever of illness. I temporized and left them where they were. I simply did not know what to do with them.

One afternoon a reporter from the *Bulletin* appeared in my office to get a story. "I'm terribly sorry," I said, "but I haven't anything for you today, and besides I'm very busy. You'll have to excuse me."

The reporter settled himself more firmly in his chair. "The editor says you're always good for a story, and I'm supposed to stay here until you tell me one."

I was suddenly inspired. Filipinos were very fond of children. It occurred to me that, if properly approached, they might be induced to adopt my babies. I had no qualms because the risk was slight if they were taken into private homes. "I'll tell you a story," I said to the reporter. "But I'll do it only if you'll promise to put it on the front page and give it a four-column head."

It was a slack day for news and the reporter agreed. I then told him about my homeless babies, whom I could not put in the orphan asylum because I might thereby be endangering many others. I urged him to pull the *vox humana* stop as much as he liked but, in order that nobody might be misled, he must make it perfectly clear in every paragraph that these were the children of leprous parents. "Put in your article that we'll have them at the office at eight in the morning day after tomorrow. There will be lawyers on hand to draw up the documents for legal adoption, and the babies can be taken away at once."

The reporter did a beautiful job. Martin Egan's *Manila Times* and the other afternoon papers seized his story and elaborated upon it. When I arrived at the office the following morning, I could not imagine at first what the shouting, milling crowd was there for. It turned out that these hundreds of people were clamoring for babies. I pushed my way into the office and found that the infants were being disposed of with great celerity. Guarantees were being given, signed, and sealed before a notary public, and everything was in perfect form. I left the details to the office force, and turned to my daily routine.

At ten o'clock the chief clerk sought me. "You'll have to go out there," he said.

"Why, what's wrong?" I asked.

"The babies are all gone."

"That's fine. What more is there for me to do then?"

"But the people are still there. They want babies. They won't go away without babies. And there aren't any more babies."

"Well, tell them there aren't any more."

"I have told them, but still they won't go away."

There was nothing to do but tend to the matter myself. Barely had I opened the door when I heard the cry, "We want babies! We want babies!"

"My good people," I expostulated. "With the best intentions in the world, we cannot produce babies on such short notice—"

"We demand babies! You promised us babies!"

At this moment a second inspiration struck me. Among my other responsibilities was the orphanage. Without any great success I had tried for years to arrange for the adoption of these orphans, who were without home care and love.

I held up my hand to still the clamor. "All right, you'll have babies," I promised. "We'll have more babies in here tomorrow morning—a choice collection and plenty to go around."

Fifty orphans were brought to the office and by noon they too were all gone. As quickly as possible I installed a regular baby department with shelves put up where the babies could be placed.

Rarely were the foster parents particular as to type. Usually they took the babies as unquestioningly as those bestowed by nature. But one morning a woman returned, carrying a baby on her hip. "I don't want this one," she complained.

"Why, it seems like a nice baby. What's the matter with it?"

"I think it has some Japanese blood. I don't like the Japanese."

"That's all right, we'll take it back." I tossed it up on the shelf, pulled down another, and handed it to her. "How is this one?"

"Oh, this one is fine," she said, and departed.

But in no time she was back again. I was slightly annoyed. "We can't keep exchanging babies every few minutes. What's wrong with this one?"

"I bought the Japanese baby a whole outfit of clothes. This baby is much bigger. Nothing's going to fit him."

I turned to the shelves, looked here and there for a moment, and then pulled down a third baby. "Will this one fit the clothes?" I asked.

"Yes," she agreed, and went away with it.

On the whole my device had been a great success, but it was only an expedient and could not be repeated.

Children born thereafter at Culion, during the Harrison régime, were left in the colony, and many of them contracted leprosy. When General Wood took control some permanent compromise had to be found. The plan ultimately adopted was to allow the babies to remain with their mothers for six months, and then place them for two years in a nursery situated outside the leper limits. Those who became afflicted with the disease during that period were returned to their parents; those who remained free of it could be sent, with their parents' approval, to Welfareville near Manila. Only a small percentage of the children treated in this manner became leprous.

When I went to the Philippines little was known, except in a general way, about the treatment of leprosy. The prospects of cure were most discouraging. Hundreds of remedies had been tried, but only failure had followed. From time to time an isolated cure had been reported. This could be ascribed to a number of reasons: the diagnosis might not have been satisfactorily confirmed, the recovery might have been spontaneous, or the reliability of the reports might have been in doubt. Experience with thousands of lepers in the Islands taught me that occasionally individuals alternately recovered and relapsed, and during the period of temporary recovery it was impossible to prove leprosy, even by microscopical methods.

Many treatments for leprosy, like those for tuberculosis, seemed to cause some improvement. Furthermore, under better hygienic conditions and hospital care, or for other reasons not understood, the disease is often arrested; in a few instances improvement results, so that occasionally apparent cures may take place without any treatment.

The people of the Islands had employed various native remedies.

The Filipinos used to tie on the leprous lesions certain leaves which had a caustic effect. The Moros, who called the disease *Epul*, practised charms upon it. The patient was taken to some unfrequented spot in woods or mountains, put naked into a disemboweled bullock, and left there twenty-four hours, during which the tomtom beat incessantly to accompany the incantations of the medicine men. This was supposed to transfer to the carcass all the impurities of the human body. Whether the charms had any effect is doubtful, but throughout the treatment of leprosy it has been observed that heat may have a beneficial reaction. In Japan the value of thermal springs has been known for hundreds of years.

Hot baths to elevate the temperature are a desirable part of all modern treatments. The protein reaction and fever caused by vaccination was also decidedly helpful. For a time we had high hopes from the use of X-rays, applied as near the burning point as possible without actually inflicting permanent injury. In two cases slightly burning the skin produced an apparent cure, but the method was so severe that it could not be generally used.

The Bureau of Health continued a policy of trying any suggested remedy which seemed to give hope of affording relief. Other apparent cures occurred, but unfortunately all of the cases relapsed or died from some other disease after a period of one year. In the case of relapse the infection had simply existed quiescent, unperceived, only to break out again under propitious circumstances.

It sometimes seemed as though the mere intuition of the less progressive people grasped more than the scientific wisdom of the Western World. The common people of the East can often, by a mere glance, detect a leper when the American or European physician, after a clinical examination, fails to find evidence of the disease. In such cases, bacteriological examinations will often show that the ignorant native is right. Dr. Strong was once riding through the streets of Manila in his carromata when a Filipino sanitary inspector stopped him and informed him the driver was a leper. Dr. Strong was outraged, but the inspector's diagnosis turned out to be true.

It has long been known to the natives of India that chewing the leaves and the twigs of the chaulmoogra tree has a beneficial effect on leprosy. There was a pre-Buddhist legend, centuries old, that a leprous king of Burma had entered the forest and cured himself by eating the raw seeds. Eventually the Indians deduced that it was the oil of the chaulmoogra tree, and this is found most abundantly in the nut, which contains the curative substance.

In 1907 Dr. Isadore Dyer, Professor of Dermatology at Tulane University, brought the properties of chaulmoogra oil arrestingly to the attention of the scientific world by reporting its successful use at the Louisiana colony for leprosy in Iberville Parish. I visited there the following year and gained a most favorable impression of the treatment.

As soon as I had returned to the Islands Dr. Dyer's treatment was given a thorough trial. The drug had to be taken by mouth, and most patients became so nauseated that only one out of three hundred could retain the oil over a period long enough to be effective. The poor lepers would say, "Doctor, I'd rather have leprosy than take another dose!"

Then began an extended series of experiments to develop some method of administering the remedy without the resulting nausea. Chaulmoogra capsules were coated with salol or other substances so that they would pass through the stomach without digesting. Enemas were tried. Most of all we wanted to inject chaulmoogra hypodermically, but the oil would not absorb.

At this point a letter was written to Merck & Company, in Germany, in which we asked whether they could suggest any substance to add to the chaulmoogra oil which might cause it to absorb when injected hypodermically. They replied that they had no practical knowledge, but theoretically it was possible that the addition of camphor or ether might give the desired result. The testing of this possibility was done by Elidoro Mercado, the house physician at San Lazaro. He added camphor to Unna's old oral prescription of resorcin and chaulmoogra oil. To our great joy we found that this combination was readily absorbed.

Many came forward to volunteer for the new treatment. In fact, had I announced to the lepers of Culion, "If your right arm is cut off, you will be cured," dozens would have stepped forward.

The camphor-resorcin solution proved a great advance. After the first year we were able to announce to the world that a number of cases had become negative. We promised that if any patient remained so for two years we would release him. When this actually happened, for the first time in history hope was aroused that a permanent cure might be found for this most hopeless disease.

Few can imagine with what a thrill we watched the first case to which chaulmoogra was administered in hypodermic form, how we watched for the first faint suspicion of eyebrows beginning to grow in again and sensation returning to paralyzed areas. We took photographs at frequent and regular intervals to compare progress and to check on our observations, fearing our imagination might be playing tricks upon us, because in hundreds of years no remedy had been found which had more than slight influence on this disease.

But I was not satisfied. The treatment was still so slow in bringing about improvement or recovery that, after the first flush of excitement, the interest of doctors, nurses, and patients all began to wane. To remedy this and to discover more effective preparations of the oil, we brought over chemists from America. They failed. As we went deeper into the subject it became more and more clear that the world's knowledge of leprosy was still very primitive. If further progress were to be made, the resources of science should be coordinated.

In 1915 I visited Calcutta and there met Sir Leonard Rogers, who had just succeeded in curing amoebic dysentery with the emetine treatment. I endeavored to interest him in our research work, telling him we were on the first rung of the ladder but, strive as we would to reach the next one, we could not secure a footing.

Although Sir Leonard was interested he said, "I've been in India many years now, and I feel I'm entitled to a rest. I'm just about to retire and return to England." But he had made a mistake in having me as his guest. I kept after him hammer and tongs until he agreed to postpone his retirement and work on my problem. In only a few months, with the assistance of an Indian chemist, he was able to make a chaulmoogra oil preparation which halved the time of treatment.

I continued my efforts to enlist the services of as many scientists as possible. When I next passed through Hawaii, I called the attention of the Molokai authorities to the progress in India, and suggested that they take up the work in their laboratory from a new angle. The use of ethyl esters allowed us to ascend at one bound several rungs of the ladder of progress. Many cases so treated recovered and only eight percent relapsed after a year or so.

By this time the United States Department of Agriculture considered chaulmoogra of such vital importance that J. F. Rock was sent around the world to make a survey of the potential supply. The true chaulmoogra is the Taraktogenos kurzii. It has a fruit about the size of an orange, covered with a tawny-colored, fibrous rind and containing numerous oval, bean-like seeds. The oil in warm weather is a brownish-yellow liquid; when cool it is a soft solid with a characteristic odor and acrid taste.

The collection of the seeds, which were offered in the native bazaars of Burma, Siam, and even in China, was in the hands of the jungle people of Burma, who allowed at least fifty percent of the crop to be eaten by wild pigs and other animals, when they were not themselves frightened away by tigers and elephants. The dealers in the oil had never seen the tree in its native state.

When the crop of Taraktogenos failed in 1912, the oil of a related species, the Hydnocarpus wightiana or anthelmintica was used. This led to years of experimentation to see whether the oils of allied trees had the same effect as Taraktogenos.

As experience accumulated it gradually became apparent that the oils of any of the trees of the family to which the chaulmoogra belonged were equally efficacious. Many contradictory reports, however, had to be sifted and tested.

Mr. Rock had found forests of Hydnocarpus in Burma, some of the trees fifty to sixty feet tall, covering the steep hillsides in the back country. In Siam the trees were, in some places, so common that soap was made from the oil. Plantations have since been started in many countries, so that the supply of chaulmoogra will be assured.

The Hydnocarpus group is now most commonly used in the form of ethyl esters, which cause less local irritation than the other chaulmoogra oils. However, the choice of which to use is determined by the ease of procuring, cost of delivery, purity and freshness, and keeping qualities.

Success in treating leprosy has become as important a factor in preventing its spread as segregation. It is obvious that if a child with an infective lesion is promptly discovered and successfully treated a most important focus of infection is eliminated. The course of leprosy is of such great chronicity that final conclusions about the therapeutic value of a drug or method cannot be arrived at until after it has been used for several years. Both clinical estimates and microscopic examinations are subject to many errors.

I sometimes compare the treatment of leprosy with an automobile which has been going down hill with no brakes. Present day treatment has provided brakes. These do not always stop the car, but they do slow it down; sometimes they stop it completely, and occasionally it is possible to reverse the machine and put it back on the road to health.

Although of no case is it possible to state definitely that it can be cured with the present chaulmoogra oil treatment as standardized at Culion, ten percent of the patients recover, and fifty percent have a cosmetic cure, that is, the outward lesions disappear and the disease makes no further progress. In the case of thirty percent the disease is arrested, and ten percent are entirely uninfluenced and keep on getting worse. Among lepers who have not had the disease more than four or five years and are not beyond the period of young adult life, in certain groups varying with the country, sometimes twenty-five percent can be paroled. Such lepers are ordinarily examined at stated intervals for a reasonably safe period.

The earlier a case of leprosy can be detected, the greater the likelihood of recovery. In Zamboanga live two girls who were paroled in 1911 when they were ten and twelve years old. I have been watching them since their childhood. They are grown up and married, and have children of their own. They bear a few scars which will never disappear, but they are well, and show no signs of leprosy.

Several thousand lepers have now been freed from Culion after having the treatment, but one of the great unsolved problems is what to do with those who have recovered but who are badly disfigured. Many were deeply conscious of the stigma attached to them when they returned to their old homes. Often they begged to be allowed to stay at Culion, and a clean section of the Island was set apart for them where they could earn their living.

253

Although chaulmoogra oil produces a certain measure of success, the search continues constantly for more effective remedies. Mercurochrome, bismuth, neo-salvarsan, X-ray, diathermy, anything that offers even the remotest hope is tested out. Dr. Gordon Ryrie, an expert in dye therapeutics, became interested in leprosy and went to the Sungei Buloh Leper Settlement, near Kuala Lumpur, in Malaya. He argued that since coal tar dyes, which are used to stain bacilli, promptly kill them in the laboratory, why should not the same result be produced in the human body?

After some experimentation Dr. Ryrie found that the blue dyes had a definite therapeutic effect. First he tried methylene blue, and then trypan blue. It was a most startling sight to see him work. Within a minute and a half after the intravenous injection, the surface lesions of leprosy became clearly outlined, just as though they had been painted upon the skin. Even lesions not ordinarily visible to the eye became blue, and gradually the whole body turned indigo. At the end of a week the leprous nodules began to soften and to be absorbed. The blue color vanished about six weeks after the last injection. Sometimes in three months all the external symptoms disappeared and the case became negative. For a time it looked as though a real remedy had been found, but unfortunately many of these cases shortly relapsed.

Fluorescin is being given intravenously, and acts as well as trypan blue. Recently a California pharmacologist named C. D. Leake produced a synthetic preparation which he called chaul-phosphate. This is now being tried out at the Brazil leprosarium at Rio de Janeiro, and the lepers of Panama are being injected with it.

Too many disappointments in the past prevent us from becoming excited about a supposed new remedy until it has been completely tested. So far none has proved more efficacious than chaulmoogra ethyl esters. But meanwhile the quest goes on.

Dr. Ernest Muir of Calcutta, one of the foremost leprologists of the world, has made many contributions to the theory of the disease. I have never seen any man whose whole soul is more in his work. He is always ready to talk of leprosy, works with it all day long and probably dreams of it all night.

PRISONERS OF HOPE

The British Empire has more known lepers than any other political entity. After Sir Leonard Rogers returned to England he was instrumental in organizing the British Empire Leprosy Relief Association which, in turn, organized branch societies in India and many of the colonies, and made a survey of leprosy in Africa, Ceylon and the West Indies, and through its sister society a survey of India was made. Recently, with adequate isolation, much has been done in Jamaica, British Guiana, Cyprus, and other places.

Christian religious societies have always interested themselves in caring for lepers, and have been virtually the only ones. All other religions have, as a rule, held aloof. But sympathy for the afflicted, a Christian tenet, has done much to alleviate the sufferings of these unfortunate people. The American Mission to Lepers, fostered by the American Churches, works in many foreign countries, particularly in India.

Leprosy in the United States, although not commensurate in importance with many other diseases, has received a great deal of attention. Estimates of the number of lepers here vary from twelve hundred to two thousand. Most of the sufferers are aliens in whom the disease had not been sufficiently advanced to be detectible at the time of their admission. But, since they were here, their care automatically became a national obligation. As early as 1913 Surgeon General Rupert Blue was advocating a National Leprosarium. The American Mission to Lepers took a leading part in demanding such legislation. In 1917 Congress appropriated two hundred and fifty thousand dollars for the construction of a hospital in which all lepers in the United States should be cared for free of cost.

The government then had the problem of selecting a site. Almost insurmountable obstacles were encountered. Senators, representatives, chambers of commerce, business men, one delegation after another, raised a tremendous uproar at the slightest rumor that a leprosarium might be established in their particular vicinity. A well-known publicist began writing articles criticizing the government for its delay in choosing a site. A year had passed and no hospital had been started. The government could make no adequate defense.

I happened to be in Washington at this time. The Assistant

Surgeon General, who had been on my staff in the Philippines, said, "I'm worried over all this criticism. Nobody wants to have a leper hospital anywhere near. Haven't you any suggestions?"

"It sounds easy enough to me," I replied.

"What would you do?" he asked eagerly.

"I'd appoint a committee of three to locate this disputed site, and since this man has been your chief critic, I'd make him the chairman. Cut out the red tape. Let them have a liberal traveling allowance. They think it's so easy. Let them struggle with the problem."

The members of the committee set out on their travels. Like Yellow-Dog Dingo, they ran until their tongues hung out, and wherever they picked out a likely place, no one would let them stop.

Their hunt went on and on and on; I had forgotten all about them. One drizzling November night I arrived at Gulfport, Mississippi, with no idea in my head except how comfortable it would be to get to the hotel and into bed. But no sooner had I stepped off the train than I was surrounded by an exceedingly determined-looking crowd of men.

"This is the guy," one of them shouted.

"Come along with us," growled another threateningly.

I could smell pungent hot tar, and caught sight of a bag of feathers not very well concealed in the offing. "What have I done?" I demanded.

"You've done enough," came the menacing reply. "We're going to make an example of you."

Things were going very badly until one of the ruffians, peering more closely, said, "Say, we got the wrong fellow. This guy hasn't any whiskers."

Then, rather belatedly as I thought, they asked who I was, and when I was able to prove my identity, they let me go with rather surly apologies, but with no explanation as to what it was all about.

As soon as I reached the hotel I asked the clerk at the desk if by chance any member of the leprosy committee were staying there.

"Shshshshshshsh," he whispered. "Keep quiet!"

"Why, what is it?" I whispered back.

The sibilants continued. "There's a vigilance committee that wants to tar and feather one of them. It's suspected he's going to recommend locating a leper colony on Ship Island just off the coast. He's hiding up in his room and we're going to smuggle him out of town on the first train in the morning."

The next time I saw the Assistant Surgeon General he was again despondent. "The whole committee wants to throw up the job," he complained. "What shall I do?"

"Don't accept their resignations. They undertook to do the work. Let them finish it."

Eventually the committee recommended the purchase of the Louisiana State Leprosarium at Iberville. The avarice of man intervened between this charitable purpose and its accomplishment and Louisiana put a prohibitive price on her institution, plainly trying to hold up the federal government. But finally the purchase went through in 1921.

Leprosy had been endemic in Louisiana more than two hundred years, and had been sustained by contact with tropical America. Not until 1894 had any attempt been made to segregate the lepers. Before that they had begged on the streets, eaten at public restaurants, and traveled in public conveyances. Even after a home had been found for them on Indian Camp Plantation, Iberville Parish, seventy miles from New Orleans, they had had to be transported there by night on a coal barge, towed by a tug, and the feeling in the parish for a long time had been so strong that the existence of the home had been threatened.

On the site of the old leprosarium the government has now erected at Carville the best equipped leper colony in the world, until recently in charge of Dr. Oswald Denney. Its laboratories contribute much to the study of the disease. Most of the four hundred inmates are Asiatics or West Indian Negroes.

Saddest of the inmates are the leprous representatives of the creole families of New Orleans. Because of the assumed disgrace attached to their state, they rarely report their cases until they are in so advanced a stage of the disease that it is impossible to help them. A large percentage of the creoles develop leprous iritis, one of the most agonizing afflictions in the world. Leprosy itself is not normally painful, but it frequently takes this particular form in Louisiana. Its victims suffer so frightfully that morphine can hardly be given in large enough quantities. Most of the time they sit begging pitifully to be killed. There was one woman of the highest social class there, once handsome, now horribly disfigured, who day after day suffered this torture. I, a doctor, felt sad and humble that I could not prevent such suffering.

Everything imaginable is done at Carville to make the lot of the lepers easier. Specialists of all sorts come weekly for consultation. I particularly admired the resident dentist. Leprosy affects the jaw bones frequently, and artificial reproductions have to be made. When leprosy gets into the respiratory passages the breath becomes unbearably foul. A special machine has been devised to pump gas into the affected areas to make them less offensive. But what makes the work heroic is that this dentist is constantly running the danger of breaking the skin of his hands and allowing the infection to enter. Not long ago a surgeon in Paris cut himself while operating upon a patient and later developed leprosy.

Golf and tennis instructors are available, and a moving picture machine affords entertainment in the evening. In the magnificent new hospital building every inmate has a private room, beautifully furnished and equipped with a radio.

This seemed to me a very paradise, and I said to one of the lepers, "You must be very happy in your new quarters."

"Ahhhhhh, the government should a done it long ago."

The inmates of any public institution usually feel that they are entitled to whatever they can get from the government. At Carville the independent spirit is enhanced by the fact that the patients are allowed to decide for themselves what treatment they want to take and how long they want to take it.

No other leprosarium in the world approaches Carville in comfort or lavishness of equipment. At Culion I had always had to struggle with pitifully inadequate funds. Even so, it took approximately a third of all the appropriations of the health service and a twentieth of the entire revenue of the Islands to care for leprosy. When Governor Harrison handed over the reins to the Filipinos, I sadly watched the calesin of government hurtle toward destruction. It is true the Philippines were poor, but they were wasting what money was available in non-essentials, or misusing it like children.

I had many detractors among the Filipinos, who for years had conducted a campaign against me. The Oriental is adept at making charges. If I had permitted it, all my time would have been taken up in answering the accusations leveled against me. But when the Legislature decided to cut in half the appropriations for the Health Department, thus threatening our provisions for lepers and insane, I knew the time for action had come.

I appeared before a Committee of the House, all hostile, all with their minds previously made up. For a whole day I talked to them, pointing out the inestimable services the Health Bureau had performed for Manila and for the Philippines. I made no impression. They merely listened imperturbably. After I had argued for half the next day, I realized that I was losing rather than gaining ground. I had only one recourse left.

Before the Americans had come, the insane had often been chained like dogs under the houses. Fires were common in the dry nipa palm huts, and, in the frantic rush to escape, the insane had usually been forgotten and abandoned to horrible deaths. We had gradually built hospitals for the insane and taken in as many as we could of the worst cases.

Grimly I played my last card before the impassive Committee. "Gentlemen," I said, "you know that the only lunatics in your asylums are of the most dangerous kind. Among them are murderers, incendiaries, and the like. I can barely maintain them with my present funds. If you cut the appropriation according to your proposed bill, I shall have to release half of these maniacs. But to make it clear that the responsibility is not mine, I shall have a sign fastened around the neck of each: 'Dangerous Lunatic. Likely to Kill. At Large Because the Philippine Legislature Refuses to Provide for My Care.' This will make a great newspaper story. It will go over the whole world, and bring you a reputation."

"You wouldn't really do such a thing, would you?" one of the Committee asked in obvious alarm.

"Certainly I would, and, what is more, the same holds true for Culion. Half the lepers there will have to be turned loose. They are in an advanced stage of the disease, and not pleasant to view. They are capable of spreading leprosy wherever they go. I have just enough money left to bring them to Manila. But I want everybody to know that when the lepers are freed in the streets, I am not responsible for this act, either, and around the neck of each will be a sign: 'Released and at Large, Because the Legislature Refuses to Appropriate Funds for My Care.'

"That will make an even better newspaper story. It will be news everywhere, and particularly in America. You are demanding your independence and say you are capable of self-government. What impression do you think this will make in the United States?"

They capitulated and the appropriation was restored.

I had won my victory, but it was short-lived, because, with my departure to join the Rockefeller Foundation, the Legislature had its way.

Governor General Leonard Wood took particular interest in the leprosy problem. He was horrified to find that, because of lack of funds, only one out of six of the patients at Culion was receiving the ethyl ester treatment. To secure further appropriations, he used all his influence with the Legislature, which in the early days was great. A more scientific staff was installed, a first-class chemist employed, and an expert on nutrition set to work. Dr. H. Windsor Wade was transferred from the chair of pathology at the University of the Philippines and made pathologist at Culion. Most important of all, the manufacture of chaulmoogra oil ethyl esters was undertaken at the colony itself, thereby reducing the cost of the treatment and permitting many more to receive it. The effects were almost instantaneous; two thousand cases became negative in a few years.

But the lack of funds was still a severe handicap. Every morning General Wood used to meet with his advisers and conduct informal discussions on every conceivable project which might be of utility to the Islands. Leprosy was often on the table. General Wood was of the opinion that it would be a comparatively simple matter to raise one million dollars from the generous American public to establish a laboratory at Culion and build a hospital for lepers at Cebu.

It seemed to me that it would be essential for General Wood to lend his name to the undertaking. But he could not be made to see that this would have any drawing power. I talked to him off and on for days, saying that what he had done for Cuba would soon be forgotten, but the world would always remember him for his efforts on behalf of lepers. His other advisers were unanimously with me in this opinion. Finally he agreed.

Mrs. Dorothy Paul Wade, the wife of Dr. Wade, offered to help in any way she could. General Wood said he would write out an appeal, and, if she could get this published in the press of America, he was sure the response would be ample. Those who had had experience in raising funds were not so certain that this method would get us what we all wanted, but, since Wood enjoyed such popularity, they admitted they might be wrong. It must be said to the credit of American journalism that, although Wood had incurred much opposition during his candidacy for the Presidential nomination on the Republican ticket, the entire press of America, Republican and Democratic alike, published his appeal in the form of an editorial. The results, however, were disappointingly small; only a few hundred dollars were raised.

It was then suggested to the General that the only way to make the campaign successful would be to place it in the hands of experts in the money raising field. This was abhorrent to his New England conscience. Believing that the entire amount should be devoted to the purpose for which it was intended, he could not bring himself to allow a percentage of any money raised to be diverted toward the cost of the campaign.

Mrs. Wade worked with amazing celerity and by the end of a month had arranged for a series of magazine articles on this great human need. The magazines, like the newspapers, were liberal with their space, but again the results were terribly meagre. After trying faithfully to do the job as General Wood wanted it done, Mrs. Wade begged him by cable to allow the campaign to be put in the hands of professionals. Among those who seconded her appeal was Peter B. Kyne who wrote the General in part as follows:

"The needs of a lot of poor Filipino devils of lepers on the other side of the world will appeal to our public with just about as much force as the starving Armenians appealed to them. The Filipino isn't a romantic figure and nobody cares a hoot about him. . . . I have no faith in the average human being having born within him a hunch that he ought to do something for another average human being; I think there are about five percent of the human race who have anything like a noble aspiration . . . About ninety percent of man's inhumanity to man is quite unconscious and unmeant. However, we cannot escape acknowledging the fact that all human beings appear to have a little peacock blood in them. They like to do the popular thing and they like to get credit for it. The humble worker in the vineyard who sits quietly down at his desk and mails his check to the Bureau of Insular Affairs for the spiritual satisfaction it gives him will be found to be as rare as the dodo. Somebody has to set a public example, somebody has to take them by the nose and lead them forward while somebody else prods them from the rear. Then and then only will you achieve results."

Time was slipping by and nothing was being accomplished. It fell again to my lot to appeal to the General, and, after "much argument, about it and about," although not altogether convinced, he bowed to the wisdom of his more practical-minded advisers. The campaign was then handed over to professional money raisers, two million dollars were secured, and the Leonard Wood Memorial for the Eradication of Leprosy came into existence. It has on its Board such men as Henry L. Stimson, General James G. Harbord, General Samuel McRoberts, and Owen D. Young. The purposes and plans of the Wood Memorial, quite different from those of charitable organizations, are "to the extent of its financial ability to leave no scientific step untaken that holds any promise of finding the ultimate solution to this age-old curse of the human race."

Half of the initial two million dollars went to erect a new hospital for lepers at Cebu and to improve the Culion laboratory, both in equipment and personnel. The Cebu hospital was helped by a large donation from Eversley Childs, and was transferred to the Philippine government, which now maintains it.

The Memorial considered that the physical care of lepers was the merest start in solving the leper problem. The income from the second million was used with business efficiency in the research field. One of the first actions of the Board was to call the Leonard Wood Memorial Conference on Leprosy at Manila in January, 1931. Only scientists who had done distinctive work in leprosy were invited, and they laid down a set of principles for the guidance of leprosy research throughout the world.

The next international activity undertaken by the Memorial was to subsidize the International Leprosy Association so that it could publish a quarterly *International Journal of Leprosy,* under the editorship of Dr. Wade. In the past a discovery made in India might not be known in Brazil. Now the Association attempts to coordinate the fields of research carefully, so that there may be no duplication of effort. It serves as a clearing house for information, and focuses the newer methods of research upon leprosy. The Memorial also financed a world-wide survey of tropical diseases undertaken by the National Research Council. A Medical Board was formed to supervise the research activities in pathology, bacteriology, and epidemiology of leprosy.

Great acumen has been shown in husbanding the resources of the Memorial. The trustees desired to use the brains of the best possible scientists, but salaries for such men would have been a tremendous drain. Therefore, they arranged to work through various American universities; each year, for example, a professor of one of the sciences goes to Culion on his Sabbatical leave, his traveling expenses being defrayed by the Memorial. He approaches the problem with a fresh point of view, and usually tours the tropics, observing progress elsewhere, before returning home. He becomes so interested in the subject that, upon reaching his university, he utilizes the resources of his own department on leprosy, thereby tremendously enlarging the scope of research.

The Memorial aids as well in discovering young scientists with talent who need more training, and gives them fellowships to go to Culion or other places to study. It also works in close conjunction with the League of Nations, which several years ago appointed a Commission on Leprosy with a full time Secretary. The efforts of this Commission have resulted in steps to organize international research centers at Tokyo and Rio de Janeiro.

For thousands of years any man, woman, or child on whom the blight of leprosy had fallen, knew himself condemned to a living death. Even thirty years ago no hope could be held out to these unfortunates, who were not even permitted by an unkind Providence to die of their disease, but must linger on for years of untold suffering and degradation. Wherever I have gone over the face of the earth I have visited colonies of lepers, and the change that has taken place is no less than miraculous. Nothing in my life has given me so much joy as to see the light of hope slowly kindled in faces once set in lines of despair. The lepers now feel themselves on the threshold of deliverance. They are patient because of the chance, however slight, that they may be once again restored to the world of men and life.

"In his nipa hut, high on the hill of the Leper City, old Lazaro de Paerusza sits in the little bamboo doorway staring seaward with eyes that leprosy has long since blinded. He turns over and over in gnarled patient fingers a battered pair of binoculars. One of the padres gave them to him when his sight first began to fail to help his dimming eyes grope seaward towards the ships—the little trudging coastwise ships that, once in three weeks, in four, in six, come tacking through the reefs with help for Culion. Each day he waits, listening, for the new ship that is to bring America's mercy to those who live beyond the grave. 'No ship today, *matanda?*' they ask him at the end of an empty day. He listens. He hears the night. The reefs chant under the moon. The wild dogs howl in the hills as they rummage among the shallow graves. He shakes his old head and smiles, wisely and believingly as children smile. '*Darating. Darating din Bukas,*' he says in the vernacular—says it for all the patient, buried thousands at Culion—'tomorrow. Tomorrow it will come.' "

CHAPTER 16. DIVIDENDS FROM PHILANTHROPY

BY 1914 I believed that my work in the Philippine Islands had been accomplished. The great pestilences had been brought under control, and the Archipelago had become a healthful place for the white man to live in. The Filipinos, who had been a nation of invalids, were well advanced in convalescence. A permanent health organization had been established. In the course of creating this, it had become increasingly apparent that the logical method of eradicating disease was to attack it at its source and to create conditions under which it could not flourish. It was this larger field of preventive medicine which drew me, but I was not certain as to the precise form my participation should take.

I was still a member of the United States Public Health Service, which had expanded from the Marine Hospital Service, and I had remained in close touch with the Surgeon Generals. The Service was constantly spreading out, and at the moment was undertaking a campaign for pure water, a matter which would affect millions of people and in which I was vitally interested. Furthermore, many opportunities for usefulness outside the Service had presented themselves during my later years in the Islands. The Canadian Pacific Railroad had asked me to install a combined railway and steamship medical system which would be more economical and efficient than their existing one. I had been consulted frequently on sanitary measures, and had often drawn up plans for civic health organizations. I had contributed various suggestions to a new state health law for Massa-

265

chusetts which Governor David I. Walsh had asked me to administer as soon at it was passed.

This was the opportunity which appealed to me the most, and I was negotiating with Governor Walsh when Wickliffe Rose, the able, resourceful, and constructive leader of the newly-created Rockefeller Foundation, came to Manila to discuss proposals for the development of health work throughout the Eastern Hemisphere.

We considered plans for the prevention of disease, which subsequently came to have tremendous influence upon the destiny of the inhabitants of the Orient. This opened for me an opportunity for world-wide service. I told Mr. Rose that I was coming to the United States in a few months and then would go further into the matter of joining the Rockefeller Foundation.

On July 13, 1914, I left Manila with mixed emotions. I was in many ways glad to get away but, on the other hand, I was leaving the place which had become home to me. As I sailed down the Bay, almost every building on the skyline called up memories. I had hard work overcoming the sad reflection that, after all, the masses of the people had no conception of what had been done.

On my arrival in the United States I went to see Governor Walsh. I told him how much I appreciated his courage in placing training and experience above political clamor in favor of a native son and seeking a health officer from far away Manila. Having heard that he had obligated himself to appoint me State Health Officer to organize the service under the new law, I realized the embarrassing position in which I was placing him, yet I had to ask him to release me. The potentialities for world service under the aegis of the Rockefeller Foundation seemed to fit in better with my aspirations.

I joined the Rockefeller Foundation forthwith. Nobody had any clear idea exactly where any of us were to fit in, but we already had our motto. We were to become heartily sick in the ensuing years of its incessant repetition; nevertheless it expressed the concept on which we were to conduct our operations—"The Well Being of Mankind."

Before Mr. John D. Rockefeller, Sr., began to dispose of his wealth on a large scale he sought a plan for distributing it commensurate with the superhuman efficiency with which it had been accumulated. He allowed it to become known that he was open to suggestion. Naturally, innumerable ideas were eagerly presented. He looked into them carefully; none appealed to him.

In 1901 the Reverend Frederick Taylor Gates, who had begun his association with Mr. Rockefeller by securing from him six hundred thousand dollars for the University of Chicago, read Sir William Osler's *Practice of Medicine*. With unbounded admiration and enthusiasm he rushed to Mr. Rockefeller and said, "I have the idea! The world isn't getting its full share of benefit from scientific discoveries. This knowledge must be distributed in a practical way to relieve the ills of the world."

Mr. Rockefeller was already convinced that education and health, two words almost synonymous in his mind, rather than indiscriminate charity, would make philanthropy produce dividends. The Gates suggestion coincided with his own sentiments, and the attempt began to find a definite application. In 1901 the Rockefeller Institute for Medical Research was chartered with a pledge of two hundred thousand dollars from Mr. Rockefeller for grants-in-aid to investigators in institutions. Later, millions were available. Dr. Simon Flexner, Professor of Pathology at the University of Pennsylvania, became its leader and the Rockefeller Institute developed into the outstanding research laboratory of the country.

Intensive investigation was begun on a special group of temperate-zone diseases about which comparatively little was known. The resources of the Institute were brought to bear upon the medical sciences for science' sake, but practical application was also kept in mind. Studies were made and improved treatments were developed for such diseases as rheumatism, infantile paralysis, diabetes, and heart affections. The knowledge of pneumonia was greatly extended and mortality tremendously lowered by various sera.

With Dr. Flexner was associated Dr. Alexis Carrel, whose manual dexterity in special phases of surgical technique is unsurpassed. He became famous particularly for his successful transplanting of living organs, and growing tissue in a test tube.

In accordance with the changing theories of the importance of preventive medicine, however, Mr. Rockefeller did not wish to spend his money primarily in curing disease, but also desired to educate man in avoiding it. This process would extend over many years and require millions of dollars. It must inevitably prove futile unless a way could be found to reach uneducated minds.

Mr. Rockefeller invited a small group of leaders of the medical profession to meet him. "I want to ask you gentlemen a question," he said. "Is there a disease affecting large numbers of people of which you can say, 'I know all about this and I can cure it, not in fifty or even eighty percent of the cases, but in one hundred percent'? Furthermore, it should be possible to prevent by simple means. It should be a disease of which the cause can be clearly seen—nothing so vague as microscopic bacteria, but something visible to the naked eye. If you could name me such a disease you would not have to discourse in vague generalities about public health, but would have something concrete which the masses could understand, and concerning which they could be convinced by large-scale demonstrations."

Nobody had ever before presented such a problem to these eminent physicians. They shook their heads and said, "We must have time to think this over."

Fortunately for the answer, Dr. Charles W. Stiles of the United States Public Health Service was writing and propounding the tremendous importance of hookworm, or uncinariasis, in the South, and Dr. Bailey K. Ashford had pointed out the destruction it had wrought in Puerto Rico.

Fortified by this information, the little group of scientists returned to Mr. Rockefeller. "We have your disease," they said. "It is hookworm. It affects millions. We know all about it. It can be definitely cured, it is preventable, and the worm can be seen."

The hookworm first came into prominence in connection with the building of the St. Gothard Tunnel in 1880, although it had been identified by the Italian Dubini in 1838, who named it ancylostoma, hook-mouth. The Italians, who are the tunnel builders of the world, supplied most of the laborers for the St. Gothard. They fell sick in such numbers that the work came to a standstill. The calamitous illnesses were ascribed to the evil eye or to the mountain's anger at being bored full of holes.

But science offered another explanation. The tunnel had been polluted by the workers. Through ova in the feces the disease was diagnosed as ancylostoma infection. The heat had compelled the men to work naked, so that the worms had been allowed free entrance through the skin, and the disease had spread rapidly. Not until sanitary measures had been taken was it brought under control. Somewhat later the common affliction among miners, known in Cornwall as Miners' Anemia, was found to be due to the same cause.

But the flurry in hookworm was soon over, and for many years the disease became merely a matter of record in medical textbooks.

Hookworm next became a subject of importance just after the United States had occupied Puerto Rico. When a frightful hurricane had wrought tremendous damage, Dr. Ashford, of the Army Medical Service, observed that the people were not recovering from their privations as speedily as, with good food and proper care, they normally should. Their skins were white and colorless, their gums pale, their hair dry and brittle. Their blood was of such poor quality that it was incapable of nourishing their bodies properly. Their appetites were unnatural and they were constantly fatigued. Children were stunted; their bodies so emaciated that they had angel-wing shoulder blades. Obviously they all were suffering from anemia.

Dr. Ashford wanted to find out why the inhabitants of an entire district should be anemic. In examining them thoroughly he found, first, ova and then the worms themselves. Although the latter did not correspond to the description in his textbooks, he had no doubt they were hookworms and responsible for the unparalleled anemia. He brought specimens to America which were later examined by Dr. Stiles, his former Professor of Helminthology.

Dr. Stiles had already suspected that the people of the South had hookworm. The cotton-mill workers, like the Puerto Ricans, suffered frightfully from anemia. They would rest all day Sunday, work well Monday, get along fairly Tuesday, be all tired out Wednesday, and thereafter do little work the rest of the week. In North Carolina the sufferers were eating clay. Nobody knew exactly why. Nature may have been appeasing a hunger in this strange diet, since the native clay contained iron, one of the best remedies for anemia.

Dr. Stiles identified Dr. Ashford's find as a new variety of hookworm, which he named the necator americanus, or New World hook-worm. It was slightly smaller in size than the ancylostoma, which was about half an inch long, the thickness of a coarse thread, and had fewer hooks. The difference between them was slight and their effect identical.

As time went on it was discovered that the necator was not at all a New World hookworm, but had been brought over from Africa with the slave traffic. Folk migrations have been traced by studying the occurrence of the worm. Dr. Samuel T. Darling has made a good case for such a movement of peoples from South to North in India. The necator has proved itself to be one of the world's greatest travelers, and wherever it has established itself, it has remained.

Hundreds of thousands of dollars have been spent in the study of the life cycle of the hookworm. These parasites live in the small intestine. They usually occur in great numbers; one person may harbor as many as ten thousand, although it takes only five hundred to produce serious symptoms. They attach themselves by their little hooks to the inner coat of the intestine and suck blood. Ten thousand worms can drink a great deal, and the wounds they cause in securing their horrid meals continue to ooze more blood. These tiny punctures leave openings for infection, and when they heal leave scar tissue. It has been asserted by some investigators that the worms cause further damage by throwing off toxins of their own.

Hookworms live a long, long time in the small intestine, creating havoc all the while, but they cannot multiply there. In the course of six or seven years they die, and the human host would be free of hookworm if reinfection did not usually occur. The worms lay eggs in tremendous quantities, sometimes ten million at a time. If these eggs, when expelled with the feces, happen to fall on warm, moist soil in dark places, in one or two days they hatch out into microscopic embryos. These little creatures rapidly acquire organs of digestion, and eat any available animal or vegetable matter. After casting their skins for the second time, they begin to stir about, and can explore the terrain for four inches around. If they are not destroyed by sun or cold they can climb up any vertical surface, and if this should happen to be a blade of grass, as is likely, they stand there on their tails, waving coaxingly back and forth in the breeze. They are capable of remaining in one spot for many weeks in patient anticipation of a foot or ankle.

It was once believed that the young parasites entered the human alimentary canal by being swallowed in water or food or carried on earth-soiled hands or utensils to the mouth and thence to the stomach. This is possible in theory, but, actually, never seemed to occur.

Later investigations have shown the worms have elected to travel by a much more complicated route. Looss, the German Professor of Parasitology at the Cairo Medical School, put a patch of infected mud on his hand and discovered from the small punctiform places that the worms had penetrated the skin. He mistakenly supposed entrance had been made through the hair follicles, but it has now been determined that the worms can squirm directly through the epidermis with astonishing rapidity, sometimes even overcoming the obstacle of socks or stockings. The resultant irritation, known as ground itch, produces ulcers when scratched. Those who go barefoot are more likely to contract hookworm, because their feet are apt to come in direct contact with ground which has been soiled by human discharges.

Once inside the human body, the young worms wriggle their way into the lymphatics or veins, are carried along to the right heart, and are then pumped to the lungs, where they abandon swimming and take to the air. Nature tries to expel these foreign substances; they are coughed up through the windpipe and then swallowed. Down the oesophagus and through the stomach they go, finding their journey's end in the small intestine, where they set up housekeeping and in less than a week begin in their peculiarly roundabout way the business of raising a family.

Any people who have to feed a collection of intestinal worms as well as themselves are bound to lose the race against those not so handicapped. By dwarfing their bodies, inhibiting the development of their minds, and rendering them more susceptible to other diseases, directly and indirectly, hookworm has caused incalculable damage. It has slaughtered members of the human family by the thousands, and rendered them ill by the millions.

Mr. Rockefeller made available a million dollars to develop methods for the control of hookworm. Having set the machinery in motion he characteristically retired from all further connection with it. Wickliffe Rose was lifted from the chair of philosophy at the University of Tennessee to head the Rockefeller Sanitary Commission, as it was called. This new organization was to operate in the South, where the Rockefeller General Education Board, favored with a Federal charter and endowed with more than thirty million dollars, had already broken ground with its agricultural improvement program.

Mr. Rose, himself a Southerner, was well aware that merely setting up dispensaries in rural communities for treating hookworm under the Sanitary Commission's auspices would not prove feasible. Local jealousy of this Northern philanthropic invasion would immediately be aroused, and the project would be stopped before it was well started. The longer way, but the only promising one by which the desired ends could be obtained, was to secure the goodwill of the already existing state health agencies and work through them. This plan had the added advantage of supplying a permanent organization which would be prepared to continue when the Rockefeller Sanitary Commission should withdraw. This theory of having the government carry on the work, and other principles which Rose laid down, made him one of the soundest administrators I have ever known. They were the signposts which later guided the International Health Board in a far larger sphere of activity; success was assured as long as they were adhered to.

The beginning was not auspicious. The name Rockefeller reeked of oil and all its unpleasant connotations. The view of Judge Kenesaw Mountain Landis that Mr. Rockefeller, for his Standard Oil misdeeds, should be "thrown into jail like a common felon" was widespread. The people were suspicious and the press inclined to be hostile. The abuse of the Rockefellers was worse than anything Ida Tarbell ever penned in her muckraking exposés. Even in Congress resolutions were constantly being introduced to stop the work in the Southern states for fear we should corrupt them.

As Rose had foreseen, indignation was also loudly expressed in the South itself. "We do not have hookworm," the papers stated. "Such an accusation is a reflection on the fair name of the South. But even if we do have it, our own doctors are good enough to look after it. We do not need any Yankee help." They chose the surest way to kill any campaign, showering hookworm with ridicule by dubbing it the "lazy worm disease."

Dr. John A. Ferrell had been chosen to lead the attacking forces in North Carolina. Under his direction survey after survey was made, with the utmost caution and care, to determine the extent of hookworm incidence in the South before any further step should be taken.

Dr. Ferrell happened one day to meet Josephus Daniels on the street in Raleigh. Mr. Daniels, then editor of the *Raleigh News and Observer*, had obligingly been running a great deal of publicity in his columns showing the widespread hookworm infection as proved by the surveys. Latterly his attitude had changed.

Dr. Ferrell seized his opportunity. "What's the matter, Mr. Daniels? You don't seem to like our hookworm campaign any more. You've been pretty critical lately. Why?"

"You've told us how bad we are in the South. But you don't do anything about it. When are you going to start?"

"Right now, Mr. Daniels," Dr. Ferrell said. "You are a fair minded man. I want to make you a fair proposition. You know what a ne'er-do-well John Doe is. We believe he's a ne'er-do-well because he's too tired to work, and he's too tired to work because he has anemia, and he has anemia because he's filled with hookworms. Will you do me a favor and watch what happens to him in the next two months?"

"That's fair enough," replied Mr. Daniels. "Certainly I will."

Inside the allotted period, by the use of thymol, which was then the accepted hookworm vermifuge, John Doe gained weight, was proud of his muscles, got a job, and started in earnest to support his family. Mr. Daniels was as good as his word; he observed the cure and faithfully reported it.

When dispensaries were opened in rural communities and each and all were invited to come for examination and free treatment, they were at first, even though under semi-public supervision, eyed askance. But other wonders continued to be worked. The same children who before hookworm treatment had shown low mentality according to the Binet test, when given the same test after treatment

273

showed a vastly increased intelligence quotient. Among the adults a grateful population was eventually restored to gainful occupations. Those who were cured were the best allies. Even the physicians, who had been so hostile, claiming that the Commission was taking away their business, came to realize that the gradually increasing earning power of the breadwinners after treatment enabled them and their families to seek medical aid much more frequently for minor ailments, and business was actually growing. Ultimately the doctors also lent active support.

Slowly the tide began to turn. The first demonstration had been made; the disease could be cured by eliminating the worms from the body. The next step, a far more difficult one, was to show how it could be prevented. Over half the rural people of the South polluted the ground as nonchalantly as the animals of the field. Every conceivable method of instruction was used to convince them that, if they would build proper latrines and use them, they would do away not only with hookworm but with typhoid, dysentery, and other intestinal-borne diseases. The process was slow but the idea was finally implanted.

When the converts saw the results, they asked in their simple way, "Can't you rid us of other diseases?"

"You yourselves have got to do something first," the Commission doctors replied.

"What?"

"Support your local health department."

"Is that all?"

"Yes, because in that way you will be aided in controlling other diseases that are preventable."

Hitherto a Southern health service had been mainly a statistical bureau where men untrained in preventive medicine might find a political haven. In all twelve states of the South only two hundred and fifty thousand dollars annually had been appropriated for health purposes, and even this had been given with reluctance. But now the most illiterate farmer who paid taxes on his small holding could see that his few pennies were bringing tremendous returns in wellbeing. For the first time in the history of Southern sanitation, money was freely offered. Health services began to spring up in the wake

274

of the Sanitary Commission. The outcome resulted in ideas which, at comparatively low cost, affected the human race fundamentally. Eventually the expenditures of the states themselves increased to two and one half million dollars, or tenfold over what they had been.

Mr. Rockefeller himself was pleased. "This thing seems to have worked out very well," he commented. "I know now what I want to do with my money. I made it all over the world and will spend it there. Get the people interested in their diseases. Hookworm seems the best way, although something else may come up later. But get knowledge into the minds of the people." Accordingly he capitalized the Rockefeller Foundation at a hundred million dollars.

As the field of activities broadened, many changes were to take place, but the Rockefeller Foundation as first organized, had four subsidiaries. An investigation of Industrial Relations was to be undertaken under the directorship of Mr. W. L. Mackenzie King, but since he was unable to participate because of the War and his rapid political advancement, this portion of the program was dropped.

In the War emergency a temporary War Relief Commission was established which dispensed vast sums to the stricken nations of Europe.

The function of the China Medical Board was to establish higher standards of medical education in China. The already existing missionary schools, owing to the paucity of their financial resources, were badly staffed. The China Medical Board undertook the job of substituting schools which would function more efficiently. Eventually it bought out the Medical College at Peiping, and built in its place one of the finest groups of medical school buildings in the world, sending members of the existing staff to America for further education.

The Rockefeller Sanitary Commission, which had operated only in the South, was superseded by the International Health Board, which disregarded boundaries, working among any peoples and in any climes. The eventual aim of this organization was to build up the health departments of countries needing assistance in dealing with their own diseases. We would help them set up a machine with the hope that in time it might be able to function efficiently by itself. In order to do this, an opening wedge had to be driven by teaching control and preventive measures against hookworm, malaria, and yellow fever.

Wickliffe Rose, the Director General of the International Health Board, was assisted by Jerome D. Greene, Secretary of the Rockefeller Foundation. Among the members of the International Health Board were Starr J. Murphy, Mr. Rockefeller's confidential lawyer and personal friend, President Charles W. Eliot of Harvard, my old confrere General William C. Gorgas, and Walter Hines Page, publisher and Ambassador to the Court of St. James. All these men were specialists in fields in which Mr. Rockefeller considered himself a novice.

One of my first duties with the Rockefeller organization was to attend a conference of some of the leaders in medicine called to discuss the question of a school to train men for public health service. Among them were Harry Pratt Judson, President of the University of Chicago, Dr. Milton J. Rosenau of Harvard, whose volume on Preventive Medicine was a classic on the subject, and Dr. William H. Welch of Johns Hopkins, honored as the dean of American medicine.

Unexpectedly the demand from the South for men trained in public health had surpassed the number of those available to fill the jobs. The ordinary physician lacked the special education to fit him for a position of this type. Unless the demand were met quickly, much damage might be done by improperly trained doctors. Experience had proved it unwise to place an M. D. without additional qualifications at the head of a health service. He might concern himself too greatly with direct questions of medical relief, rather than the larger problems of preventive medicine.

It was decided to establish master schools to train leaders and teachers. After a thorough survey Johns Hopkins was endowed with a million dollars and Dr. Welch became Director of the first modern school of hygiene in the United States. A few years later Harvard was similarly endowed.

I had been introduced to the great Dr. Welch for the first time when I had been a medical student. At this second meeting we became great friends and remained so during his lifetime. He was probably the most brilliant and able medical man produced in the

United States. After studying extensively in Germany, he had returned to found the first pathological laboratory in this country at Bellevue Hospital, New York City. Later, in the nineties, he was mainly responsible for the organization of the Johns Hopkins Medical School on a system which ultimately had a profound influence in shaping American medical education and giving it world leadership. Many of the most eminent members of his profession, such as Dr. Simon Flexner, Dr. William G. MacCallum, and the Nobel Prize winner, Dr. George Whipple, had been his pupils.

When Presidents and other high officials wanted medical advice, Dr. Welch was sent for. He was acclaimed not only in his own country but throughout the civilized world. Nobody knew how he managed to keep up with all his appointments; he faithfully attended the meetings of the Rockefeller boards, and also those of the Carnegie, the Milbank, and other benefactions. He engaged in countless additional activities, and never missed one of his classes.

Now, at the age of sixty-five, Dr. Welch was undertaking to organize this new School of Hygiene and Public Health at Johns Hopkins. He traveled over the world and in the end evolved a postgraduate public health institution, different from the others, which has become the model for all later schools.

Nobody ever saw this fat little man, perfectly bald, with pointed Van Dyke, take any exercise. But he had most amazing physical stamina. He was over seventy-five when he attended the opening of the Peiping Union Medical College. Some of us had laboriously climbed the Mountain of the Ancients at the Summer Palace, from which one of the finest views around the Chinese capital could be obtained. As we reached the summit and the beauty of the vista spread before us, one of our party panted, "Too bad poor Dr. Welch can't see this," just as we caught sight of the old gentleman himself, calm and unwinded, smoking away on his big cigar.

One of the outstanding characteristics of Dr. Welch was his intellectual curiosity. One day as we were walking in Manila and I was detained for a moment, he wandered off and returned beaming. "What's the history of the monument in that little square around the corner?" he asked.

"What monument?"

AN AMERICAN DOCTOR'S ODYSSEY

"The one to the Spaniard who introduced smallpox vaccination into the Philippines."

During all my years at Manila, and in spite of my intense interest in the subject, I had never known that such a statue existed.

Dr. Welch was never too busy to talk to those who sought his advice, and was kindly and gracious to all. But he would seldom answer letters. The Filipino doctors were naturally most anxious to meet him. He was extremely affable and would say, "Now you must write me what you are doing. I'm always interested to hear." But I knew that in his room in Baltimore were piled stacks of letters which he had never opened. In fact, the only way to get a reply from him was to send a telegram. He could not be reached by telephone except at the school or at the Maryland Club which, in his day, used to revolve around him.

The personality of this human dynamo was so vivid that all present were electrified when he entered a room. Conversation ceased; everyone waited for what he might have to say. To any medical subject he could bring color, and could hold the uninitiated enthralled. He could discourse brilliantly on politics, or, if the conversation should turn to New England cemeteries, he could quote quaint epitaphs by the dozen.

The stories told about Dr. Welch were innumerable, particularly in regard to his uncanny memory. Once he was traveling across the Pacific with Dr. Flexner on the Committee that resulted in the organization of the China Medical Board. At one of the inevitable ship's entertainments Dr. Flexner recited a poem of sixty verses. Dr. Welch, who had listened attentively, murmured apologetically afterwards: "Dr. Flexner, didn't you make a mistake in the second line of the eighteenth verse?"

Dr. Flexner, who took great pride in his own memory, was annoyed. "I couldn't have done such a thing. I'll show you the text," and sought the correct version in the ship's library. But Dr. Welch was, as always, right.

Dr. Welch was as familiar with other medical subjects as with his own. On one occasion at Peiping Dr. Robert T. Leiper, of bilharzia fame, in the midst of an address on helminthology, was taken ill and fainted. The situation was awkward. Dr. Welch was asked whether he would speak to the audience. He obligingly took up Dr. Leiper's speech and to our amazement continued it.

Nobody ever saw a note on the innumerable speeches made by Dr. Welch during his many years of public life. When honored by President Hoover on his eightieth birthday, he considered it would be discourteous not to have something prepared. He ascended the platform, put his manuscript down on the desk, and, as he went along, regularly turned page after page. Afterwards a reporter asked him for a copy. "Certainly," replied Dr. Welch, with a twinkle in his eye, and handed over the sheaf of perfectly blank pages.

But after Dr. Welch died, bundles of musty papers and memoranda were discovered under an old stairway in his home. Many and many of the postprandial talks he had given had been previously outlined on scraps of paper. Apparently anticipating that he would be called upon, he had prepared himself, and at need had probably directed the conversation along lines to which his talk would be apropos.

My first month with the Rockefeller Foundation I spent at its offices in Washington, going over the various phases of future operations with Welch and Rose. It was agreed I should make a thorough survey of the East and thereafter propose a plan based on the same effective methods already in use in the United States. First of all, I had to return to the Philippines to close out my work there, and then continue to Borneo, Java, Malaya, Siam, Ceylon, India, and Egypt.

In addition to making surveys of health conditions and the possibilities of working in the various countries, I was to report on the status of medical education. Rose believed that one of the important means of extending medical knowledge was to provide fellowships so that earnest young men from Tokyo, Sydney, or Bangkok could learn from Paris, Berlin, or London, Boston, Baltimore, or New York.

According to the system we developed, our fellows were not necessarily recruited among those who had graduated at the heads of their classes. By the more usual method of selection, a fifty percent success had been high. We chose instead those who had in practical work demonstrated ability and capacity for leadership. It was sometimes difficult to make this plan understood in the countries for which fellowships were being considered. The Indian government, for example, kept presenting me with lists of those who had passed their examinations with the highest marks. By our method we rarely had a failure, and a large number of our fellows now occupy leading positions throughout the world.

In the course of many years I interviewed thousands of these enthusiastic seekers after knowledge. I always tried to give personal attention to those whose choice had fallen upon American schools, and arranged to have them invited into homes, so that when they returned to their far countries, they would have a broader picture of what we were like.

It was equally necessary to present the habits of the East to our own young staff members, not only to show them how inexorably the Orientals were yoked to their ancient and onerous customs, but that patience must be cultivated before the yoke could be removed. These promising young men were being trained variously as specialists, directors, advisers, and teachers. Many did fine work in the field. I have always been proud of them and profoundly grateful, for they were constantly dealing with people who did not understand what they wanted, who were often suspicious, sometimes antagonistic, and almost always apathetic. At extreme personal sacrifice they isolated themselves from home ties and friends and, year after year—three hundred and sixty-five days on end—faithfully carried out our projects.

One of the hardest abnegations was entailed by our stipulation that the local health organization should receive credit for whatever success might be accomplished. As a rule our men were never heard of in the outside world. Scientists usually want the fruits of their labor in the shape of public recognition, but we could not allow this. I sympathized deeply, but could do nothing save encourage them in their work.

Some of our men received flattering offers outside the Foundation at much higher salaries than our organization paid. We were not sorry to see them go elsewhere, because in so doing they were carrying out the larger purpose of extending health knowledge; in many cases we even helped them to go. We ourselves always made a special point not to employ persons who were already doing good work under other auspices.

When I joined the Rockefeller Foundation, Mr. John D. Rockefeller, Jr., had already given up his business directorships and was devoting himself to social service under the able tutelage of the men his father had chosen. But before many years had elapsed he had taken his place at the head of the table, not by right of inheritance, but by right of ability. Sober and serious, with a stern sense of moral obligation springing from his religious background, home environment, and the strict school of piety in which his father reared him, he regards himself as a trustee for the millions placed in his keeping.

On the other hand, Mr. Rockefeller, Jr., has a lighter side not often realized by the public. He has a fine sense of humor, loves good stories, and likes to tell them himself. He has found time to make himself a connoisseur of porcelains, one of the most esoteric of collectors' hobbies. At Hongkong we went through Sir Paul Chater's collection, which was supposed at the time to be one of the best in the world. As his discerning eye wandered over the cases, again and again he would point to a piece and say, "That is not genuine." When Chater died and the collection went to the British Museum, many of the items were discarded as counterfeit.

Traveling with Mr. Rockefeller was an amazing experience. He was hyper-conscientious about his customs declarations, sometimes including more than the law demanded. He was equally sensitive to the requirements of the swarms of newspaper reporters and photographers who awaited him at every station. While the rest of us would employ our brief stops in stretching our legs and pacing up and down the platform, he would devote himself to the unpleasant duty of being interviewed.

The incredibly bad-mannered curiosity about the whole Rockefeller family was a revelation to me. On shipboard Mr. Rockefeller could never escape impertinent inquisitiveness. Everybody would gather around to watch him play deck tennis. As we would sit after dinner in the Rockefeller suite, a window would be raised cautiously, and several pairs of eyes could be detected avidly peering in.

Not a day passed that Mr. Rockefeller did not receive several dozen letters from passengers on board, all asking for aid. When we visited the Philippines, airplanes circled overhead dropping requests on the ship. He took all letters seriously, insisting on knowing the contents of each, so that nothing might be overlooked for which he felt responsibility. He spent his time indefatigably on such matters. I always felt sorry for him, because he seemed to have so little time for recreation. Almost everybody who came near him had an ulterior motive. As we left the hall after one of the big banquets during the dedication ceremonies of the Peiping Union Medical College I sought to get a few words with him concerning our program for the next day, but during the short walk from the table to the door, at this purely social function in his honor, he was accosted by three different individuals begging for money. Dozens of times I have been asked for letters of introduction by people who sought to use me as an approach.

The magic of the Rockefeller name extends to the Foundation. Innumerable requests are received which are not included within the general scope of its divisions; these range from the reasonable to the ludicrous. "I'm a widow. I have a mortgage coming due next week. I need two thousand dollars. Please send a check by return mail"; or, "Would like all literature on the harmfulness of cigarette smoking. My boy is twenty-one and smokes a cigarette a day." A mother asks help for her baby suffering from eczema, a man wants aid to improve his eyesight, a woman desires medical advice about her sister's sinus, a father would appreciate a monthly pension of forty dollars to educate his five daughters, a doctor wishes a subsidy to permit him to reduce his fees, amateur societies suggest infallible schemes for world peace if provided with funds, an inventor seeks investigation and promotion of his hair root resuscitator, a note from an immigrant at Ellis Island says, "Here I am, Mr. Rockefeller, please send my check for a million dollars here."

All such mail is carefully perused. The same courtesy is shown in the offices of the Foundation as Mr. Rockefeller himself displays in his personal correspondence.

The scope of the Rockefeller Foundation was not sufficiently broad to include all the philanthropies of Mr. Rockefeller, Sr. His wife had had many charities which he wished to have continued, including the Constantinople College for Women. But one of the peculiarities of the existing Rockefeller organizations was that each one, almost immediately after birth, had developed a policy. In referring requests for aid to his various philanthropies, Mr. Rockefeller, Sr., would often be met by the reply, "This does not fall within our policy." Finally he established the Laura Spelman Rockefeller Memorial, which among other things was to carry on Mrs. Rockefeller's benefactions and serve as a catch-all. Following the policy of all the other philanthropies, however, the Memorial promptly developed a policy of its own.

Mr. Rockefeller, Jr., experienced the same type of difficulty as his father in his benefactions. When insulin was first discovered the appeals were almost beyond belief in number and poignancy. Although the wording was practically identical at times with the fantastic examples just given, the genuine need behind them was obvious. "My only son has diabetes. I'm a poor woman and a widow. I cannot afford to buy insulin. Can you, Mr. Rockefeller, with all your millions, sit still and see my son die?"

Mr. Rockefeller showed these pathetic letters to the Institute, and asked whether something could not be done about them. "This matter does not fall within our policy," he was told. "It would interfere with our other work."

He then appealed to the Foundation. "Oh, no," was the reply. "We're only interested in preventing people from getting sick. We're very sorry indeed, but we can do nothing."

He finally took his problem to the Spelman. "Oh, no. We cannot go into this, it does not fall within our program."

In one of our conversations, Mr. Rockefeller told me of his deep concern. "This is a real need and must be met somehow," he said.

"Then you'll have to set up some organization to take care of it," I warned him. "It's humanly impossible for one person to investigate all those claims, some of which are certain to be fictitious. You would also have to have some method of distributing the insulin to the authentic cases."

"Can you suggest how this could be worked out?"

"I can think of one way. The administration of insulin requires a great deal of skill and knowledge. The medical profession now has no opportunity to learn the necessary technique. Why not give money to several big hospitals, strategically located throughout the country. Fifty thousand dollars to each would suffice. They could then give free instruction in administering insulin, and supply the drug free to those who applied. Each appeal could be directed to the nearest center, which could handle the whole matter."

The plan was adopted and proved successful.

Mr. Rockefeller continued his benefactions and by 1926 the following separate entities had come into existence: The Rockefeller Institute for Medical Research, which occupies several blocks in New York at Sixty-sixth Street between York Avenue and the East River; at 61 Broadway there were first, the General Education Board; second, the Rockefeller Foundation, under which the International Health Board operated, the Division of Medical Education and the Division of Studies; third, the China Medical Board, which was under the joint direction of the General Education Board and the Rockefeller Foundation; fourth, the Laura Spelman Rockefeller Memorial; and fifth, the International Education Board. All of these organizations worked independently, and subsequently they were partially consolidated. By 1936 the Rockefeller Foundation had added divisions for the Social Sciences, the Natural Sciences, and the Humanities.

It was under the Presidency of Mr. George E. Vincent that the Rockefeller Foundation so largely expanded its activities. Mr. Vincent, a past master in the art of public speaking, could say things that from anyone else would sound outrageous, but he phrased them so amusingly, and was so lacking in malice, that he never gave offense or was even criticized for his remarks. Once one of the vice presidents of the Foundation was delegated to substitute at an address during one of Mr. Vincent's absences. Much worried that he might make some strategic error, he procured an outline of one of Mr. Vincent's most successful speeches. He committed this carefully to memory and delivered it, secure in the conviction he was doing the safe thing. The next day the newspapers assailed him for expressing such views.

I have traveled with Mr. Vincent for a week at a time and heard him give virtually the same address each night in a different town. But always it was as new to me as though I had never heard it before. The framework was identical but new trim had been substituted. Speaking on one occasion at the same banquet with Winston Churchill, Great Britain's acknowledged best, in English in which the most critical could find no trace of abhorred Yankeeism, he aroused vociferous praise from audience and press alike.

Mr. Vincent's memory was comparable to that of Dr. Welch. Like the best public speakers he was able to incorporate into his repertoire any anecdote or bit of description. We would often ride uptown together on the crowded, rumbling, rattling, rolling subway. His attention would apparently be divided between his newspaper and the amusing incidents I was telling him. A week or two later my stories would appear refurbished in his own inimitable manner.

Whenever anybody wanted to know anything that might have a remote connection with the health field, he came to the International Health Board. At the home office, the most important achievements were frequently off the record. Countries unable to obtain laboratory and hospital supplies asked for assistance in filling their orders. Cities large and small, near and far, solicited advice—how to plan and staff their health organizations, where to obtain competent instructors for their medical schools, how to purify their water, how to build their sewers, and how to construct their hospitals. We welcomed the opportunity to extend aid of this character.

The International Health Board's achievements in proving the importance of hookworm eradication had aroused interest in the medical laboratories of the world, and many were anxious to do research for their own countries. The laboratories at Amsterdam were exceedingly desirous of studying dog hookworm, which was analogous to the human type, but, because the canines of the Netherlands never had been attacked by uncinariasis, we were requested to send them a thoroughly infected animal.

Rose asked me whether I could supply one. I wrote to a dozen friends in the South, trusting that among so many I could procure a specimen. But not a single reply was forthcoming. When the time came for a follow-up, I resorted to speedier methods and sent twelve telegrams. A few days later, to my amazement, not one but twelve dogs arrived, all in the same afternoon. The offices were filled with sounds of yelping, whining, and barking.

Sailings to the Netherlands were infrequent. Each of twelve girls of the office staff agreed to take a dog home for a few days. But when the next sailing was delayed, it was too much to ask them to keep the dogs longer. I secured quarters at the Rockefeller Institute.

On the morning the ship was to leave I took a sad-looking little yellow cur, the commonest of its kind, to the American Express Company. No sooner had it been delivered on board, however, than rumors began to spread that it had a strange disease. An hour later the dog was put off and returned to me. I hurried down to the pier and argued the captain into accepting it. But further complaints that the dog was a menace to the passengers caused it to be put ashore just before sailing time.

I taxied the forlorn little object back to the Institute to join its fellows, all of whom were being cherished in case something might happen to the yellow dog. I was getting desperate. With good food and care the dog appeared to be losing his hookworms rapidly. From time to time I used to look anxiously to see whether there were any left. I sought other means of transportation, ultimately finding the captain of an Antwerp freighter who agreed to take the dog if I would secure him a certificate from the Dutch Consul that it would be admitted to the Netherlands and would not remain on his hands.

Another snag arose. The Belgian Consul refused altogether to give the diseased dog a permit to travel across Belgium. I made a return visit a few days later, this time appealing to his emotions rather than his problematic love of science, reminding him of the services of the United States in feeding the Belgians during the War, and pointing out that they owed us a debt of gratitude. He was still doubtful. I then said, "If you can't do anything about it, I'll have to send a cable to the King himself," and I sat down at the desk and determinedly took up a pen.

"I'll do it! I'll do it!" the Consul hastily interjected, and cabled his home office, shortly receiving permission for the dog to land, provided he did not stop anywhere in Belgium.

It was with a sigh of relief that I saw the little dog, who had appeared sadder with each frustrated trip to the pier, sail down the Bay on his designated mission.

In spite of their varying policies, all the Rockefeller organizations had the same end in view of serving people everywhere. When they were needed, the International Health Board borrowed the brighter lights of the Rockefeller Institute. For example, Hideyo Noguchi helped us in our yellow fever research.

When Dr. Flexner had first been in the East, Noguchi had wanted to return with him to the University of Pennsylvania, but Dr. Flexner had refused on the ground that there was not room in his laboratory, and had forgotten the incident. A year later Noguchi had walked in, saying, "Here I am. I'm your assistant." He had proved such an apt pupil in Philadelphia that Dr. Flexner had found him indispensable and had brought him to the Rockefeller Institute. Sometimes he would work night and day for forty-eight hours steadily, without eating or even telephoning his family. He was full of temperament and scarcely anybody but Dr. Flexner could get along with him.

This curious little fellow had been so long from home that his own countrymen could not understand him, and his English was equally incomprehensible to us. But in a siege of typhoid he unexpectedly learned Spanish, which apparently came easier to him, and thereafter he and I compromised on that language.

Though Noguchi was valuable to the world, the members of the accounting department could have dispensed with him gladly. He drove them almost frantic. They would give him a thousand dollars for expenses and a little book in which to note down his daily disbursements. But when Noguchi returned, his little book would invariably be blank. It went without saying that the money had been legitimately used, but it was only possible to guess in a general way the manner of its spending.

Publicity came to Noguchi unsought; he was a man who attracted attention. But he was unfortunate in that his undertakings which seemed to promise the most brilliant results did not always eventuate. When he was sent to Guayaquil, Ecuador, to study yellow fever, which he had never seen before, cases were produced for him which both the local physicians and a clinician sent down from Chicago certified as authentic.

Noguchi took blood from these patients and found organisms new to science. He cultured these and injected them into guinea pigs and rabbits, thereby producing a disease which was apparently yellow fever. Assuming that the diagnosis of the physicians had been correct, he believed he had discovered the yellow fever organism; unfortunately for his reputation, it turned out to be one which caused a form of the infectious jaundice known as icterohemorrhagica, or Weil's disease. He had already worked on this disease, but the type of organism he found in Ecuador differed from that with which he was familiar.

Since icterohemorrhagica had first been discovered in Japan, Noguchi was extremely anxious to obtain some of the original strain for comparison with American jaundice, and two unsuccessful attempts were made to transmit the culture. Once when I was at the Kitasato Institute in Tokyo, Dr. K. Shiga, head of the bacteriological laboratory, asked, "Will you help us get a strain of icterohemorrhagica to the Rockefeller Institute?"

"What do I have to do?"

"Oh, very little," I was assured. "You just have to take a few guinea pigs with you on the steamer, and every eight days you inoculate a healthy one from one that is dying or has just died. We'll supply you with everything necessary, and put the guinea pigs on the ship."

"All right," I agreed, and promptly forgot about the whole matter. The Canadian Pacific liner, *Empress of Russia,* was crowded; every cabin was taken. In mine I found waiting for me six guinea pigs, two of which had been inoculated the day before, and four healthy ones to carry on the strain, together with bales of leaves and cabbages. My room companion at once objected violently to the idea of traveling with sick pigs. I sympathized with his repugnance, because the odor in the hot confined space was undoubtedly disagreeable. I had only been in the room a few moments when the steward informed me the guinea pigs must go back on shore. My only hope was to interpose delays. The steward was still objecting and I was upholding my end of the argument with undiminished vigor when the ship got under way.

"If you'll let this go overnight, I'll fix it in the morning," I promised, and he finally departed.

But before I could do any fixing, the captain and the purser and the doctor all paid me an official visit. The captain delivered the ultimatum. "You'll have to get rid of the whole lot. We can't run the risk of infecting our passengers from sick pigs."

"But it is most important for me to get them to the United States."

"I won't have them on my ship. The whole business has got to go—all your old fodder and everything else."

"Could I discuss this first with the doctor?" I asked.

With the captain's consent I appealed to the doctor's professional instincts, explaining my objective. "You tell the captain it's perfectly safe to have these pigs on board. You know they can't infect the passengers. I can understand the objections to having them in the room, but if you ask him to let me keep them in the ship's morgue, I'm sure he'll agree."

The doctor added his entreaties to mine, and cages and food were transferred to the morgue. For a few days the gentle guinea pigs, which suffer so uncomplainingly from so many of man's diseases, scampered around merrily and nibbled their cabbages, unaware of how nearly they had come to an ignoble end under the butcher's cleaver.

From the time we left Tokyo it was raining and blowing, and almost all the passengers on board were seasick. But the pigs remained in good health. On the eighth day I inoculated a nice little white-eared pig. The next morning the pigs found a new roommate lying on the rubber slab above them. A Chinese passenger had died. According to the custom of his race he had paid a deposit in return for a guarantee from the steamship company that he would not be buried at sea, but would be returned to the tomb of his ancestors, in order that he might receive proper homage from his own descendants.

That morning the storm reached gale proportions. I found that my guinea pigs were apparently very sick from the effects of the formalin with which the corpse had been embalmed. The second Tokyo-inoculated pig had died during the night, and it was necessary that one of the well ones be inoculated immediately. I sat flat on the floor with my feet well braced and picked up the healthy black pig. According to instructions, I prepared him by shaving the hair from his belly, and put him aside temporarily. Selecting a shiny scalpel, with the greatest of care I began to cut out the liver from the dead pig.

Just as I was at the most delicate stage of the operation, the ship gave a tremendous lurch. The dead Chinese above me slid off the table, and sat on my shoulders, with his legs around my neck. I did not dare move. The slightest slip might mean a cut and consequent infection from a disease with a particularly high mortality. With the pig before me and both hands occupied with scalpel and tweezers, I had to continue. The ship would roll one way and a cold naked leg would swing in front of me, then back it would roll in the opposite direction and the other leg would jolt my arm. I had to leave the icy, stiff body straddling my shoulders until I had finished extracting the liver and rubbing it on the denuded belly of the black pig. The moment I had finished I heaved the body back on the table and, with the aid of the morgue attendant, lashed it down so that such an accident might not recur.

When we reached Vancouver, only three pigs were left. They had already endured much and the condition of two of them was dubious. It was midwinter and they had to be kept warm. I took them into the sleeping-car with me, concealed under my raincoat. But that evening they were discovered; the conductor peremptorily told me to remove them to the baggage car.

"But it's so cold the guinea pigs will die."

The conductor pulled out a book of regulations, and I had no recourse but obedience. By this time we were well up in the Canadian Rockies and it was eighteen below zero. The first thing in the morning I hurried forward the long length of the swaying train to look at my guinea pigs; they were all frozen stiff. I sent a telegram to the Institute at once, informing them of the mishap, and received a return wire to bring them along, but be sure to keep them frozen.

Tremendous excitement attended their arrival at the Grand Central Station. A Rockefeller Institute ambulance, uniformed attendants, and even Noguchi himself were there. The train had barely slid noiselessly to a stop when the guinea pigs were snatched from the baggage car and rushed to the laboratory, where Noguchi, in spite of the many misadventures, succeeded in reviving the icterohemorrhagica organisms.

The pigs had fulfilled their destiny.

CHAPTER 17.   A DRUMMER OF
IDEAS

IN undertaking the position of Director for the East of the International Health Board I was obligated to spend most of my time away from the United States and practically ostracize myself from any permanent ties of family or home. For twenty years I traveled furiously on my mission, peddling my line of ideas. Research workers in the United States would be brimming with experiments they wanted tried out in the tropics, and tropical health officers were eager to have projects tested in the big laboratories of the outer world. I carried in my head health ideas gleaned up and down the whole creation.

Until a few years earlier the various medical services of the East had been united only in their laissez-faire policy toward the native populations, looking with suspicion upon one another and jealously guarding their own secrets. Each health service had revolved smugly in its little sphere, and much labor had been wasted in solving problems which had already been successfully met in other lands.

Governor General Forbes had given concrete form to the idea of international medical cooperation. He had issued invitations to all countries East of Suez to send delegates to the first meeting of the medical men of the Far East to be held at Manila, March, 1910. Japan, China, Tsingtao, Ceylon, Hongkong, Straits Settlements, the Federated Malay States, India, Siam, Netherlands East Indies, and Australia had responded, and the Far Eastern Association of Tropical Medicine had come into being.

More important than the papers read or even the ideas exchanged had been the personal relationships established among the medical representatives of widely divergent races and countries. Yellow, brown, and white had met in a common cause, and each had learned that the essentials of his problems were common to all. Thereafter our brethren throughout the East, in full fraternity, had met with us every other year at some Eastern capital. The results of these meetings were so gratifying and so valuable that on my trips for the Rockefeller Foundation I varied my itinerary whenever necessary to attend them.

Usually I followed the sun on my journeys, and Vancouver was my first stop. British Columbia already had a health service, but sometimes officials were unsure of themselves and felt the need of being confirmed in their procedure. They would present me with many problems, and we would pore over them, trying to pick out the sound kernels which might bear fruit.

Generally I traveled from the Pacific coast to Honolulu. Although we had neither personnel nor money invested in Hawaii, not only the government but also private organizations of business men were spending liberally in promoting health. The Americans in Hawaii had established such high standards of plantation sanitation as to make Hawaii a paragon throughout the East. Here I could learn much. The give and take in ideas exceeded that in any other place. I could study the methods of leprosy treatment at Kalihi, and in return help with plans for the eradication of plague, which was endemic in the back country of Maui, and which was looked upon as a stigma.

Each country I visited had a different set of questions to be answered. The Japanese would accumulate a huge quantity of statistical data without being themselves sure of what to do with it. Their interest in science as practised in the laboratory was tremendous, but not sufficiently vital to induce them to sink their professional rivalries for the good of the country. The aim of the Foundation was to bring about concerted action in health work and I, as its representative, tried to make myself persona grata to rival factions. Out of respect for the Rockefeller Foundation they would come together, and this was a big step toward conciliation.

A DRUMMER OF IDEAS

From Tokyo I went to Peiping, where the China Medical Board was already at work. Its activities did not fall within my province, but I was frequently consulted.

I already had had experience in China. In 1911 I had been asked to organize a health service in South China. Many of the questions put up to me, however, had been far afield from sanitation. The first thing the authorities had wanted to know was what to do with the army which had just conquered Kwantung Province and refused to go home. "How can you disband an army?" they asked me.

After prolonged cogitation I suggested that the wall along the water front of Canton should, in the interests of sanitation, be demolished. "Why not set your idle army to tearing it down?" I suggested.

The soldiers were put to work, and the wall had practically vanished before, one by one, the disgruntled laborers had abandoned their unexpected task and had slipped away to their homes. At one and the same time the ends of health had been attained and the army difficulty settled.

The problem in China was controlled by the value placed on human excreta. China has no sewers. Each night in urban centers the excrement is collected by coolies, who carry it in wooden buckets to barges along the river. These are pushed up the streams and canals into the interior, and almost everywhere farmers and gardeners may be seen purchasing their supply, which they convey to their fields of rice and mulberry. There they dig it into the ground for their crops, or moisten it with water and sprinkle it over growing vegetation. Thus a relatively light infection in Chinese cities may become a serious factor in spreading the disease to agricultural districts and, through the infected vegetables, back to the cities. All gardeners and rural coolies work barefooted or bare-legged. Under the mulberry trees, where it is dark and shady, the hookworms wait for the unwary.

At Shanghai, as a private individual, I used to meet the authorities of the International Settlement at dinners and luncheons, and talk over a dozen different things. I used to impress upon newspaper editors the need for better water, so that they would begin intensive campaigns; ultimately both water purification plants and sewers were built in Shanghai. In the normal course of events, this would have

293

taken place of itself, but perhaps I helped to speed it up. I could do such things without having them appear in any reports, and the results in health were infinitely greater than could have been accomplished in fighting any particular epidemic.

After a quick swing through the interior of China, I usually ended at Hongkong, which in my opinion vies with Sydney as being one of the most beautiful harbors in the world. From the water front at night when the mountain side is lighted, the scene defies description. Along the zigzag road which curves back and forth up the Peak, the traveler can be carried in chairs or take the inclined railroad, all the way passing homes built into the hillside, each with its beautifully terraced garden radiant with bloom.

In Hongkong diplomacy was essential. The British prided themselves on having created an island oasis of health, despite the fact that it happened to be inexplicably ridden with malaria. I would cultivate the chief medical officer, reporting progress in malarial countries here, there, and everywhere, but never mentioning Hongkong. Finally he would say, "We have some malaria here. What do you think we should do about it?" Since this was the opportunity for which I had been waiting, I would promptly make my suggestions.

The University of Hongkong and the Health Service had long been furiously jealous of each other. The latter controlled the hospitals. Hence the medical school, which the British had started, could not secure clinical material. Due to this feud, as well as lack of funds, the school was not doing the good work it should. The Foundation judged it exceedingly important that the school should graduate well-trained doctors who spoke Cantonese and would have influence on the governmental affairs of South China. My job was to effect a rapprochement between the University and the Health Service, which eventually took place.

Sometimes I used to take ship from Hongkong to Saigon where the French have reared a little Paris from the swamps of Cochin-China, and with typical insularity have transported there the boulevards, shops, sidewalk cafés, and hotels of their *patrie*. On arrival I paid my respects to the health officials of Indo-China. The service was primitive; it protected the French population, but little was done for the natives. Cholera had been raging in Indo-China for years and had never been brought under control although, as always where French influence predominates, a Pasteur Institute had been erected. One thing that impressed me was the intense French jealousy of other nations. I was told, for instance, that it was a criminal offense for any native of Indo-China to come to the United States for an education; he would forfeit his citizenship thereby.

The ruins of Angkor Wat in Cambodia rank with the seven wonders of the world. A complete city, with a magnificent style of architecture to be seen nowhere else, had been built by the Khmers. Where this race had come from nobody knows, and where it has gone is equally shrouded in mystery. This amazing city, supposed by the natives to have been built not by men but by mighty demons, was only discovered in 1860, and no start to clear away the jungle was made before 1908. Since then the French have worked long and hard to make it accessible to travelers. They also desired to bring home to their own people some impression of its grandeur, and when I was there they were taking impressions of some buildings for the French Colonial Exposition in Paris of 1932. To test out their carefulness, I made scratches on a block of stone; when I examined the replica later in Paris I saw even these scratches exactly reproduced.

Since I could bring little to the French in Indo-China and take little from them, I went there seldom. More often on leaving Hongkong, I sailed to the Philippine Islands, where I was coming home. I was still regarded as Director of Health, and was deeply touched by the many kindly attentions of the Filipinos, who had come to realize what I had been trying to do. At Malacañan with each Governor General I would go over the problems which, though familiar, were always changing. I would greet old friends, revisit old haunts, never failing to pay a friendly call at the Culion leper colony.

After about six weeks I would start South, invariably stopping at Zamboanga. Here Dr. Fajardo, head of the Mindanao health service, displayed the affection of an old boy greeting his former master. He was trying out all sorts of advanced preventive methods, among them cholera vaccine, which up to that time even Manila had hesitated to use.

From Zamboanga across the Sulu Sea to Sandakan was not a long jump. British North Borneo was run by a chartered company for dividends, and was, naturally, not particularly interested in health expenditures. The task there was to arrange for hookworm surveys and to show the planters how better sanitation would not only improve the health of their laborers but, what was of more immediate interest to them, decrease their operating costs. The planters were not at first able to see the self-evident connection between profits and health.

In 1915 a heavy outbreak of beriberi had been serious enough to handicap the production of rubber, for every pound of which a world at war was clamoring. The impotent health service was well aware beriberi was caused by eating polished rice, but was powerless to induce the planters to accept the idea. Upon my suggestion Governor Pearson, who had autocratic powers, issued a mandatory order that only unpolished rice should be used on plantations. Not until this order had gone into effect and beriberi had automatically disappeared in its wake were the planters convinced.

I received every consideration at Government House, and being the Governor's guest had certain great advantages. He would ask me whom I wished to see. "I don't know," I would answer, "but I'll tell you what I have in mind."

The Governor would then invite the particular group of people who were in a position to tell me what I desired to know. Because everybody who came to Government House was supposed to talk, I was able to secure a mass of information which would never have come my way in the course of ordinary interviewing.

Governor Pearson told me about an interesting criminal case which had arisen in connection with a Malay woman who was subject to the nervous affliction called latah. The characteristic of this disorder is that the afflicted person will involuntarily imitate every motion made by another. In this instance the woman was traveling on a steamer with a baby in her arms. A man near her made a motion to throw something into the sea, and she imitated him by throwing the child into the ocean, where it drowned. The court held that since the man knew she suffered from latah, he was guilty of the crime.

I spent a great deal of time visiting the various plantations, often starting in the early morning and enjoying the gorgeous sunrises, the infinite variety of birds, the cool air, and the winding trails. One nine hundred acre plantation was run by a canny Scot who had made the steps to his house double the ordinary height to save lumber, and was tapping his trees in two places, although it was an accepted fact that a rubber tree could stand no more than one.

Another rubber estate was located on rich soil, said to be ten feet thick, which had been the bottom of a lake within the memory of the older residents. Between the trees had been sown the creeping passiflora fetida, which shut out all other growth and could, at intervals, be rolled up like a carpet, leaving the ground bare and free of weeds.

The poles of the recently completed telegraph line between Sandakan and Jesselton, the other capital of Borneo, were kapok trees, which have only straight, right-angled branches upon which the wires were strung. These telegraph poles had the advantage of not deteriorating and also of raising a valuable crop of cotton. In other places where ordinary poles were used, for some unknown reason, wild elephants took exception and pulled out the posts and threw them away almost as soon as they were replaced.

The Rockefeller Foundation representatives in Borneo sometimes had a hard time socially because the feeling against Americans was very strong, and few amenities were extended. The planters blamed the Americans for the bursting of their rubber boom; from the height of opulence in 1925 they had been plunged into depression a few years later. It is not a simple task to gain the cooperation of people who believe they have been robbed.

I would go along the coast of Borneo, occasionally stopping at the Island of Labuan and the Protectorate of Brunei on the way to Kuching, the capital of Sarawak. There I was the guest of Sir Charles Vyner Brooke, the White Rajah, who governed the country under British protection.

To my surprise the British in Sarawak seemed to have lost the art of polite living in the British sense. My experiences gave me the distinct impression that visitors were not particularly desired. The Brooke family took little interest in health work, and the authorities in charge seconded this attitude. I was amazed to see that everyone seemed so afraid of the Rajah that he was not discussed even in whispers. Because I had credentials from the Colonial Office in London, I was admitted to conference with His Highness and explained to him how two courses were open in a backward country such as his. A little might be done in many fields, and such action, though it would have only a slight effect on sickness and death rates, would be commended by the lay critic; or, something essential, although less spectacular, might be done which, at comparatively small outlay, would produce larger results.

We kept a man there under salary for over a year and a health plan was worked out, but the government never put it into effect.

From Kuching I sailed to Singapore, in Malay, the "City of the Lion," which had been transformed by Sir Stamford Raffles from a fishing village into the Emporium of the Orient. It was now a great world trade center and Great Britain's monster naval base in the East. Chugging to Johnson's Pier through the diversified shipping was a fitting introduction to the conglomerate life of this extraordinary cosmopolis. The Raffles Hotel, one of the famed hostelries of the world, was almost always crowded. World tourists were arriving on every steamer and people were dropping in from China, Japan, the Philippines, Siam, Burma, India, Ceylon, and Europe. On the huge verandas overlooking the Bay, amid beautiful palm trees, the punkahs swayed noiselessly back and forth, ice tinkled in glasses, and constant calls were heard for stinga whiskey and soda.

Before Rose had started his 1914 tour of the East, he had realized that knowledge of hookworm control was not yet perfected. A fundamental question had to be answered, "Was anemia from hookworm distinguishable from that caused by malaria or other diseases?" Malaya seemed to offer the best opportunity for a survey. With the cooperation of the government a commission was appointed by the Rockefeller Foundation, composed of the American doctors, S. T. Darling and M. A. Barber, assisted by the British doctor, H. P. Hacker.

Dr. Darling, the head of the Commission, had been in Panama with General Gorgas, where he had made important contributions toward the success of the health service. Dr. Barber had been Professor of Bacteriology at the Kansas Medical College. One of his most brilliant laboratory achievements had been the discovery of a way of isolating a single bacillus. The great Koch was told about his method at the Tuberculosis Congress of 1908, but Koch had pooh-poohed it. Dr. Barber had then successfully demonstrated it to him. Because he had so well proved himself, we brought him over to the Bureau of Science in the Philippines, where he made many practical discoveries, brilliant in their simplicity and revolutionary in their effect on the control of disease-bearing mosquitoes and other aspects of tropical medicine. After he joined the International Health Board, he developed a method of segregating hookworm eggs by which examinations were immensely facilitated and speeded up.

One of my first jobs in the Federated Malay States was to prepare the way for the Darling Commission, find a place for its members to stay, arrange interviews, and, since they had no licenses to practise there, to secure the necessary permission. In addition, I drew up a list of points on which further hookworm knowledge was desired, such as whether thymol or chenopodium was more efficient, the after effects of the treatment, what kind of purge to use, the diet, the relation between the age of the patient and the severity of the infection, and whether necators were less resistant than ancylostomes. The final point was to determine to what degree uncinariasis infection was a menace to the health and working efficiency of the peoples of the Orient. The Commission planned to make the same type of survey in Java and Sumatra, and to check their findings in Fiji, where no malaria existed to complicate the study.

Much hookworm work was eventually done throughout the Straits Settlements. Dr. Paul Russell gave many lectures at Malacca, where large numbers of Chinese and Tamil laborers had been imported to build a new dam. His audience took to heart the letter if not the spirit of his exhortations. A group of Chinese coolies, after hearing one of his talks on hookworm infection, almost killed two Tamils who had violated some of the regulations he had laid down. Another Malay convert was inspired by his teachings to build a latrine of which he was so proud that he fastened the door with a padlock lest anybody defile it.

In Java as well as the Federated Malay States I secured permission for the Darling Commission's survey, but accomplished little else for many years. It was difficult to make headway against the hard-headed

Dutch who, because of their brilliant achievements, considered themselves self-sufficient. In the beginning, I was under suspicion on the theory that I was there for the chief purpose of winning approval for a Standard Oil concession. I could have answered any direct charge, but nebulous implications are not so easily combated. The Dutch authorities, however, were always hospitable and courteous in listening to suggestions. It required a long time for an idea to penetrate the heads of this stubborn people, but, once it was in, they could be counted upon never to let it go. And so I persevered.

From Batavia I retraced my steps to Singapore, and thence continued to Siam, where in the uplands of Chiengmai we turned old Buddhist temples to our uses, transforming them into theaters where we could display the life cycle of the hookworm. Thence I took the train back to Malaya, stopping for a few hours at the beautiful island of Penang. The congestion of small watercraft at this port of entry into Siam and the northern coast was terrific. No adequate docking facilities were available, and people and merchandise had to be landed in small boats.

It is an overnight journey by train from Penang to Kuala Lumpur, known locally as K-L, the capital of the Federated Malay States. It was one of the first cities in the world to adopt town planning, brought about by a woman's organization. Every house plan had to be submitted and accepted as harmonious to the whole. At Kuala Lumpur, during and after the War, I saw flourishing one of the most affluent governments in the world. The shipments of rubber and tin were so large that only a slight export duty on them sufficed to provide for all government needs. It was a taxpayers' Utopia. Commodities of all sorts could be had for little or nothing; good Havanas were ten cents apiece. I thought travel in the United States was comfortable, but it did not compare with that of Malaya. For fifty cents I could acquire a compartment with a bed, screened windows, shower bath, fans, and running water.

Owing to its tremendous wealth, the government of the Federated Malay States did not feel in need of our financial assistance; all it desired was ideas.

In Sumatra, by suggesting methods of hookworm and beriberi control, I was able to prove the commercial value of sanitation to foreign firms with huge plantations just coming into production. The Dutch treatment of the malarial mangrove swamps taught me in turn much which could be used elsewhere.

From Belawan Deli, the chief port of Sumatra, I went to Rangoon, capital of Burma, rich with oil, rice, teak, and rubber, and boasting the great golden Shwe Dagon. The Burmese were a docile, easily led race, inclined to be lazy. The health service sought the help of the Hpungis, the priests, who would assist, for example, in rounding up the people for vaccination. The upper classes assimilated knowledge readily, but gambling and the pursuit of pleasure often made them unreliable in medical work. Students had to be paid to attend the medical branch of the University, and the government had to let them bring along their valets. The Burmese were so ashamed of their medical school that they would not even permit me to see it.

Personal habits were not a problem among the Burmese. They were cleanly and used latrines. But the heavily populated part of the country was low-lying, and when the subsoil water rose in flood time, the people became infected with hookworm from the overflow.

Next I landed at Colombo and spent approximately three weeks looking over operations and studying, in the field, the development of the hookworm campaign. Ceylon was one of the most important stops on my route. In the early days the Foundation was using this island to demonstrate the results of hookworm research. We concentrated much effort there, because we believed that what was accomplished in Ceylon would be applied in other British colonies. Even though the obstacles were great and the discouragements many, in Ceylon we learned more about the practical application of hookworm knowledge than anywhere else in the world, and in the end the results were gratifying.

Then I crossed by Adams Bridge into Southern India, first stopping at Madras, and afterwards going north to Calcutta in Bengal. I would spend days and evenings getting acquainted with the men of the Indian Medical Service, the most effectively organized body of medical men in the world, who had contributed the great bulk of our knowledge of tropical medicine. The British who composed it, able, efficient, and unassuming, proceeded steadily toward their goal in spite of the magnitude of their problems.

Sometimes it would seem desirable for me to go to Simla. Two nights and a day were consumed in a journey which might have borne a superficial appearance to a vacation, but it was made for a purpose; I met the important people there at a time when they had leisure for discussion.

Many of the research problems of India were being worked out at the Bombay Bacteriological Laboratory. I used to stay with the commanding officer on the grounds, and, consequently, valuable time was not taken up in establishing my status. The Indian Medical Service was trying to start a school of hygiene, a project dear to my heart and one in which I was delighted to be of assistance. Bombay, one of the scientific medical centers of India, was disputing with Calcutta for its location, although ultimately Calcutta won.

On the long voyage from Bombay through the Red Sea and the Suez Canal I had time to collect my thoughts, and most of my material had been organized when I reached Egypt. The World War had stopped our hookworm labors there, and for years my visits were of an advisory nature only.

Egypt was one of the most tempting countries in which the Rockefeller Foundation could be of service. Its resources were tremendous but the knowledge of how to apply them effectively was meagre. Egypt also offered unequaled opportunities for research, being one of the few places in the world where the ancylostoma exists alone without the necator. Furthermore, it is afflicted with the outstanding problem of bilharzia.

Thousands of tourists, the cultured of all countries, well-informed, intelligent, and thinking people visit Egypt each year, and have been doing so for a century or more; scarcely one among them has even heard of bilharzia. Yet out of the twelve million Egyptians who are crowded into the narrow, desert-bordered belt of fertile green that fringes the sinuous course of Father Nile from Alexandria in the Delta to Assuan by the cataracts, six million have this disease, three million are seriously handicapped by it, and one million are bedfast. A tiny trematode worm, called a fluke from its fish-like shape, holds the descendants of the Pharaohs in a self-imposed but none the less vise-like grip.

Here, as everywhere else in the tropical world, the chief responsibility for disease rests upon the lack of cleanly habits. Bilharzia could be eradicated if these could be inculcated. With other research workers the Rockefeller Foundation is now engaged in attempting to solve this problem. Until Egypt has been freed of this devastating disease, she will always be under a serious disadvantage in taking her place among the nations of the world.

From Alexandria I embarked, sometimes for Athens, because we were conducting malaria investigations in Greece, sometimes for Naples, and sometimes for Constantinople. Wherever I landed, after a short stay I would take the train for a brief tour of the capitals of Europe. I would spend a few hours at Budapest to inspect the Institute of Hygiene, and then go on to Vienna which, long before the social conventions had permitted it in other countries, had made clinical material available for students.

Czecho-Slovakia held special interest because it had a newly-organized government with young ideas and an enthusiasm unhampered by an already existing bureaucratic administration and weighed down with precedent.

In Germany the great problem after the War was to know how to apply sanitary measures with the consent and help of the people. In the imperial days an order had no sooner been given than it was carried out, and usually carried out well. But the Republic had to instruct and persuade.

I never omitted Paris, where the Foundation maintained an office for the Commission on Tuberculosis, which was making extensive surveys—a work later taken over by the French. I learned a great many things that could be successfully applied in such places as the South Seas, where the tuberculosis incidence was high.

The French, although they may well claim to be among the world's most intelligent people, had steadfastly refused to be convinced of the soundness of our conception of medical education. Because we wished to disseminate this special type of knowledge through French-speaking people, the Foundation tried to accomplish this purpose by helping the Belgians at Brussels to develop a modern medical school.

At Amsterdam and The Hague I would interview people from cabinet ministers down, and discuss particularly the problems of Java. My chief point of contact was Dr. W. Schüffner, famous authority on tropical diseases, whom I had first met in Sumatra. It was through these Netherlands visits that I eventually broke down the barriers to our entrance into Java.

London, although last, was the scene of my most important diplomatic labors. The health officials of the colonies looked to my visits there to help them get through measures they desired. The Colonial Office in turn was anxious to have impressions of its agents abroad. The authorities made my path infinitely smoother by seeing to it that I was officially received wherever I went in British territory, and secured for me the necessary invitations to make surveys.

From a health standpoint, Russia was, without doubt, one of the most interesting countries of Europe. Although I traveled there in 1929 as a private individual, naturally my chief interest lay in finding out what was being done in my own field. Because I wanted to guard against receiving purposeful misinformation, I was careful to confirm what I heard from the Soviets by checking at such unprejudiced sources as the Jewish Relief, financed from the United States, and the well-informed Americans at the Near East Relief headquarters. In no case did I find I had been deceived.

Under the Czar medicine had been encouraged as an art, but had not been widely disseminated among the general populace. But under Soviet rule Russia had evolved a modern health organization which was laying particular stress on popular education, using all the resources of propaganda, at which the Soviets have proved themselves so expert. The government acted on the theory that the public must be intelligently prepared for health measures. The radio, which could be heard in farthest Siberia, was of inestimable value in reaching the illiterate portions of the population. Foreign pamphlets and posters from all over the world had been collected and such parts as were applicable to Russian conditions were being used.

At Moscow I had a most interesting interview, conducted in German, with Dr. Vera Assatkine, one of the chiefs of the Bureau of Health. She described the Soviet health achievements—general mortality in Moscow had been reduced one-third, infant mortality one-half; attendance of mothers at post-natal clinics had been increased over ninety percent, health protection was being extended rapidly to rural districts. When populations were transferred from unprofitable lands to virgin fertile regions, the train that carried the people had a hospital car with doctor, nurses, medicines, and complete hospital equipment.

A special plague section had been formed in the Health Department. In various cities larger and more scientific laboratories had been erected which made smallpox and cholera vaccine. Before it had been possible to organize health work, a great smallpox epidemic had broken out and many deaths had resulted. But now every infant over four months old had to be vaccinated. Russia also had had frightful malaria after the War, but within a few years had installed the most approved system of combating it. Anti-malaria stations were opened and distribution of quinine arranged. Russian delegates made a practice of attending foreign meetings on malaria, and working industriously they steeped themselves in the world's knowledge of the disease.

I was particularly struck with the manner in which the Health Department handled venereal disease, which was being treated solely from the infectious standpoint. This is in great contrast to our attitude; ostrich-like, we stick our heads into the sand and refuse to recognize that syphilis causes greater havoc than any other disease in the Christian world, and that efforts to deal with it should not be handicapped by regarding it as punishment for sin. Venereal disease, like cholera or plague, is primarily infectious and should be handled accordingly. The situation will remain hopeless as long as a prominent health officer of the leading state in the Union can be refused the use of one of the great radio broadcasting systems because he mentioned the word syphilis.

After the Revolution of 1917, when the experiment in Communism was just beginning, the Soviets made one serious error in the health field. They had assumed that no special preliminary education was needed before a student could enter medical school. Four or five years were lost before they learned that good doctors could not be made in this way. Their excuse was that the Marxian doctrine is not complete; here were beams too short for Marxian houses. Nevertheless *Das Kapital* remained their Bible, albeit in modified form.

The friend with whom I was traveling was accustomed to paying well for what he desired. But at the hotel in Moscow, in spite of his lavish tips, we received practically no service. We could seldom finish a meal in less than two hours. A party of Germans seated near us would come in, be expeditiously waited upon, and depart while we were still impatiently awaiting our first course. Finally I went over to their table to ask them their secret.

"You don't do it right," was the answer. "You can't buy these people with money or treat them as servants. If we want a fork we say, 'Kamerad, would you mind, when you are coming on another trip from the kitchen, to bring us a fork? We would be so glad if you would.'"

We changed our tactics and stopped tipping, and thereafter received every consideration.

The aim of the Soviet is, as I understand it, in simple language, to work out better sociological conditions, and if they succeed other nations will, no doubt, wish to adopt them. As long as they confine these activities to Russia, we have little cause to object if they choose to turn themselves into a social laboratory.

I often altered my itinerary at other points than Russia. Occasionally my trips were varied by a tour of Central America, which was recognized as a health menace to the United States. Lack of public order made stable health services there impossible. The men in charge of the Foundation work had to be encouraged and heartened over and over, because only a Disraeli could have survived the ups and downs, the fusillade of bullets, the constant repetition of "the President has been shot, long live the President."

Sometimes I went to the South Seas or Australia. In the latter country at first I encountered such opposition that it was difficult to tell whether the bitterness was due to the Rockefeller name or directed against Americans in general. Certainly capitalists were not popular. But in the end the country united to laud the efforts of the Rockefeller Foundation in promoting health.

Whatever my route, once a year I returned to the United States where one of my busiest times began. Progress in medicine and health would have been so rapid that after my long absence I would find myself far behind. I would go to Canada, Boston, Philadelphia, Baltimore, Washington, Chicago, San Francisco, delivering lectures and attending meetings, renewing old associations, making new contacts and investigations, and picking up new ideas which would be helpful during my next world tour.

CHAPTER 18.   MUCH HAVE I
TRAVELED

MOVEMENT, change, flux have governed the pattern of my life for many years. The throb of engines, the mournful warning of foghorns, white-jacketed stewards, tourists vocal with erroneous information; gentle seas, rough seas, calms, and typhoons, landfalls once strange but later familiar, golden sand and green jungle, heat and dripping humidity; alien customs and alien faces, white skins, yellow skins, brown skins, black skins, the patter of many tongues; trains swaying along uneven roadbeds and hurtling over level ones, shrill whistles in the night, hotels with sleepy porters; cots, feather beds, wooden pallets; low-humming Rolls Royces and rattling Fords, flat roads meeting the horizon, white roads curling up mountains; cities large and small with prideful citizens anxious to display civic wares; hospitals everywhere, "This is the ward for such and such, and this is our operating theater, and this is the laboratory, and so on"—I can still repeat the whole story backward and forward— it makes me weary now to think of the hundreds of miles of hospital corridors traversed in contemplating medical education in lands near and remote; interviews with those friendly and hostile, tongue dry with hours of talk, pointing sprightly stories with hidden morals, explaining the same thing over and over, mustering the old arguments of merit against politics.

Almost always I took with me one of the younger doctors, either from New York or his post in the East, to show him what was being done in countries other than his own. Often I had pleasant companionship which was not directly in the line of duty. In 1916 I was accompanied by one of my old friends, Dr. William George MacCallum, who had become one of the world's leading pathologists, and was author of one of the best textbooks on this subject. Dr. MacCallum, who was then enjoying his Sabbatical leave from Columbia University, said he was tired of performing autopsies on victims of the same old diseases and the same old races; he wanted to see what he could learn from the victims of tropical maladies. But in the beginning of our journey the opportunities for autopsies were so few that he was reduced to dissecting sharks.

MacCallum was still harping on autopsies when we arrived at the Fiji Islands and loudly expressed his annoyance because nobody had died recently in Suva. At the Governor's dinner I sat next to the Chief Justice and endeavored to amuse him by describing MacCallum's macabre enthusiasms.

"Well, I think I could arrange something for him," the judge remarked.

"How?"

"Two criminals are going to be executed here next Monday. I could easily arrange to have their bodies turned over to him."

I explained that unfortunately MacCallum could not wait until Monday, because we were sailing Sunday.

"Oh, that's easily enough arranged. I'll have the execution advanced to Saturday. That'll be a simple matter."

Confronted with this proposition, I had to beg off on the ground that I could not feel responsible for hurrying two wretches into eternity before their time.

I preceded MacCallum to Manila where I arranged to have him temporarily appointed a city pathologist. I told him the glad news when I met his boat at six in the morning, but, omitting all mention of the current cholera epidemic, warned him that, if he once accepted, he must perform autopsies on all bodies brought to the morgue. MacCallum was so delighted at this opportunity to increase his knowledge that he hurried through his breakfast and rushed me off to the morgue. Five bodies were already awaiting him. I left him bubbling with enthusiastic anticipation. He did not appear at lunch, nor at dinner. At eleven in the evening he dragged himself wearily into the hotel, having seen a great deal more of cholera than he had bargained for. Ten more cases had come in before he had finished the first five. After the second day he was ready to resign, but I told him he would have to remain at least two weeks to establish his good faith. The result was that the cholera chapter in the revised edition of his book was one of the best.

MacCallum had done special research on malaria and had made one of the great contributions to the knowledge of the disease by his discovery of the sex life of the malaria parasite. At Singapore he was overjoyed to find many victims of malaria on whom he could perform autopsies. These were so profitable in adding to his store of information that some years afterwards he returned to make further studies. But in the meantime the British had performed the Herculean task of reducing the disease to a negligible figure. Practically nobody in Singapore was now dying of malaria. He railed at me for months thereafter. "You sanitarians have ruined the business of the poor pathologist."

Unfamiliar with the vagaries of tropical climates, MacCallum had great difficulty in adjusting his clothing to the differing temperatures. On reaching Vancouver he had stocked up with winter clothing and discarded his light weight suits. At Fiji he had reversed the process, throwing away his newly-acquired winter outfit, and buying a summer one. At Sydney he had purchased new winter clothes and left behind his summer ones once more. I lost track of the number of times he went through this jettisoning process, but when he arrived in Java he was in his winter clothes and dripping in the insufferable heat, always protesting to me that he was, "Very comfortable, thank you." Not until his resistance had been overcome to the point where he would admit he was genuinely suffering did I produce his latest edition of tropical clothing, which I had surreptitiously retrieved. His pride by this time had completely melted, and his gratitude was unalloyed.

Through so much traveling I had had to learn all sorts of expedients and prepare for all sorts of emergencies. My wardrobe had to provide for a wide range in temperature, and social, business, and sport requirements. I found there was only one way of being sure I did not leave anything essential behind. I made an all-inclusive list, a copy of which was kept in each bag. By this means nothing was ever lacking, even when I had to pack and set forth at short notice.

I carried an office desk with me in the shape of a specially designed wardrobe trunk. When it was opened, a leaf in the middle could be pulled down, thus converting it into a desk. There were plenty of pigeon holes. One drawer held a traveling library, another served as a catch-all for papers, and below was a suitcase ready packed with everything I needed for brief trips, including a typewriter and complete desk equipment. In the other half of the trunk my clothes were concealed behind a folding door.

It was a painful experience to see the massive trunk being moved inch by inch up the ship's gangway; one slip and it would have gone to the bottom of the sea. Only in Egypt where the stevedores are reputed the strongest in the world did I ever feel confident; but there one of them would pick up the three hundred pound load, walk up the gangplank with it on his shoulder and deposit it on the deck. A turn of the key and I would be ready to work; through the tropics it was pleasanter on deck. I always suffered considerable anxiety until I had the trunk in my possession. Once when I had to search for it in the hold, I found it labeled, "Dr. Heiser, deceased," and had great difficulty in proving that I was alive.

Seasickness is a malady of moment only to the sufferer, but it is nevertheless very serious to the constant traveler. I am not one of those fortunate ones who are naturally immune, but I did learn how to prevent its occurrence. Until I had become more or less immune, my simple but effective remedy was to lie in bed with my feet higher than my head, even eating with my head at this lower level. A still better cure is to have some absorbing interest to divert the mind. Once in weather so rough I could hardly stay in my bunk, where I was coddling myself, a sick call came from the steerage. I somehow staggered to my feet and answered it. Shortly I became so occupied that I forgot all about my unpleasant nausea.

In 1915, when the War was well under way, some of the steamers delegated for neutral passenger traffic were unspeakable. I always chose an upper berth, because of its advantages; I could look out the porthole and, if my cabin mate were seasick, I preferred to be located aloft. One night, while traveling on the Union Steamship Line, I was awakened by the most terrific pain in my big toe. Wriggling it only made it worse. I thrust my foot over the edge and my anguish increased. When I hurriedly switched on the light, there was a huge rat hanging on with a bulldog grip. The more I shook, the harder the frightened rodent held on, and the further his teeth sank into my toe. But as soon as I pulled my foot back on the bed, he let go and scampered off, leaving me to dress my wounds.

In addition to rats, the ship carried a full complement of roaches. They would run over the tables, even in the daytime. But they had some compensatory attributes. No chiropodist could have made his living on this line. Passengers who were afflicted by corns would find them neatly removed by morning. The roaches would gnaw down until they reached a sensitive spot, the foot would then automatically be moved, and, thus disturbed, they would scamper off.

Even more annoying than the Union Steamship Company was that far famed line, dear to all British hearts—the Peninsular & Oriental. I have experienced all the vexations and humiliations which Kipling has described so well, and, in addition, many of my own. My introduction to the P. & O. came when I boarded one of their ships at Suez, en route for the first time to the Philippine Islands. I had left my heavy baggage at Port Said while I went to Egypt, and had arranged for the ship to pick it up there because I planned to meet it at the other end of the Canal.

The officials of the line would not vouchsafe the time of the vessel's arrival at Suez. But, fortunately, I had one eye open when it finally came at three in the morning. With a natural anxiety to find out before we left whether my baggage had come on board, I repaired to the purser and made inquiries. He was as offended as though never in his life had he heard such a question. He grew redder and redder, and swelled and swelled like a turkey gobbler. Finally he managed to sputter, "The luggage is the business of the Fourth Officer."

"Where is the Fourth?"

"I don't know."

After searching here and there on the darkened ship, I finally crawled down the hatch ladder and located the Fourth in the hold with the cargo. Again I inquired politely for my trunks. He looked at me in a stern and lofty fashion. "Do you really expect me to keep in mind all the luggage that comes on board?"

"I thought you might be able to refer to your list."

"We have regular hours for attending to luggage. Tomorrow at four."

I could not see how that information would avail me if my trunks were not on the ship. But his decision was final, and I went to bed.

I was still tired when I awoke at nine and decided to have breakfast in my room. I rang for the steward. He came. I ordered breakfast.

"Are you ill, sir?" he inquired.

"No."

"Breakfast is only served in the cabin when the passenger has a certificate from the doctor that he is too sick to come to the table," he parroted.

I tried to induce the steward to change his mind, but he persisted it was against the rules of the company. Since I was more tired than hungry I stayed in my bunk until noon. Then I repaired to the dining room for lunch, expectantly anticipating my soup. When I indicated to my waiter that I was ready, he corrected me with the information that I might be ready but the captain was not. Fortunately for my appetite, the captain, a proud individual in a grand uniform, soon entered and was majestically seated. Then, and not until then, a special steward by his side banged on a big gong, and the soup course appeared.

I soon learned the rigid etiquette of dining on the P. & O. A hardy individual who said, "I won't have any soup, steward, I'll have the fish," was met by a stolidly reproving glance. "The soup is being served, sir."

The hungry man would have to possess his soul in patience until another sonorous bang announced the captain had finished his last spoonful of soup and the fish was being borne ceremoniously through the swinging doors. Whoever came late had to start with the course which the captain was then engaged in consuming.

I remember one dinner at Aden where we had arrived late in the afternoon. The customary rule on most lines was dinner jackets in the evening, although if a passenger had been ashore until too late to dress, it was automatically waived. But not so on the P. & O. Sitting next to me at table were a young Hungarian count and his bride, neither of whom spoke English. He came on board just as the soup gong had struck, rushed into the dining room, and sat down.

The steward said, "I'm very sorry, sir, but we can't serve you."

The Count obviously did not understand and pointed again to what he wanted on the bill of fare.

"You'll have to leave the dining room, sir. We do not serve anyone who is not in evening dress."

Still the Count did not understand. The waiter then stepped behind him, lifted him out of his chair, and escorted him from the room.

In later years a great concession was made to the tropic heat going through the Red Sea. I saw a sign which read, "Gentlemen will be permitted to dance in flannel trousers, but this will not excuse them from formal dress at dinner."

Conversations on shipboard are always the same, people get tired of deck tennis, organizing ships' concerts, betting on the daily run, and avoiding bores. By way of divertissement, I sometimes submitted my list of ten words, which nobody yet has spelled successfully. I usually prefaced it by remarking that President Eliot of Harvard had missed three, and that newspaper editors had been known to miss five or six.

The spelling test worked with equal efficacy on land. On one occasion the copper king, John Ryan, was present, took the test, and missed four. A few weeks later I met him walking along Broadway. He came up to me with his big beaming smile. "I haven't seen you since I boasted I was the champion speller of Michigan."

"Are you sure you can spell those words now?" I asked.

"Of course I can."

"I doubt it."

"I'll show you. I'll do it right here."

There in the middle of crowded Broadway, jostled by passers-by, he scribbled out the words as I gave them to him. Again, to his great chagrin and surprise, he missed four. His experience was by no means unique.

I learned to count upon certain responses which were almost in-

314

variable. Though numerous and diversified, the explanations offered for mistakes followed a set pattern. The British always used to claim I was using the American way of spelling. I would refer them politely to the Oxford Dictionary. With eager look one of them would rush to the ship's library. Sure that he was right, he would skim over the pages until he came to the word. Momentarily dashed, he would then rush with equal confidence to the next word he had missed, only to have his hopes once more blasted.

On one trip I had been asked by Mr. Rockefeller to make a report on the Constantinople College for Women, which was anxious to secure additional funds. I went through the various divisions until finally I reached the English Department. I was introduced to the head, a spinster, forbidding in demeanor. To alter the monotony of the inspection I began as follows: "You're the head of the department?"

"Yes."

"You teach English?"

"What else would I teach?"

"I suppose you give instruction in spelling?"

"We pride ourselves on our spelling."

"Would you mind if I tested you?"

"What do you want to test me for? I know how to spell."

"Of course," I said, "if you don't want to give me information—"

The President of the college, who was standing by trembling in her boots, conveyed to the English teacher in whispered asides that it was important to treat me with civility. An abrupt change in attitude followed. "Certainly you may test me," the English teacher said.

"Have you a pencil and paper?"

"I usually spell out loud."

"We'll use pencil and paper if you don't mind."

I gave her the list. Confidently she wrote down the words and handed the slip to me. Seven were wrong. Further whispers followed, which evidently convinced her of the enormity of her guilt; I never saw a balloon collapse more quickly than she.

I had already determined that the time was not propitious to recommend more money for the institution, but to this day those

315

women probably believe they did not receive a further grant because the head of the English Department had fallen down on the spelling test.

These are the words—inoculate, embarrass, harass, supersede, innuendo, rarefy, vilify, plaguy, desiccate, picnicking.

The Australians, on whom I also experimented, countered with "Can you name for us five adjectives ending in 'dous'?" I was delighted to add this to my list of parlor games. When I tried it on General Wood, he was so exasperated with his inability to name them that he had his secretary go through the dictionary until ten had been painstakingly culled.

Pleasant memories stretch behind me of kindly hospitality in government mansions and native huts, friendly clubs and charming homes. Everywhere people went to great pains to entertain me. In addition to the round of dinners and banquets, my hosts produced for my delectation the local forms of diversion, among which dancing was naturally prominent.

In all Eastern countries dancing is a highly formalized art to which the performers are usually trained from childhood. It has attained a degree of perfection remarkable to behold, though often unintelligible to Western minds.

One of my trips stands out for the quantity and variety of dancing exhibitions to which I was invited. The Japanese government, always lavish in welcome, wished to show me the beauty of the graceful geisha dances, and staged an elaborate display. I found it delightful and said so. My next stop was Peiping. The Chinese, who had heard how impressed I had been with Japanese dancing, were not to be outdone, and produced the best their sing-song girls could offer. I then went to Canton, and the Cantonese did their utmost to prove that dancing in South China was the finest in the land. When I reached the Philippines the girls at the Normal School had been learning old Filipino folk-dances, and proudly reproduced them for me. At Bali I saw the world-famed symbolic interpretations of Hindu legends, acted by masked dancers whose every tiny gesture was significant. But at Djokjakarta the Dutch said the genuine Javanese dances performed to the haunting melodies of the gamelan orchestras were incomparable, and proved it. I even saw the temple dance at

Angkor Wat, which is supposed to be the acme of Oriental perfection.

Unaware that their efforts were being wasted upon me, country continued to vie with country. But by this time I knew that I did not care to see more dancing. When not a word of it was breathed at Singapore I sighed with relief. I thought I was finally done with spending evening after evening at this business.

But at Siam the word that I was a connoisseur of dances had again preceded me. The Crown Prince had arranged a special exhibition, beginning at nine and ending at three in the morning. Beautiful as they were my appreciation was dimmed by the fact that I had to be up and about my duties at eight.

I was now sure I must have seen the end of dancing, but hardly had I stepped ashore at Rangoon than the wife of the Governor said to me, "We've held up our annual dancing fête until your arrival. We thought you, as an authority on Eastern dancing, would be particularly interested to see it." That afternoon she gave a tea party to which all social Rangoon tore its hair to be invited, and I was regaled with the native dances of Burma.

I went to India. In Madras, Travancore, and Bombay the nautch dancers swayed to the shrill piping flutes. I continued to Egypt—the dancing girls of Cairo swung wildly to the monotonous minor of Arabic music. Not until I had left the East did the competition for my unofficial approval finally end.

In the diverse forms of entertainment offered me I could more readily adapt myself to the dinners and the luncheons, though they were often composed of strange foods consumed according to strange customs. I remember my first formal Chinese dinner. Graciousness is inherent in Chinese hospitality. When plans were being perfected for a National Health Service in China, I was tendered a banquet at the Winter Palace of the former Empress Dowager. We were rowed in the moonlight to one of the lake pavilions on a barge, beautifully decorated with palms and wistaria and varicolored paper, which might have belonged to the glamorous Tsu Hsi herself.

Apologies were many and profuse that the sixty-course dinner was not enough for my honor; it should have consisted of one hundred and twenty. At seven o'clock we were seated at a round table, each with a little bowl before him. In the center of the table was a large bowl from which the guest of honor first served himself with chopsticks; after that a general scramble took place. Each diner retained his own bowl, but the center one changed as course followed course in amazing succession—sharks' fins, birds' nest soup, unrecognizable foods which, nevertheless, had a delicious flavor. The ordering of such a formal Chinese dinner was a fine art; two days might be devoted to planning the appropriate dishes and their fitting sequence.

After two hours, even though my portions had been small, I began to feel that I had had enough, but by ten o'clock I had digested the first courses and had gained my second wind; it seemed to make no difference thereafter how much more I ate. The meal reached a high point when we were served eggs, black with age, buried for three hundred years. They were not so unpleasant as might be assumed, but tasted rather like poor quality cold storage eggs. The Chinese esteemed them as one of their greatest delicacies, and cherished them for their antiquity. I considered this merely part of their ancestor worship.

The Westerner at a Chinese table cannot identify much of what he is eating, but the initiate knows the dinner is nearing an end when the rice and tea appear. The fruit course is never served at the main table; the necessity for shifting to a side one where it is displayed provides an opportunity to change partners.

Watermelon seeds, which are eaten before, during, and after the dinner, are much prized. My hosts would skillfully extract the kernels with their teeth, but I found it took practice. Chinese wines of varying flavors are freely served; I found Suchow most to my taste. Glasses are constantly replenished and tongues are loosened at these bright and charming Chinese functions. The Japanese affairs often compare with them in length but not in sprightliness of conversation.

Most Chinese foods are pleasant. But occasional exceptions are found. At a dinner given me in Hangchow the *pièce de résistance* was many-legged, live bugs several inches long and resembling roaches in color. These were served in a bowl covered with a glass bell. It is bad form not to accept a helping, no matter how small, of everything offered. I was supposed to lift the cover quickly, grab the wriggling animal with my chopsticks, pop it into my mouth, and crush it before it could start to crawl. I found that I needed considerable courage to bite this unfortunate insect, and, since I was a novice at the practice, it would invariably begin to squirm around my mouth before I could administer the quietus.

I have eaten all sorts of food in all sorts of places. It has always astonished me that Americans and Europeans in the tropics spend much money importing fruits when they are surrounded by all varieties of delicious native species; on a short trip through Central America I once encountered fourteen fruits different from those in the United States.

For some reason or other when I first went to the Philippines I had never heard of the mango. The *Rohilla Maru* had landed me in Manila about six in the morning, and I reached the hotel in time for eight o'clock breakfast. My table was located near that of an American woman who had ordered a strange-looking fruit of a rich yellow color. I was avid for new experiences and wished to make myself at home in this new country. "I'd like to have one of those," I said to the waiter.

Not wishing to appear ignorant, I watched how the lady handled hers. She tilted it on end, with a dexterous stroke cut down the two sides, and then ate each of these with a spoon. It looked very simple. I tilted back my mango similarly, and started to cut. But when it did not slice with the ease of hers, I exerted force. The juice exuded and spurted over my arms and on to the tablecloth. When I had hacked it open, I set to work with my spoon, but again the juice would not stay in the fruit; a geyser spouted up to my chin. I wondered uneasily how many people were watching my exhibition.

Stealing another look at the lady, I observed her take the four-inch kidney-shaped seed, insert her fork into it, and eat it delicately with absolute unconcern. I adopted the same nonchalance. I pressed my fork against the seed as I had seen her do; it would not go in. I pressed harder, but to no avail. The breakfasters began to nudge one another, and I was conscious of eyes focused upon me. In desperation I tried again. The more pressure I exerted, the less successful I seemed. The veins of my neck became turgid and my face cyanotic. By now the whole dining room was watching me. I was determined to succeed. With a final terrific thrust the fork slipped and the large flat stone shot the length of the long dining room, hit the opposite wall with a crash, and fell to the floor with a loud thud. A roar of laughter went up from my delighted audience.

I was shortly set right as to what I should have done. My first mistake had been that I had not cut from the stem end, and consequently had been working against the grain. I had made the same error in eating the fruit, also spooning it against the grain. Finally, when I had essayed the seed, I had not known that I should have inserted the fork, one prong at a time, into the soft places between the ridges.

Even with the best of care mango eating is apt to be messy. The juice makes an irremovable stain which in a moment turns black; in mango season hardly a white napkin can be found in the Islands. It was always popularly said that the proper way to enjoy the fruit was to relax in the bathtub.

After my not too brilliant first performance I set to work to master the fine art of mango eating and this eventuated in securing me many dinner invitations at Malacañan. Whenever any Governor General had distinguished visitors who had never eaten mangos, I received a summons. Since it would have been indelicate for him to give directions on how to handle the fruit, he would introduce me as the Director of Health, who would expound the proper method of eating mangos hygienically.

I became Philippines instructor in the technique of mango eating.

A very strange fruit is the durian, which grows on a large tree and is larger than the largest orange. It is protected by spines and filled with seeds which turn black as it ripens. I once tried to eat one. I held my nose and found it not so bad as I had feared. A traveler, who more than half a century ago wrote a book on the Malay Archipelago, described the savor of the durian as a "rich butter-like custard, highly flavored with almonds . . . but intermingled with it come wafts of flavor that call to mind cream cheese, onion sauce, brown sherry, and other incongruities." It possesses one of the most penetrating and disagreeable of all odors in the world. A polecat or limburger of the ripest vintage are mild in comparison.

On one occasion I was traveling with my chief assistant, Dr. Wilbur A. Sawyer, now Director of the International Health Division, on the train from Bangkok to Penang. The train had no diner, and we had, therefore, taken our luncheons in a hamper. About the middle of the day a Chinese, the only other occupant of the compartment, bought a ripe durian at a station and began his lunch by slicing it carefully in half. Bad as a durian is while yet unopened, it is infinitely worse when the rind is cut. We called a guard, told him we were absolutely overpowered, and asked him to persuade our traveling companion to eat his durian on the platform. The Chinese gathered it up and obligingly departed.

We unwrapped our ham sandwiches and began to eat them shortly after our fellow-passenger had come back. We had scarcely bitten into them when he started to make gestures of repulsion, shook his head, and ejaculated, "Whew! Whew! Whew!" as though he were overcome with disgust. Then he, too, called the guard to whom he spoke in Malay. The guard turned to us and asked whether we would mind stepping outside to eat our lunch. Since the Chinese had been so polite in acceding to our request, we felt we could do no less than return the favor. To a final "Whew!" we also left. When we had finished our innocent sandwiches and returned, the jocular Chinese looked up at us with a big, broad grin on his face.

I cannot imagine why, but nothing would satisfy Dr. Sawyer after this until he also could secure a durian. Not finding any ripe enough for immediate consumption, he compromised on a green one. At Penang he packed it away in a wicker hamper which, with the rest of our baggage, was left in a storeroom of the hotel at Colombo while we made an inspection trip of the provinces of Ceylon. As we approached the hotel on our return, even a block away we were aware of a terrible odor. It grew stronger and stronger as we drew nearer. We were astonished to see the whole courtyard in an uproar. The hotel staff was opening doors, poking at the ground, searching vainly to find the source. It was as though a hundred rats had been dead for some weeks. When Dr. Sawyer called for his baggage and the door of the storeroom was opened, the smell almost knocked us down. The durian, a fruit unknown in Ceylon, had been ripening successfully in the hamper.

The dauntless Dr. Sawyer was still determined to eat it. I said, "You certainly won't be allowed to open it around here, but if you go out along the breakwater, you'll be a half mile away and perhaps nobody will mind."

With his durian Dr. Sawyer retired to the very end of the mole. Even so, occasional whiffs of the evil odor came drifting in on the sea breeze.

Amusing and sometimes dramatic experiences often befell me on my voyages. Inevitably I missed boats, sometimes because the sailing date had been changed, sometimes because ships had been condemned or had sunk. At least four times to my knowledge I have been saved from almost certain death by pure coincidence.

In 1901 I had come down from Canada and was stopping at the Murray Hill Hotel in New York City, awaiting orders from Washington. When several days had passed without reply to my report, I sent a telegram, "Still awaiting orders."

The answer came almost instantly, "Return to Canada." I took the train at once. That same night an explosion occurred in the old Interborough tube, then under construction. The Murray Hill Hotel was badly damaged, and the man who was sleeping in the bed I had occupied was killed.

The second event occurred in Mexico during the Revolution. I had had great difficulty getting into Mexico City by the San Antonio-Nueva Laredo route for a conference with Carranza. I decided to return by way of the longer but less uncomfortable road to El Paso. I had already bought my ticket, made arrangements, and notified the Foundation of what I proposed to do. But just before train time I received a wire, "Services urgently needed in Brazil. Take most direct route to New York." I canceled my ticket at once. The train on which I had planned to travel was held up by bandits the next afternoon, and all the white passengers were taken out and shot.

The scene of the third coincidence was on the other side of the world. I had always wanted to travel the road to Mandalay, but had never seemed to have time. Once when at Rangoon I had concluded my essential duties and still had a few days before my ship was due to sail. This seemed an ideal opportunity. At the railroad office I started the process, interminable in the East, of procuring a ticket. Before the extended arrangements had been half concluded my conscience began to trouble me; my time could be better employed in attending to unfinished details in Rangoon. "I'm awfully sorry," I said to the agent, "but I don't think I'll take that ticket after all."

The train departed, but had proceeded only a hundred miles when it was wrecked; over fifty persons were killed and several hundred wounded. My three days were employed in helping to set bones and sew up wounds.

The fourth escape occurred at Bagdad. Mr. Charles R. Crane, the former Minister to China, with whom I was traveling, urged me to accompany him in his motor car the next morning, but the exigencies of my itinerary called for my arrival at Damascus at a certain time. We were both dinner guests of King Feisal, and as we parted at eleven o'clock I announced my decision that I had to go by the more direct route. Mr. Crane left at six in the morning; at nine his automobile was ambushed by Arab tribesmen. The man sitting next to him on the back seat of the automobile was killed. I would almost surely have been that man.

My first trip for the Rockefeller Foundation in 1915 was in many respects the most interesting of them all. The War, so recently under way, complicated almost all of our undertakings. But having set ourselves to the task, we could not turn back, even though we had to mark time in some places and surmount unexpected obstacles in others. Echoes of the battle could be heard in many countries of the East.

At this time the British had their hands full not only with their avowed enemies the Germans, but also with native unrest. When I arrived at Singapore, the recent mutiny of the Fifth Light Infantry, an Indian regiment some seven hundred strong, was still the all-absorbing topic of conversation. Nobody knew the exact cause of the outbreak, but the mutineers had killed Britishers wherever they could find them, thirty-seven in all. They had then gone to a camp where three hundred Germans were interned and, after driving off or killing the guards, had invited the Germans to come out and lead them. This offer had been refused.

Singapore had been entirely unprepared for the outbreak, and pandemonium resulted. The small British gunboat *Cadmus* landed seventy-five men, and these, with a few hundred Singapore volunteers, met the largest groups of mutineers and dispersed them. Four hundred gave themselves up within forty-eight hours, and said they had been forced to join the mutiny by their comrades, but had never fired a shot. Two thousand territorials shortly arrived, a Japanese gunboat landed some marines, and the man hunt was on. At first, the mutineers were shot on sight, but many escaped and hid in nearby swamps, where they were not found for several weeks. As soon as they were caught they were tried by military court martial and many, as examples, were condemned to be shot.

I attended the impressive function, March 25, when twenty-two of them were executed before a crowd of ten thousand, mostly Malay and Chinese. Outside the grey, moss-grown walls of the prison the white volunteers formed an open square. To the beating of drums and the blowing of trumpets, the prison doors were flung open, and a section of turbaned Sikhs emerged with the prisoners. Each of the twenty-two marched steadfastly, without a sign of fear, to a post of wood, quite new, which had been driven into the turf. Each came to attention while being tied, and, with eyes unbandaged, stoically faced the square. The officer in charge read in clear tones the findings of the court martial. The khaki-clad territorials faced the condemned men. "Present"—a pause, "Fire!"—and a sharp crash. The territorials were willing but their marksmanship was not perfect. All the mutineers were not dead, and the officers of the firing squad had to despatch those still living with final bullets.

I watched for an expression of hatred, or pity, or horror, on the faces of the multitude. No emotion whatsoever was displayed—nothing but stolid indifference.

Borne by human, animal, and machine power, on sea, on land, and in the air, I have traveled over the globe. Almost everywhere in the East human muscle is the most important factor in transportation. Rickshaws are omnipresent, pulled by one man on level ground with amazing speed and endurance. But in the mountains of India, where the grades are steep, rickshaws are manned by two, four, and even six runners. At the base of each hill in the uplands of Japan pushers wait and, at the rickshaw's approach, dash out to assist their fellow coolies up the hill, and then, with their coppers, return to resume their patient waiting.

MUCH HAVE I TRAVELED

Often where trails forbade wheeled vehicles, I have reclined in litters carried by four bearers. In China I have been lifted in sedan chairs, and also bumped in wheelbarrows with huge wheels which have benches along each side where four or more passengers sit back to back and have little places for their feet. One coolie trundles this enormous load, the wooden axle groaning and howling with each revolution of the wheel. The excellence of a wheelbarrow is judged by the character and volume of its squeak; no luck will attend the journey on a squeakless one.

In some places I have been carried ashore from boats, my legs dangling around the neck of a porter half my size who somehow staggered through the shallow water under what must have been an almost overwhelming weight, invariably landing me dryshod.

I have embarked on every imaginable type of water craft—hand propelled houseboats, lighters, barges; canoes on Canadian rapids, punts on the Thames, gondolas in Venice, sampans on the Yangtzekiang; in the Philippines unstable bancas and enormous cascos holding fifty tons; on the Nile, dahabeahs, aided by soft winds against their towering sails; in the vale of Kashmir, luxurious, awninged boats, made comfortable with cushions of gay colors, drifting down the Jhelum toward the Indus, past the towering peaks of the Himalayan wonderland; sailing vessels of every description—schooners, junks, praos, and swift, two-masted lorchas, which used to speed from Iloilo to Negros with such celerity that only a good steamer could keep up with them; greyhound liners, battleships, private yachts, coastwise steamers, tug boats, and wheezy launches in which I would sit by the hour waiting for the engine to be started.

On land I have driven behind six-mule teams and the horses of Egypt, of purest Arab stock, racing the twelve miles from Cairo to the Pyramids in an hour. I have ridden in the gharry of India, and the four-wheeled carriage of Singapore; calesins, carromatas, calesas, carretelas, and carts of the Philippines; buckboards, droshkies, sleighs, and sledges. Perhaps the most amusing animal-drawn vehicle was the two-wheeled sadu of Java, sometimes pulled by a horse so small that, reversing the role of passenger and burden bearer, I have stuck my head between his front legs and carried him. On one occasion, when the horse apparently saw the house in which he had been born and started toward it, my companion and I simply leaned backward in the sadu and lifted him off the ground between the shafts, holding him pawing ineffectually in the air until he had recovered his mental balance. The only smaller animal that I have known was the diminutive trotting ox of Ceylon, clatter-clattering along on his tiny, shod hooves, a joke edition of the more common and stolid specimen.

I have jogged hundreds of miles on horseback—ranging from polo ponies to percherons. I have bestridden minute donkeys, hunching up my legs and gripping them with my knees to prevent their walking out from under me. I have clambered into the howdahs of ponderous elephants and clutched the cumbrous, wooden saddles of the nasty-tempered, rocking camels.

I have journeyed thousands of miles on luxurious Pullmans with seats of comfortable plush—corridor and compartment—combination freight and passenger, and even construction trains; funiculars, and baskets swung perilously from crag to crag in the Dolomites; camions, trucks, and buses; and airplanes and hydroplanes, swiftly winging over mountain, desert, and river, even the Great Wall of China winding snake-like below.

I did not roam from wanderlust or curiosity as to other lands, not to criticize ways alien to my own, not to bring back adventurers' tales to those who must travel in armchairs. My mission was to open "the golden window of the East" to the gospel of health, to let in knowledge, so that the teeming millions who had no voice in demanding what we consider inalienable rights should also benefit by the discoveries of science, that in the end they, too, could have health.

CHAPTER 19.   SNAKES IN EDEN

WHEN the British in 1795 added Ceylon to their Empire, they became overlords of a country with a storied past but no apparent future. The massive ruins of Anuradhapura, once a city covering two hundred and fifty square miles, was no more than a shrine for pilgrims, who came to gaze with reverence upon the sacred Bo tree, grown from a slip of that under which Buddha himself had sat at Benares. It had survived two millennia, and bade fair to continue for several more. The island, which had known the yoke of Hindustan, Portugal, and the Netherlands, retained only vestiges of its ancient riches—few divers descended to the famous pearl fisheries, the gold mines were abandoned, the people had grown weary, and grubbed but listlessly for topaz, sapphire, and ruby, the palaces were tumbled down, and the jungle had crowded into the groves of cinnamon and cardamom; it was said the British had conquered no more than an empty shell.

But, once again, after many vicissitudes, the Fragrant Isle has bloomed. Although not many decades ago the coffee trees on the great plantations were destroyed by blight, and the cinchona industry was lost to Java, in place of these, pungent tea shrubs now flourish luxuriantly on every mountain side, and latex flows from the rubber trees and have brought new prosperity. In the lowlands the fronds of the useful cocoanut shade broad roads, and add to the country's riches.

Because of its economic prosperity, Ceylon was looked upon in the East as a prize colony, although many serpents flourished in this Garden of Eden; the hookworm infestation was heavy and widespread. If we could prove the importance and the practicability of a hookworm campaign, funds would be available to carry on the work, and the already existing Health Service would provide the machinery. A second reason for concentrating on Ceylon was that other British colonies tried to emulate it, and hence a successful campaign there would serve as an entering wedge elsewhere in the Orient.

But the internal situation in Ceylon was exceedingly complex. Economic, political, and social conditions made it desirable for us to work first on the large estates, which, in turn, required securing the cooperation of the powerful planting interests. This was necessary but dangerous, because a hostile-minded press might have attacked us on the ground that we were one group of rich men working for another group of rich men rather than for the poor down-trodden masses.

Living is easy in Ceylon, and the Sinhalese, the native born, choose not to work for the planters. Therefore, laborers had to be imported for the year-round task of gathering the leaves in the tea estates. Fortunately, an inexhaustible supply of Tamils exists in the great Presidency of Madras, which sprawls down the eastern and up the western coasts of South India. When the Rockefeller Foundation decided upon Ceylon as a demonstration center, about one hundred thousand coolies, including their families, were going annually to the Ceylon tea and rubber plantations.

These primitive Dravidians of Madras, coal black with Caucasian features, ignorant, superstitious, and servile, unresponsive, uninterested, only five percent literate, entirely lacking in ambition, were also docile. They were willing workers, but depressing to look at because of their blank countenances; there was hardly a smile in the entire race. They still spoke in their ancient dialect, and had brought with them to Ceylon their own habits and preferences. They ate their strictly vegetarian meals from banana leaves, and objected at first to the substitution of tin plates.

A detention camp had been built at Mandapam, at the tip of India, through which half of these coolies passed on their way to the estates. According to contract, the planters provided their living and hospital care, but otherwise did little more than cater to their insurmountable caste demands. Hindus, for example, lose caste whenever they leave their country and travel over water. This could be restored by religious ceremonies at the temples of Dhanushkodi or Rameswaram when they returned from Ceylon.

Because the Tamils had a superstitious fear of light, no windows were built into the barrack-like "lines" in which they lived on the plantations. Each family had two rooms; in one they slept, and in the other cooked on the floor. Smoke and dirt were everywhere. More insanitary than all else was the indiscriminate soil pollution. This was a greater health hazard to the Tamil than to many other peoples because his skin was as thin as that of the white man, and hookworms could penetrate it easily.

The planters had long before made up their minds they would allow no interference from the local health authorities. They would neither give nor receive aid in dealing with the hookworm situation, because they were convinced the intrusion of sanitarians would hurt business. I was well aware that Lord Crewe, when at the India Office, had threatened to stop their labor supply unless they took active steps to deal with the hookworm situation; they had then made evasive but plausible answers, and things had gone on as before.

The resistance of the planters had to be overcome, but our policy demanded also that we conduct our work under the official auspices of the Health Service. Consequently, my first step on landing at Colombo was to call upon the incoming head of the department, Dr. G. J. Rutherford. After the amenities had been complied with, we began discussing the new venture in health launched by the Rockefeller Foundation and what it purposed to do. "What's the present hookworm situation in Ceylon?" I asked.

"It's frightful," he promptly admitted.

"Why should that be? You have laws enough to cover any action you might take, haven't you?"

"Yes, we have, but the tea planting interests are all-powerful, and they are opposed to taking adequate measures against hookworm. We issue a regulation—they get it suspended. We're helpless."

"Would you have any objection to a survey made under the auspices of the Rockefeller Foundation—supposing it could be arranged with the planters?"

"Not at all, provided your men operated under our Health Service."

Since this had been my objective from the beginning, I assented readily to his condition.

That evening at the Colombo Club I was fortunate enough to meet the Chairman of the Estates Agents Association, which represented the absentee landlords of England and was the dominant force in local politics. In the pleasant club atmosphere I was able to establish friendly relations. "They tell me you've lots of hookworm in Ceylon," I said, seizing the opportunity, "but they also say you planters won't allow anything to be done about it."

"You're jolly well right we won't."

"Why not?"

"We're not going to have a lot of health fellows crashing into our affairs. Look at what happened last year. There was a plague scare just when our best harvest was due. It amounted to nothing, but those health inspectors came along threatening to inoculate our laborers, and almost before we could turn around thousands of them were on their way back to India. It nearly ruined us. If we ever let the Health Service get started on hookworm, all our laborers would run away, and we couldn't harvest our tea and rubber. No! No health business for us."

"Well," I replied, "I'm not a reporter or a writer for muckraking magazines. But if I wanted to, I could make your actions look like the Belgian Congo atrocities. Here you are—rich Englishmen—sacrificing thousands of lives just to get your tea harvested."

"But we have no such intentions," he indignantly protested.

"It's actually happening. Why don't you do something about it?"

"Nothing can be done with Tamils," he asserted with an air of finality.

"That's all I've heard in the East for fifteen years. When I first began working with a peasant population, I was informed everywhere 'Nothing can be done.' But it was done in the Philippines."

"Perhaps American millions did accomplish a little there. But nothing can be done with our coolies."

"We won't get very far by my insisting it can, and you that it cannot. Let's talk about this as a business proposition. How much does it cost you to bring a laborer here from Madras?"

"That's a commercial secret."

"I don't care about your exact figure. I'm not in business. But does it cost you a hundred rupees?"

"All of that."

"How many laborers do you have to import?"

"About a hundred thousand a year."

"That runs into quite a sum of money, doesn't it? Now, on every estate you have a hospital. It may be large or small, but it is constantly occupied. Doctors and nurses alone must cost you a lot. And am I correct in assuming that you have to pay your laborers whether or not they are working?"

"Yes."

"Suppose we could reduce the hospital expense by half."

"That would certainly save us a great deal."

"Here's another important point to be considered. The Tamil women tend to be sterile because of anemia from hookworm. If they could produce children, you wouldn't have to bring over fresh labor all the time. You could raise your own. Wouldn't that be advantageous in the long run?"

"It would increase our profits tremendously—that goes without saying."

"So health and the planting business have something in common after all? Now, there's a way to test out these arguments I've been giving you. Suppose you were to pick out some estates employing several thousand laborers and allow the Rockefeller Foundation to bring in experts to demonstrate whether we could cure them without having them run away. You'd be the judge of our success."

"I don't see how that could do us any harm. But we wouldn't want our own Health Department concerned in any way. They're all tangled up in red tape, and would only make a lot of trouble. You'd have to leave them out of it."

"I'm afraid we couldn't do that. If you don't like your present Health Department, it's your privilege to recommend a change. But we cannot go anywhere at the request of a commercial organization alone; we must have an official invitation from your Governor."

"Well, I'll talk this over with my Board of Directors, and let you know in a few days."

In the interval I made calls assiduously on everybody who might be concerned, hearing everywhere that all hookworm conversation ended merely in talk. I was, therefore, much gratified when the representative of the Estates Agents reported that the planters were willing to let the Foundation go ahead with the demonstration. I had some difficulty, however, in making clear to him that the Foundation must supervise its own expenditures. Finally, he accepted my condition that the planters pay their share.

The Governor of Ceylon, Sir Thomas Chalmers, K.C.B., had previously indicated that he did not want any Yankee men or Yankee methods introduced; Ceylon was capable of running its own affairs and paying for its own health work. The Estates Agents Association, however, brought its influence to bear, and in the course of a week the Governor capitulated. Letters were exchanged, and we prepared to begin operations, but, because the submarine campaign was in progress, and the Germans were constantly torpedoing boats with our supplies on them, we were delayed some months in assembling a staff.

But when finally we did get under way, as was almost inevitable, we incurred immediately the enmity of the native herb doctors, who considered we were interfering with their practice. They said we were in league with the British and were administering capsules to the coolies which would explode inside them at the end of five years; thus the Germans would find no labor when they possessed themselves of Ceylon. This rumor, which seemed so plausible to the coolies, was not easy for us to combat, especially as the War was going badly for the Allies at the moment. Our demonstrators might swallow capsules by the dozen to combat the accusation, but this constituted no proof that at the end of five years their stomachs would not explode.

For many years thymol had been used as the standard vermifuge, but owing to the War this drug became expensive and difficult to obtain. The Dutch had already discovered the virtues inherent in oil of chenopodium and had called my attention to it. Chenopodium had the advantage of expelling all worms, even the long-lived and tenacious tapeworm, and had a ninety-one percent efficiency against hookworm as compared with thymol's eighty-three. Carbon tetrachloride, tetrachlorethelene, and hexylresorcinol are being used now.

Our first action in the Ceylon campaign was to treat thoroughly a small number of estates for hookworm. The results were amazing. Hospital attendance and charges dropped immediately, and the general death rate was soon greatly reduced. Whereas before the campaign large numbers of coolies failed to report for work, afterwards the labor turnover was reduced. The treatment was rapidly extended to other estates, and in 1921 two hundred thousand coolies were being freed of worms.

After demonstrating what we could do in the way of cure, it was time to start education in preventive measures against hookworm. The coolie lines in 1915 were not equipped with latrines. Every planter believed it futile to build any because he was convinced the Tamils could never be induced to use them. But by this time we had proved the economic value of our methods so completely that we could lay down conditions. We notified the plantation owners that we would do no more work on the estates until they had installed them.

Accordingly, the planters erected latrines and we helped to instruct the coolies in their use. An effective method of enforcing compliance was to fine a coolie a few cents for each dereliction. We had not been installing latrines for many years before a Tamil who was preparing to sign on again would ask whether the particular plantation to which it was proposed to send him was equipped with them. Districts now vary from thirty to ninety percent in installation, and their use has become an accepted part of the customs of the people.

In time the number of Tamils imported from India was reduced, because the working force on the plantations was not so depleted by sickness and death, and the women, having recovered from their anemia, began to bear children. In the end the planting interests cooperated whole-heartedly and themselves went through many a struggle on behalf of sanitation.

After we had demonstrated under controlled conditions on the estates that hookworm could be both cured and prevented, the campaign was extended to the villages, a far more difficult undertaking.

We were now dealing with the intractable Sinhalese rather than the stupid but amenable Tamils, but, even so, we kept the idea in the forefront that it was their responsibility.

Ceylon, like India, was split along religious and racial lines. The Sinhalese, who made up half the population, were followers of Gautama; the largest minority were the Hindu Tamils, and next to them the more energetic Mohammedans. An important factor in the population were the Christian Eurasians, known locally as the Burghers. Under supervision by the whites they ran a great deal of the administrative machinery of the island and the plantations.

Politics in every Eastern country is inextricably mixed with religion. This always complicates the health problem to a degree inconceivable to Western minds. Our work in future years was to be delayed by the rising tide of Sinhalese nationalism. The first day I was in Colombo I heard the slogan, "Ceylon for the Sinhalese," on all sides, and was offered also a glimpse of native religious unrest.

May 25 was Wesak, a Buddhist festival, customarily celebrated by making pilgrimages to shrines, feeding the poor, and feasting. But in 1915 the religious tension seemed extraordinarily acute, particularly at Kandy, a very holy place because of its temple where one of the teeth of Buddha reposes on a golden lotus leaf within its seven jeweled caskets. Riots flared up when the Buddhists held their procession in defiance of an injunction secured by the Mohammedans. The worshippers of Allah had irritated the erstwhile peaceful Buddhists to the point of violence by disrespectfully tweaking the noses and twisting off the ears of the calm and contemplative images of the Enlightened One.

The unrest spread along the railway toward Colombo. Volunteer white guards mobilized, cannon were dragged through the streets, armored automobiles filled with soldiers dashed about. The concentration point seemed to be at my hotel.

A week later trouble began in earnest. The street cars stopped running, soda water bottles filled with sand were hurtling about, and the broken glass interfered seriously with motor traffic. Groups of people were collecting everywhere, ships in the harbor were unable to coal, the government commandeered all motor cars. The Mohammedans were the shopkeepers; hence they were the creditors and the

Buddhists the debtors. I would see a crowd gathered in the street; one man would point to a shop and all, with a concerted rush, would dive into it. Three minutes and the place would be gutted, and not a trace of "accounts due" would be left. Dr. Rutherford told me one hundred and fifty injured were brought into the hospital during one night.

This was by no means the end of the disturbance, although a Colombo paper soothingly stated that everything was "practically quiet in Kandy except a few assaults and murders." Finally British territorial troops restored peace.

The Mohammedans, in retaliation, started many lawsuits for damages, which were upheld by the courts. Bitter resentment was felt against the government by the Sinhalese, some of whom are still paying costs.

Our work was going on in Ceylon when the Donoughmore Commission's recommendation for self-government went into effect. This movement was synchronous with the rising tide of Indian national feeling. An attempt had been made in Ceylon to safeguard the rights of minorities, but the Sinhalese, who were in the majority, tended to disregard the claims of Tamils and Burghers to hold office, even though they had been born in the country. Under British control many Burghers had been taken into the Civil Service, but now their advancement was threatened by the Sinhalese.

The political situation in Ceylon was typical of that encountered elsewhere in the East. Petty politics, unwarranted attacks launched by ambitious office seekers, vague promises never fulfilled, evasions and procrastinations, public announcements conveniently forgotten, were everyday happenings. Politics had to be considered at every turn. There often seemed to be no chance whatsoever of getting action on our many plans and projects. Our representatives sometimes became so down-hearted that they recommended withdrawing until things should settle down.

But in spite of individual discouragement, the Rockefeller Foundation persevered in its attempt to make Ceylon a modern health community. Experience proved that the best way to popularize a movement so foreign to the customs of the people as hookworm prevention was to prosecute it as though it were the only thing in the universe left undone. The history of the devious life and habits of this wily worm had to be brought home to every resident of Ceylon.

To prepare the way, lantern slide lectures were given and public exhibitions arranged, showing the parasite and its eggs under the microscope. To make the demonstrations more convincing the villagers were allowed to take part. They were first asked to scoop up moist earth, and put it in a glass funnel. Water was poured through this and they could watch with their own eyes the larvae being washed out of dirt they had walked over daily.

People universally seemed to show more interest in the biological problem involved than in the ravages caused by the disease. The aim was to make even the most backward members of the community thoroughly familiar with the biology of hookworm, thus creating better understanding of the methods for its control.

A small dispensary was often opened in the house of the Headman of the town, who was instructed to persuade the villagers to apply for treatment. When they showed reluctance, the simple device was adopted of treating everyone for hookworm who applied at the hospital or dispensary, even though his complaint might be as far afield as a broken leg or a toothache. The number treated in this way rose to over a million a year.

Hookworm relief was supplemented by the establishment of Health Units throughout Ceylon, which assumed responsibility for all work in a particular district. They were staffed by a doctor, a number of public health nurses, midwives, and sanitary inspectors. When no epidemic loomed in the offing, these nurses always directed their attention toward maternity and baby welfare work, because the problems of both are constant and serve as the best avenues of approach to general education in health measures.

These Health Units did not blossom forth overnight. They met opposition from all classes and religions. A doctor would approach the Mohammedan chief of a village with a list of questions. "What's your death rate?" he would begin.

"It is the will of Allah that all die; some die young, some old."

"What's your number of births?"

"Allah alone can say."

"Is your water safe and potable?"

"History records no death from thirst."

"What is the hygienic condition of your village?"

"Allah sent Mahomet who proved the truth with fire and sword. Now, Lamb of the West, cease your questioning. It can do you or others no good."

To train doctors to cope with these and all other possible situations which might arise, better instruction had to be provided in the Medical School. This presented a major problem. The Sinhalese believed their school to be one of the best in existence, and support for any radical change was almost impossible to obtain. Practically all the instruction was by lecturers of the old didactic type. Criticism of the general lack of interest and the inefficiency shown by the doctors in the hospitals always brought the triumphant rejoinder that they had qualified before the British General Medical Council with flying colors. Though I might be convinced that both diagnosis and treatment were often incorrect, I could make no answer.

When the Sinhalese gained political control, they insisted on having the teaching of the ancient Hindu system of Ayurvedic medicine supported by the government. As the protagonists of modern science, we had to discourage a method by which a practitioner, en route to a patient's bedside, would determine the treatment he was going to prescribe by the number of buttons on the coat of the first man he met.

In the renaissance of Indian nationalism, Ayurvedic medicine had naturally been stressed, and many schools had been started all over India. One of the largest of these was at Benares. When I was taken on the usual tour of inspection, the President, a Hindu, solemnly displayed the most ridiculous things. After he had finished I said, "I trust you won't consider me rude, but how can you believe in what you have been showing me this afternoon?"

"You never get very far or go very fast by attacking an established institution direct," the Brahmin replied. "You have noticed that by the side of courses in Ayurvedic we have installed others in anatomy, histology, and chemistry. Wherever possible, we encourage our students to take these courses. Those who do so are intelligent enough to see the absurdities in Ayurvedic, and will discard them of their own volition. But if I were to challenge the Ayurvedic system

337

itself, I would not get the money I need for the school, and the little we have gained would be lost."

This answer impressed me as being sound in its psychology, and seemed to offer hope that the time would come when we would not have to contend with this particular obstacle.

Because the claims of this extraordinary materia medica were put forward by such leaders as Gandhi, who dogmatically asserted modern medicine was sorcery, the government of India, under Colonel Chopra of the Indian Medical Service, has spent thousands of dollars in the endeavor to determine whether it possessed anything of value. So far the results have been meagre. It is true that certain Ayurvedic drugs were found to have properties with which we were not familiar. But we had developed drugs for the same purpose which were far more efficacious. For example, Ayurvedic boasted about its kurchi as a cure for dysentery, but carbasone is so far superior as to be beyond comparison.

The march of medical progress in the East for a time was retarded by the poet-philosopher, Rabindranath Tagore. He had arrived at Peiping on his way through the Orient, addressing huge audiences everywhere and advocating a return to Eastern idealism instead of following Western materialism. This was virtually an attack on modern science. Because he was being hailed by all the dark-skinned races as an example of an Eastern intellect acknowledged by the West as of equal calibre, his words carried great weight and were extremely detrimental to the objectives of scientific medicine. I might very likely fail, but I thought I could do no less than try to divert the trend of his lectures.

Such vast numbers of admirers were besieging Tagore's quarters that I had great difficulty in securing an interview, but finally was ushered into his presence. He looked like a patriarch, with his beautiful, long, white hair and flowing beard, and he charmed me with his soft, persuasive voice and delightful manner. We talked for a long, long while of this and of that. He elaborated his theory that nothing permanent or worth while in health could be accomplished unless the spiritual and human interest of the masses were first won. He apparently was impressed by my observation that disease had made it largely impossible for Indians to smile, and agreed thoroughly with my stand that no government or private organization could give health; people had to achieve it by their own efforts.

Tagore was of the opinion that the Indian Medical Service had failed because it had not established itself in the hearts of the people, and intimated that if the Rockefeller Foundation were to work directly through him its results might be very much better. I answered that, though we required the formality of government cooperation, we used our own judgment and our own methods in establishing ourselves in the hearts of the people, very much as he advocated. Tagore's suspicions of us as allies of the government he so mistrusted were allayed, and he was persuaded that we had the same end in view as himself. But he was convinced that the only right way to go about attaining it was through the system of ancient India which he was so stoutly recommending.

This remark gave me the opportunity for which I had been looking. "You've had a Western education," I said, "but you're decrying everything Western science has contributed to the world. Yet the mere fact you are here is a testimonial to its accomplishments. The steamship which carried you could never have been produced by the old culture which you uphold."

"I could have come overland."

"Not in your condition of health," I replied. "You couldn't have come at all. But I'm most interested in what you have to say about Hindu materia medica. You claim it has much value. But you don't know, and the only way of testing its merit is in the modern research laboratory, the greatest institution for truth that man has ever evolved. It is absolutely impartial, its findings are not colored, it is simply seeking the truth. A lot of the remedies which you suggest as effective have been scientifically proved of no value. I think you yourself would be satisfied if you followed the steps in the laboratory that have been taken to arrive at this conclusion. Before you say anything more, would you go and see in this city of Peiping one of the finest laboratories in existence?"

The philosopher agreed to go, and I made arrangements for his reception at the Medical College. This was our only conversation on the subject, and I had no opportunity to find out when I saw him later whether his visit had converted him to my way of thinking.

But I followed his addresses carefully, and never again to my knowledge did he speak against Western medicine.

Obstacles and discouragements were of almost daily occurrence in Ceylon, but in spite of them our efforts were eventually successful. With the assistance of the Rockefeller Foundation, Ceylon now has one of the most modern health services of any country of similar population in the world. Our function was to hasten this accomplishment by several decades.

Ceylon was the best illustration that could be found of what Mr. Rockefeller had meant when he said, "Philanthropy must pay dividends." Both from the economic and the humanitarian standpoint, benefits accrued far beyond our expectations. Not only was the health of the population improved and its happiness increased thereby, but this very improvement in health produced wealth in increasing proportions. The fifty thousand dollars we spent to widen the circle still further, over the years brought about governmental appropriations for health of at least five millions.

Important as it was to complete the hookworm demonstration in Ceylon, the eventual goal was to make such demonstrations unnecessary by tracking hookworm to its place of origin and eradicating it. It would be useless to wipe out the disease in Ceylon if reinfection were constantly to recur from the source of labor supply. To persuade the authorities of India of the shockingly high Tamil hookworm infection was the first step in the long march toward stamping hookworm out of Madras, which was a radiating center of infection, sending Tamils thousands of miles westward across the world to Trinidad and British Guiana, southward into Malaya and the lower tip of Africa, and eastward to Burma and the South Seas.

As soon as preparations for the survey in Ceylon had been made, I had set off for India. Whatever elation I may have felt over the successful outcome was dampened by having to start the same laborious round over again. The provincial Health Service of Madras disclaimed all authority. In a country which had an average of one hundred and ninety-five persons living on each square mile, the idea that hookworm was controllable was denigrated. It was the old cry of the impossible job; it could not be done. After interviewing men here and there—at Calcutta, Delhi, and Simla—trading health ideas as I went along, I found, surprisingly enough, that the source of authority was the man at the top, Sir Charles Pardey Lukis, Director General of the Indian Medical Service.

I called immediately upon Sir Pardey at Simla. He was an intelligent and pleasant gentleman, but skeptical of the hookworm figures with which I presented him. He could not believe that our estimates of over seventy percent infestation could be correct, but assured me he was open-minded and willing to be convinced. He intimated, however, that it was out of the question for anything to be started in war time. I retorted with a description of British colonies in which health work was going on in spite of the War, and described enthusiastically the impression I had received that the British government was very proud of those officials who could keep things moving in a normal manner, and even undertake new things during war time.

The next day I went into the matter with Major F. Norman White, the Assistant Director General, sounding him cautiously on the prospects. He also was affable, but less easy to convince. He said he feared the government would decide to postpone any such undertaking as a hookworm survey until after the War because the Indians might take advantage of war conditions to start an uprising. Any innovation might have an unlooked-for effect, however innocent or philanthropic its real objects might be.

Major White attempted to discourage me further by saying it was inconceivable that an American doctor, new to the infinite complexities of Indian psychology, could make any headway when the Indian Medical Service doctors, with years of experience behind them, had such great difficulty. I suggested that many of the things which appeared theoretically hard often proved simple in actual practice, and we believed the best plan was to proceed cautiously with test demonstrations, working out the procedure as we went along. Any man we sent could be relied upon for tact, and with Major White as guide might achieve success.

I returned later to the attack on Sir Pardey, and we spent several evenings talking until midnight. At the end of these conferences he asked me to submit a letter with our proposals. I did as he asked, but, because the chiefs of the Indian Medical Service did not believe the hookworm situation could be as serious as I had represented it, they decided to have their own men verify my estimates. Since almost all their regular members had been absorbed in the War, Sir Pardey selected to make the investigation a native doctor, Mhaskar, and a Catholic priest, Father Caius, the latter a competent chemist who had already been working in his laboratory on various remedies for hookworm. The two investigators reported a ninety-seven percent infection, a figure far higher than ours. The Indian Medical Service was horrified over the enormity of the problem, but the War took so much of its attention that several years elapsed before we were called upon for any further part in Indian health affairs.

Meanwhile, research work on hookworm was proceeding in many quarters of the world. Dr. Norman Stoll, with Dr. John Grant, who had been studying the disease in China, evolved a method for determining the severity of infection. By counting the number of eggs in one gram of feces, he could estimate the number of worms in the individual. Dr. Wilson G. Smillie, working in Alabama and Tennessee, found that the presence of fifty hookworms or under did not constitute a serious menace to health and could be disregarded; many more were required to produce anemia.

As soon as the government of India was free of its war obligations, and had asked the Rockefeller Foundation to cooperate, we turned this newly discovered knowledge about hookworm to practical use in Madras. It had been estimated that the cost of a hookworm campaign averaged about one dollar per person. Therefore, it would cost fifty million dollars a year in Madras alone. We did not have this money; neither did the Indian government. Even had we had it and treated the population, it would all have had to be done over again the following year. Obviously such an enormous problem would remain unsolved until some new method of handling it could be evolved.

To begin with, we stationed men at each emigration camp, and ploddingly examined every outward-bound Tamil for his degree of infestation, including plotting his birthplace on an enormous chart. At the end of three years' painstaking examination, it was apparent that the emigrants with heavy infestation came from a few well-delineated districts. If these foci could be cleaned up, it was probable that less heavily infected centers would eventually become free, because hookworm tended to disappear of itself. We checked our information by looking up meteorological records of certain swampy areas and found they were distinctly correlated with the major hookworm infestations. We then knew exactly where to direct our attack at a cost within the grounds of possibility. Since this section of India was disseminating uncinariasis throughout the tropical world, a tremendous step toward its conquest will have been taken when it is stamped out of Madras.

CHAPTER 20.   THE WHITE MAN'S LAST REFUGE

CEYLON was a large scale demonstration for the entire East where the Rockefeller Foundation helped to spread modern health concepts. There we were dealing with a native population to whom sanitation and health had meant practically nothing; in the Australian democracy, with white labor already health conscious, almost one hundred percent literate, and fully vocal, little was needed except encouragement.

In 1916 I had to approach British countries armed with credentials from the Colonial Office at London. With this meagre equipment I launched my attack against the important, self-sufficient citadel of Australia. Not until some years later was Rockefeller Foundation aid eagerly sought everywhere and were we able to lay down more and more stringent conditions.

With pleasant anticipation, I entered beautiful Sydney Harbor, dotted with Goat, Shark, Cockatoo, and innumerable other islets. I saw again the sloping green hillsides from which emerged the picturesque red and pink tiled roofs of the houses. The sun was full upon the city and the sight gorgeous beyond description.

My reception at the pier was decidedly in contrast to this inviting prospect. That I was an American was proclaimed by my passport. The customs officer, glancing at it, asked peremptorily for my luggage. Forthwith, suits, shirts, handkerchiefs, collars, socks, papers, books, toilet kit, all my possessions were soon scattered over the dirty floor.

When not a single object remained in the gaping bags, he turned away. "You can go," he said gruffly.

"Who's going to put my things back in the bags?" I mildly inquired.

"You are!"

Before I could think of an effective rejoinder, there was a loud honking from the street, and a brilliantly appareled officer brightened the doorway. "Is this Dr. Heiser?" he inquired. "I'm the Governor's aide. His Excellency has asked me to look after you. Is your luggage ready?"

I waved my hand toward the wreckage. "The customs officer has been making an inspection."

The aide turned to him sharply. "Dr. Heiser is a guest of the government. Repack his bags immediately and if one thing is missing or dirty, you'll hear from His Excellency."

We left a subdued inspector, meekly dusting, folding, and packing.

On this visit I found Australia generally inclined to be inimical. In the first place the friendliness she had formerly evidenced to the United States had been metamorphosed into hostility, and the resentment against Americans as such was strong because they alleged we were avoiding the risks of war while reaping the financial benefits of neutrality. They took delight in annoying us whenever and wherever possible.

I, personally, suffered under the further handicap of being an emissary of the Rockefeller Foundation. Even the august tutelage of the Governor General could not help me in that quarter. The odium and curiosity attached to the Rockefeller name was inevitably reflected upon anyone associated with it. My life would have been a burden had I even had the Foundation address printed on my baggage.

In those days offers of help from the Foundation were looked upon with suspicion, particularly by the anti-capitalist Australians. The Standard Oil Company was in such bad repute that the health officials, although we had been friends since the days when they had visited the Philippines, shied at the sight of me. Instead of receiving me in their offices, they would conduct interviews walking up and down in the park, where our conversations could not be overheard or our association be so obvious.

Any representative of the Rockefellers was bound to be looked at askance in a country which had been pro-labor and anti-capital from its very beginnings. Most Australian legislation had been drawn up to the end of fettering capital. In the eyes of Australians I was the agent of the arch capitalist. The deep-seated hatred of large corporations was enhanced by a lurking suspicion that our work was in the nature of a scheme to superimpose American economic control upon ingenuous foreign countries.

The influence exercised by labor in Australia was enormous. Even when I had first gone there in 1911 anybody could be arrested for working more than eight hours a day, and many papers had listed violators. New South Wales carefully defined the minimum wage as one which provided food and adequate shelter for a man, his wife, and two children, and, in addition:

"fuel, clothes, boots, furniture, utensils, rates, life insurance, savings, accident or benefit societies, loss of employment, union pay, books and newspapers, train and tram fares, sewing-machine, mangle, school requisites, amusements and holidays, intoxicating liquors, tobacco, sickness and death, domestic help, unusual contingencies, religion, or charity."

I was constantly running into other examples. One of the most extravagant was in the Northern Territory. Originally part of South Australia, which saw it go with little reluctance, this vast expanse of desert, interspersed here and there with grazing land, has turned out to be a white elephant to the Federal government.

Port Darwin, the chief city, seemed like one of our own Western towns with its right-angled streets and one story buildings, its lack of trees, and the red soil which rose in clouds of dust under the great heat. Even in this latitude of only twelve degrees south the air at night felt almost crisp. The prosperity of the town had depended on a huge, million-dollar plant which the Vestry Meat Works of London had erected there, drawing its cattle from the big ranges to the south.

But labor, in the so-called slow strike, had forged a deadly weapon to satisfy its demands. The normal daily load carried by sixty-five stevedores was three hundred tons. But when a ship chartered by the Vestry Corporation would come in to take on cargo, this would be reduced to fifty tons, thereby increasing the loading time six-fold. Since all vessels have demurrage clauses in their charters, if they are delayed in port too long, the profits are entirely consumed. The meat plant had to close.

The laborers, who had thus done themselves out of the only existing jobs, were soon in a starving condition, and the Australian government had to support them. I was once on the *S.S. Montoro* which was taking free supplies to Port Darwin. When we arrived Sunday morning the foreman of the stevedores came on board. He told the captain, "If you want us to unload your ship today, you know you'll have to pay double." Dock laborers in Australia were paid a base rate of eighteen shillings, with nine extra for tropical service, and double rates for Sundays and night work. The captain might fume but, to avoid demurrage, he had to agree, even though the ship was bringing food to be distributed to these very men as a dole.

At eleven the foreman came truculently on board again and demanded drinking water. One of the ship's officers lost his temper and shouted, "To hell with you! Get your own water!"

In this labor democracy stop work orders might be issued on all occasions. The foreman, judging the water situation warranted drastic action, issued a stop work order. Immediately all the stevedores adjourned to the town, which was some distance from the harbor, for a drink. By noon they had returned, but, since union regulations did not permit them to start work until one, another hour was lost. At five o'clock their supplies were not yet unloaded and the foreman dictated, "We'll have to get double wages for night work." Again there was nothing to do but submit and pay the quadrupled rate. The captain estimated that each laborer had received twenty-five dollars for carrying his own groceries.

On another occasion the *S.S. Victoria* had cargo to transfer to another ship and pulled alongside the vessel in order to make the shift directly. The union issued an ultimatum which compelled her to dock on the other side of the wharf and pay regular unloading rates for

347

having the cargo placed on the pier. Each piece had to be weighed and then transferred on trucks the few feet to the other side. Regular rates had to be paid for the reloading operation also.

Had the *Victoria's* captain not submitted, he would have been in the same sorry predicament as the captain of another vessel on which I was once a passenger. Fifty mules were awaiting shipment at Townsville, Queensland. But because it was a holiday, though only a minor one, the stevedores refused to load them. Rather than delay sailing until the next day, the captain commandeered his crew and, with the volunteer aid of most of the passengers, the refractory animals were brought on board. But the captain paid dearly for his expedient because he found himself on the black list and could not return again to Townsville.

Australia is a country full of curious phenomena. The aborigines, termed blackfellows by the Australians who, even though they have lived in the land only since 1788, called themselves the natives, are more primitive than the Negritos of the Philippines. These survivors from the neolithic age build no houses, wear no clothes, cultivate no crops, but live on wild fruits and game, killed by boomerangs and clubs. Their only social grouping is in clans, each bearing the name of its totem, usually a bird, and their only taboo is that no man and woman of the same bird name shall marry. Though only an estimated fifty thousand are left, their wild nomadic life has kept them comparatively free of the diseases of civilized man.

The bird life is equally strange. The emu, the national bird, cannot fly, but kicks sidewise as well as backward; the mallee hen makes its own incubator out of decomposing vegetable matter; the bower bird builds playhouses and gardens, and adorns them with shells and bright seeds; the kookooburra, or laughing jackass, is a friendly fellow, with an uproarious laugh.

Australia is geologically the oldest land surface, and the rivers rise near the coast and flow inland. It was cut off from the rest of the earth before the development of mammals beyond the most primitive marsupial stage.

The kangaroo, which should have ceased living thousands of years ago, is of many species and ranges in size from that of a mouse to that of a man: the wallaby bounds along with gigantic leaps at fifteen miles an hour; the beaver-tailed, duck-billed platypus, webfooted yet clawed, lays eggs and suckles its young, has no external ear and yet can hear; the striped anteater also lays eggs, but hatches them in her pouch; the bear-like wombat and the rat-like bandicoot are other denizens of this strange land.

Lower still and more anachronistic in the scale of evolution are the iguanas which corkscrew up trees after birds' eggs, and the legless lizards, known as slow worms, two feet long, so brittle they break in several pieces when grasped, and the abundant skinks, in which legs have disappeared, leaving only a solitary toe.

My own eyes were witnesses that these things were so, but I had to take on faith the yahoo, whose feet point backward, so that when running from you it seems to run toward you, and the bunyip, the great Beast in the Bush, which none has seen and survived to record its horrendous properties.

However mythological these latter beasts may be, undoubtedly a tremendous wild buffalo with a space of ten feet between the tips of his horns roams the backcountry, and the Great Barrier Reef is haunted by shellfish which can bite an oar in two. The little brown rifle fish swims along until it sees an appetizing bug poised on a limb, takes aim, and brings it down with a well-directed squirt. At the museum in Dunedin, New Zealand, I saw the extinct moa bird, and heard the well-confirmed story of the kea bird, the harmless mountain parrot which, after tasting the fat of dead sheep, developed a voracious appetite for this delicacy, attacking the live animals and killing so many that a price was put on its head.

When some sport-loving Briton introduced the rabbit into Australia, an animal familiar to us but a novelty in this outdated land, the result was startling. Only an adding machine could cope with the rapid increase. Poisons, bounties, and packs of half-tamed dingos failed to diminish them. Finally, to keep them from digging the very grass roots out of the grazing lands, a hundred thousand miles of fences were erected. The fences had to be extended further and further until eventually they overlapped and enclosed the rabbits instead. The Australians have at last turned the tables and have converted these "vermin," which, as white men, they themselves will not eat, into a profitable crop; one ship sometimes carries a million rabbit carcasses to London.

The Australians had even more trouble coping with the cactus, which had escaped from a decorative garden bed and now covers virtually thousands of acres. The plants often grew higher than a man's head, and were so hazardous that cattle often became imprisoned among them. Scientists sought the world over for a cactus pest, and have only recently secured some promising insect enemies.

In a country where the principal tree, the eucalyptus, held its leaves sidewise to conserve moisture, and where cherries had their pits on the outside, which had to be crushed to reach the fruit, the inhabitants also naturally had peculiarities. For instance, any man or woman who resisted the opportunity for self-expression to be found at the polls, under the compulsory voting act, had to pay a fine.

Because of the laudable determination that everyone should be allowed ample time for recreation, Sunday was observed with the utmost rigidity; double fares were charged on the trams and not even a bottle of soda water could be bought. Picnicking in parks or in the outskirts of the cities was a universal pastime, and horse racing was a passion among all classes. So great was the enthusiasm for games that a cricketer who showed extraordinary prowess had a purse made up for him which sometimes amounted to thousands of pounds.

Australians were so determined that their country should belong to the white man that they put into effect the most stringent immigration regulations, even rigidly controlling British subjects. Their simple device was to present the prospective immigrant with an educational test. The Indian, for example, who was constantly appearing on the doorstep, might be asked questions on trigonometry or ancient history. Since he could not possibly answer them satisfactorily, he was automatically returned to his port of origin.

Cultists of all kinds were also unwelcome, although there was no legal barrier to their entrance. When Christian Scientists began their propaganda, the doctors of Melbourne sent them a public challenge, saying the superiority of mind over matter would be freely admitted if they could refrain from vomiting after being given a certain injection. Since sports overshadowed all else in Australia, the populace was agog to see the ordeal by apomorphine, but the Christian Scientists refused to submit, and when their answer was heralded by the press they were discredited.

Intruders might be kept out by various means, but Australian internal difficulties had by no means been settled. Warfare of one sort or another was always being waged against a neighboring city, state, or even the Federal government. Because each state considered itself autonomous, interstate jealousy, political and economic, was intense. Railroad gauges changed at each boundary, New South Wales being the only one to possess standard width. This was discouraging to a traveler, who had to clamber off and on trains five times in making the journey from Brisbane to Perth.

Great Britain itself was not exempted from jealousy. I soon learned that I would have to omit Colonial Office, governor general, and imperial completely from my vocabulary. But it was rather odd, in this democratic country, to see how knighthoods were prized, and the kingly palace in which the Governor General was maintained.

No state would consent to have the capital of the new Federation, which was created after fifty years of bickering, permanently located in the city of another state. This rivalry finally culminated in abandoning a perfectly good capital at well-to-do and slumless Melbourne, beautifully set beside the river among hills and trees and already equipped with public buildings and innumerable metropolitan facilities, for the desolate district now known as Canberra, halfway between Sydney and Melbourne and many miles inland.

A hundred years from now Canberra will probably be one of the world's finest cities. The streets are beautifully laid out in accordance with modern town planning schemes, ornamented with statues and fountains and planted extensively with trees. But at present it is a little trying for the visitor. Building has been started on opposite sides of the immense rim, and it is often miles from one government edifice to another.

I could do little at Sydney in 1916. The Federal authorities were not sufficiently powerful to compose state differences and embark on a national health program. Only Queeensland was eager to have

351

the Rockefeller Foundation make a hookworm study, and invited me for a consultation. Most of the land route to Brisbane lies through valleys and over mountains much resembling those of the Berkshires. Scenery of great beauty lies beyond Toowoomba, as the railroad winds down the jeopardous slopes through tunnels and over fantastic bridges which the Australians build three times as strong as ours, with a triple factor of safety.

South Australia was in the temperate zone; Queensland was tropical, and at Townsville was located a flourishing and interesting Institute of Tropical Medicine which was trying to prove that the white man could work and thrive in the tropics. In the sugar plantation country of Queensland I first encountered this all-absorbing problem. There I saw white men working in the fields, something unheard of elsewhere in the tropics. I observed that, although the temperature was rather low at times, a mango which I had sent as a mere shoot from Manila several years before had become a tree and was bearing fruit. Nevertheless, the country lacked the intense verdure to which I had become accustomed in hot countries. It was curious to see the banana and apple—tropical and temperate zone fruits—growing side by side. Areas of poor soil were indicated by the stupendous magnetic anthills, so called because they pointed north. These mammoth oblongs were sometimes higher than a man on horseback. A tropical region where white labor wore shoes presented unusual conditions, and may have accounted for the fact that Australia came nearer eradicating hookworm than any other country.

Dr. J. S. C. Elkington, Quarantine Officer in Brisbane, an old friend, discussed with me the hopes he and his associates entertained for a Federal Ministry of Health. I stated frankly that, in my judgment, the prospect seemed poor unless public opinion, which must be enlisted to back the project, could be assured and that local governments would cease their childish wrangling and follow a national policy.

In the five years which elapsed before I next saw Australia in 1921, the idea of a Ministry of Health became a popular issue. The troops coming home from the War had threatened the introduction of malaria, typhoid, dysentery, and venereal disease. Cerebrospinal meningitis paid no heed to the jealously guarded state borders.

THE WHITE MAN'S LAST REFUGE

The influenza epidemic, which spared no corner of the continent, brought to light the inefficiency and confusion of the states in dealing with a disease of such vital concern to all. A plan was formulated to centralize health operations under Federal control, with each state remaining responsible for most of its former functions; hence it would cooperate rather than criticize. The Quarantine Service, which was already Federal, was to be the nucleus of a National Health Service.

The great obstacle to the establishment of the proposed Ministry of Health was the alleged opposition of Prime Minister W. M. Hughes. This Australian leader, who had conducted his country brilliantly through the War, was a person of importance. The frequent requests for his presence in London had added to his prestige.

By 1921 a Rockefeller representative was no longer held in anathema. In fact, he was welcomed in an advisory capacity. As a neutral, without an axe to grind, I was asked to approach the dreaded little man with arguments for the Health Ministry. Dr. J. H. L. Cumpston, Director of the Quarantine Service, arranged the interview with Mr. Hughes.

I had no premonition of the unexpected turn the conversation was to take. In the first place, it was disconcerting to find the Premier so deaf that my arguments, well practised for intonation and phrasing, had to be shouted.

Deaf people usually fall into two categories: either they whisper so low that no one can hear their words, or they are under the impression that everyone else is also deaf. Premier Hughes belonged to the latter persuasion. He could hardly curb his impatience while I was setting forth the arguments for the new ministry. As soon as I had finished, "I don't believe in your ministry," he roared up at me. "It's ridiculous!! It's wrong!! I'm not going to have any more ministries!"

"How do you think it ought to be done?" I bellowed down.

"No more ministries!! Have enough of them already! Doctors don't know how to run a ministry! Make it a division! Start on tuberculosis!"

"That's absurd!" I practically screamed. "It's an illogical plan! There's nothing sound about it!"

353

He looked at me in amazement. "Yes," he agreed, "it's bad."

His amazement hardly equaled mine. The great man whom everybody had approached on hands and knees was actually being meek. Before he could retract his admission, I followed up my advantage with further screams, "You're only a lawyer trying to tell me about something at which I've spent my life!"

I had out-shouted him completely. He was in a virtual state of collapse. "How do you think it ought to be done?" he asked.

"You've heard the plan! That's what you ought to do! You've a great opportunity before you! If you don't accept it, you'll deserve to be called backward."

"Well, why can't we do this ourselves? We've plenty of men."

"You haven't a man with modern training," said I, still yelling at the top of my lungs.

"How should we go about it then?"

"We'll lend you our men, and we'll have yours trained for you in Europe and America to replace them as soon as possible. The whole thing is for the benefit of Australia. Great Britain has a Ministry of Health, and so should you!"

"Perhaps we should," he agreed.

I was not going to give him a moment's pause in which to rally his scattered forces. "Certainly you should," I yelled. "You ought to have done it long ago!"

"Will you help us?" He was almost timid.

"Of course we'll help you. I don't hold anything against you just because you are not familiar with health administration."

"All right, I'll do it."

I could hardly believe that I had heard aright. The tumult and the shouting died. I told him I would submit the plan for a Ministry of Health at once to the Rockefeller Foundation, and bring him the reply as soon as received.

"I'm very glad you talked this way to me," he said with a humble and a contrite heart, as I took my departure.

Dr. Cumpston was so encouraged that he said even though nothing should come of this promise, meanwhile he was living on great dreams.

In two days I had the agreement of the Foundation to its part in the plan, and returned to Mr. Hughes' office. I read him the cabled offer to assist in the formation of a Ministry of Health, and presented him the plan. With some return of his former pugnacity, he began, merely from habit, to pick out insignificant paragraphs here and there to criticize, saying it appeared we thought hookworm was as important as the Ministry of Health. "The public can only grasp one idea at a time. Any proposition which expects to win popular approval must contain sections which will apply to each individual."

This was sound statesmanship, but I could not afford to let him get the upper hand. My voice rose immediately. "Of course, hookworm is important. That's the way you're going to get people interested—focus their attention on public health. Then you'll get the thing that Australia needs the most—support for a central health service."

Having made this last stand, he whole-heartedly approved the entire proposal.

By means of an Order in Council, a Ministry of Health was established the next week. Labor gave it unanimous support. When we finally withdrew from Australia, which had been so antagonistic in the beginning, the Federal Parliament passed a vote of thanks commending the Rockefeller Foundation for its work there.

New Zealand bore the standard of the white man's last refuge even higher than Australia. The cost of democracy was equally high, and the same labor troubles were in evidence. Once my steamer stopped at Auckland during a big strike in which practically all shipping was tied up and more than a thousand people were stranded. No cargo could be unloaded. The strikers, however, respected the sacrosanct character of the mails, and were willing to undertake their delivery to the pier, but when they found that a little cement dust had sifted on to the mail sacks, they immediately demanded double rates for landing "dusty cargo"; ship and passengers were detained two days pending the settlement of their claim.

The eight-hour law was observed most punctiliously along the water front. I remember once at Wellington watching horses being loaded onto the ship. One by one slings were fastened about them and they were swung from the wharf to the deck. When the twelve o'clock whistle blew the winches stopped, and a horse was left dangling in midair for an hour, until activity was again permitted.

Even more than Australia, New Zealand was preeminently a land of strange laws and social experiments. Every farmer was obliged to feed and give a night's lodging to any swagger, or tramp, who applied. Regardless of income tax, every employed person had to contribute five percent of his salary toward the unemployment fund. The New Zealanders were cultists; the vegetarian idea had taken firm root. Nevertheless, they had their little snobberies. The bars were run with three separate counters—one for well-dressed people, another for laborers, and a third for soldiers.

Railroads, trams, telephones and telegraphs, water power, insurance, mines, totalizers for betting, workmen's dwellings, hospitals, old age pensions, banks, and arbitration and conciliation committees between capital and labor were under government control and, in actuality as well as in intent, seemed to be operated for the public benefit. I was struck not only by the number of branch libraries everywhere, but that they were so arranged that the public might draw books with the least amount of inconvenience.

New Zealand had been largely settled by missionaries and retired army and navy officers. The average intelligence was high and the illiteracy rate the lowest in the world. No smallpox, no plague, and little malaria attacked its homes. No snakes, no white ants, no ferocious animals disturbed its peace. Nearly all plant parasites were absent; few bugs or pests ravaged its gardens. The country for years has had the lowest general mortality and infant death rates. Its system of child hygiene has been regarded as a model for all to follow.

A very nice question presented itself in such a seeming health paradise. In the War New Zealand soldiers had suffered a higher morbidity rate than the English, and the same held true of New Zealanders traveling in foreign countries. Was it better to correct the environment of the New Zealanders still further, thus making them relatively susceptible to introduced infections, or to build up their immunity so they could both withstand these invasions and go abroad with greater safety? None of the members of the medical profession with whom I discussed this paradox had a solution to offer.

The New Zealand government was taking seriously its responsibilities to the original inhabitants, the Maoris, and was trying to give them the benefits of modern civilization. Over seventy-two thousand of this most advanced group of the highly intelligent Polynesians still existed and warranted every effort made in their behalf. They were found in all walks of life; the Minister for the Cook Islands and the Maoris was himself a full-blooded Polynesian.

But the conscience of the government spread beyond its own confines. Far away to the northeast it had a dependency in the shape of a small group of islands named after the explorer Cook, and supposed to be the original home of the Maoris. The Cook Islanders had by no means progressed so far as the Maoris, although they were not wild people in the sense of the Igorots or Moros of the Philippine Islands.

New Zealand also accepted the League of Nations mandate for Western Samoa, and has spent huge sums, infinitely greater than any return it has ever had, in elevating the living standards of the Samoans. These kindly, hospitable, and docile Polynesians, like the rest of the inhabitants of the South Sea Islands, were decreasing yearly in numbers. New Zealand was much chagrined over the slow progress of her health work, and welcomed our assistance. Our campaigns against hookworm and yaws among the Cook Islanders and Samoans were only two out of many such labors which we undertook in this island-studded section of the broad Pacific.

CHAPTER 21. PARASITES LOST AND PARASITES REGAINED

SOME years after the World War had ended, I was sitting one day in the office of the Australian Minister of the Interior at Melbourne, engaged in a lengthy discussion of health affairs. When it was evident that our conversation would continue for some time, the Minister asked, "Would you mind if I interrupt? There's a man outside who has been waiting to see me for some time. I know what he wants and it will only take a few minutes."

In the shabby individual who entered I recognized the man whom once I had looked upon as among the most enviable of mortals. His appearance recalled to my mind the long-ago morning when my steamer was approaching an island north of New Guinea. Slowly and peacefully it rose from the sea until it appeared like the green and gold lid of a sugar bowl resting alone on a bright blue tablecloth and crowned with a white knob which, as we drew nearer, resolved itself into a spacious house. From the white coral sands of the sea's edge thousands of cocoanut palms flowed like a green tide up the gentle slope toward the summit.

Two German brothers were the sole possessors of this enchanting island of Moron. I later stood with one of them on the crest of the rise, with the sea rim curling below us, as he described his idyllic existence. All the land that he could see was his. No work, no worry troubled him; nothing disturbed the solitude of his existence save the slow procession of ships bound for Singapore, Tokyo, Sydney.

PARASITES LOST AND PARASITES REGAINED

When the fancy took him, he might fish or cruise in his magnificent schooner yacht, or he might bide at home, reading a book from his well-stocked library, illumined by light from his own electric plant, while sipping drinks cooled by his own ice machine—a luxury then unheard of in the South Seas.

This calm and this sumptuousness were the fruits of the hundred thousand cocoanut palms, each of which produced an annual revenue of one dollar. Turn and turn about one brother would take the hundred thousand dollars and scatter them lavishly over Europe, while the other sat idly on the veranda and watched the workmen gather the cocoanuts.

But the War came and Australia and New Zealand eagerly snapped up the rich German spoils of the South Seas. Now here was my host of that halcyon day, who had lost his earthly paradise, tramping from ministry to ministry in the vain hope of its return.

From the first time the eyes of white men feasted upon the beauties of the South Seas, these islands have symbolized escape from a world that is too much with us. According to tales brought back by travelers, nature on sea and land offered a freedom from trouble and from labor, the air was soft and balmy, and the women beautiful and kind. The sea was full of fish, wild hogs ran everywhere. As soon as a child was weaned, it was put on a diet of taro root, and taro grew so freely that an effortless kick brought it from the bountiful earth. The United Fruit Company, with all its research and cultivation, produced no finer bananas than those which nature, unaided, here provided, and everywhere cocoanuts and oranges supplied both food and drink. For the Islanders life consisted almost entirely of diversion, and they questioned the greater satisfaction to be derived from work as compared with leisure. Even Europeans, after a short sojourn among them, tended to accept this view.

The South Sea Islands, generally speaking, are those east of Australia and south of the Equator. With the exception of American Samoa, they are all under the sovereignty of the British Empire or the French Republic. The origin of the Islanders is largely a matter of conjecture, but by drawing a line north and south through the Fiji Islands they may be divided racially into Polynesian and Melanesian, although the Gilbert and Ellice Islands are inhabited by so-

359

called Micronesians, light in complexion, but with the slant eyes which betray a Malay strain.

To the east are the Polynesians, the pure race of tall, brown, straight-haired men. To the west the Polynesian strain fades out until it vanishes in the negroid interior of dark Papua. In the middle islands the admixture is called Melanesian. The course of the Polynesian migration eastward may be traced by isolated islands still remaining predominantly Polynesian.

The long, straight hair found in the Cook, Samoan, and Tonga, or Friendly, groups gradually coils to become a frizzy mass on the head of the Fijian, and kinks tighter and tighter until in Papua it is a mere wool. The Fijian dandy takes such great pride in his black, or sometimes reddish, poll that he spends hours in trimming it, so that not one hair shall be out of place. He will, however, have no hair on his face. Should any have the hardihood to appear, he, with equal hardihood, usually plucks it forth with two clam shells. Sometimes he shaves, using sharks' teeth, broken bottles, or perhaps a knife of split bamboo.

The Fijians, with their beautiful shoulders, narrow waists, great thighs, and handsome calves are more perfect physical specimens than the Polynesians who, although large and well-formed, are apt to be soft from too little exercise. The beauty of the Fijian body was well displayed by the picturesque *lava lava*, much like the Malay sarong, six feet long and a yard wide, varying in fashion and color with the tribe. For women the modest Mother Hubbard, the missionary's contribution to morality in the South Seas, was universal. Only now, with the decline of missionary influence, is some small trace of waist line beginning to creep in.

Throughout the South Seas the missionaries were, in the Nineteenth Century, the dominating force. On their arrival they found the Islanders enjoying a system of communal ownership. If a new house were needed, all joined in and built it. Nothing was spent on maintaining law and order; there was nothing to steal because the goods of one belonged to all. For any little infractions of their customs, the elders of the village held court of a kind; but there were no prisons nor jails.

The missionaries were horrified at these conditions. In the Cook

Islands they insisted that property must be secured from aggression by posting it with cocoanut branches nailed to the house. If a man should take a pig for his own use, he must not only return the one feloniously removed but an additional one as well. In their efforts to reform native morals, they had enacted some highly amusing legislation. No gentleman, for example, could go walking with a young lady after dark unless he carried a lighted torch in one hand.

The Islanders amiably but stubbornly clung to some of their ancient practices. In spite even of recent government pressure, the Fijians will not be persuaded to give up *kere kere*, a custom which requires that anyone must surrender any possession another of equal rank may demand. The Governor told me the unhappy experience of a Fijian Oxford graduate who imported silk shirts which so caught the fancy of his friends that he lost them as fast as they arrived.

Some connection might be traced between the universal aversion to work and the popularity of religion which, until the advent of the movies threatened to displace it, furnished diversion but required no expenditure of effort. The Tonga Islands seemed to me to consist almost exclusively of churches and yet more churches. Methodism was the state religion and long wielded enormous power. Even as recently as twenty years ago, when a restrictive sanitary and medical act was drafted and about to be voted upon by the native Parliament, the Church quashed it in its entirety because it contained a provision that only qualified doctors could practise medicine, and the proponents of the bill refused to excise it. As a means to an end the missionaries had been dispensing a tract with each pill, hoping that both would reach the proper destination. They would lose prestige if, merely because they did not know how to practise medicine, they were debarred from doing so.

Anthropologists believe that Rennell Island, one of the Solomons, although it lies far to the west of the dividing line, is Polynesian, or possibly even pre-Polynesian. The Rennell Islanders have had practically no contact with white people, and their religion is undiluted by Christian doctrines. Here is to be found a primitive religion in a practically pure form. Two main gods, a grandfather and grandson, are tremblingly worshipped. The sinner entreats his ancestors to intercede with the grandfather god, who may thus be induced to intercede with the greater and more fearful grandson god. The priest, however, standing before his people with his talking stick in his hand, communicates directly with the grandson god in a strange hobble gobble, and interprets the holy answers to a cowed and submissive populace.

The taboo is all-powerful; the Rennell Islanders are governed by fear of everything—their environment, their enemies, and even their friends. Ritual directs every act of their lives, and all sickness is, ipso facto, punishment for some infraction of the taboo; they recognize that somehow they must have offended against the orders of the grandson.

Not far from tiny Rennell lies the huge mysterious island of New Guinea, peopled by a myriad wild tribes. Only the fringe of Papua has been explored thoroughly; no one knows what riddles of race or sorcery lie hidden in the jungly interior. The cannibals and killers who dwell there are also ruled by terror of unknown forces. As throughout the South Seas, sickness and health are dependent upon *puri puri*—witchcraft. *Puri puri* is not picked up casually; the finer points are expounded in a school which accredits its graduates in sorcery.

The death of an enemy may be secured in Papua with great simplicity by employing the village sorcerer. This medicine man, who always has some distinguishing mark upon his house, serving the purpose of the doctor's shingle, assumes full charge of the affair, and the person seeking revenge may retire from active participation. In the Mekeo district, the sorcerer studies the habits of the prospective victim, particularly the paths along which he is accustomed to go and the hours at which he frequents them. Next the witch doctor secures something which has been close to him, such as a loin cloth, although it is claimed even a hair will do.

The sorcerer unstops the end of the bamboo rod in which he keeps a venomous snake always on hand for just such emergencies, releasing it into a pot. Then he builds a fire under the pot, in which the piece of cloth has already been placed. The unsuspecting victim walks along the usual path at the accustomed hour and the snake, released from the pot, associates the odor of the man with that of the maddening heat, and makes straight and unerringly for him.

PARASITES LOST AND PARASITES REGAINED

Another Papuan method of carrying out vengeance is for the witch doctor merely to point a sharpened human bone in the exact direction of the man to be killed, the theory being that the bone will speed straight through the air, pierce the body, and return to the sorcerer's hand so quickly that its flight may not be seen. Strange as it may seem, cases of death from such fantastic conjurations have been reported on evidence that cannot be lightly dismissed. In such instances, however, the man who is to die has been informed a curse had been put upon him. Bad aim is impossible; if death does not follow, the failure is ascribed to the employment of a more powerful opposing sorcerer.

Opportunity to observe *puri puri* at first hand was afforded on the sugar plantations of Queensland, which had been obliged to import hundreds of Kanakas, as the South Sea Islanders are popularly called, to serve as temporary labor. A Kanaka worker from one of these plantations once came into the little hospital at Mossman, and said the finger had been put upon him—he was going to die Thursday at eleven. "Sun he come up," he pointed to the horizon. "He come along here," his hand rose almost to the meridian. "Now he stop along place," his outstretched arm was motionless. "Close up me die."

Dr. Philip Clark, the physician in charge, examined the Kanaka thoroughly—blood, urine, heart, liver, lungs—nothing was wrong. Nevertheless, the man persisted he was going to die, lay down upon a cot, and refused to rise again. Dr. Clark had had previous experience with the effects of mental suggestion upon Kanakas. When he could not jolly the victim of the spell out of his *idée fixe*, he sent for his foreman to persuade the Kanaka nothing whatever was the matter with him; that he was not going to die. The foreman came, leaned over the bed, peered into the black man's eyes, shook his head, and turned away. "Oh, yes, Doctor, close up he die."

At precisely eleven o'clock on Thursday morning the man's heart, which Dr. Clark testified to be normal, suddenly ceased to beat.

Dr. S. M. Lambert, then in charge of the Rockefeller Foundation's work in Queensland, several times came into direct contact with this form of *puri puri*. On one of these occasions he happened to stop at a Seventh Day Adventist Mission Station, around which was a

collection of Kanaka villages, largely dependent for food and tobacco on the missionaries. The latter were puzzled by the strange
condition of a Kanaka named Rob who had come to them in terror
announcing that Nebo, most influential of the neighborhood witch
doctors, had placed a spell upon him. Rob, without physical appearance of illness, was at the point of death. Dr. Lambert found he had
no temperature but an alarmingly weak pulse; since he could discover no trace of disease, there was little he could suggest as a remedy.

As a last resort, one of the missionaries went directly to Nebo and
spoke severely. "If you do not remove the spell upon Rob, you and
your tribe will get no more food or tobacco. You come back with me
and tell Rob that he will get well."

Dr. Lambert watched carefully what happened. Rob was lying
helpless on the bed. In spite of all that had been done for him, his
vitality was steadily ebbing. Nebo leaned over the sick man and assured him no spell had been cast upon him; it was all a mistake and
there was no need for him to die. Rob's face slowly broke into a
broad smile. Before the day was over, his grey, dull skin, that infallible index of illness in the black man, was shining healthily and
he was about his work as usual.

In Fiji the witch doctor's curse is known as *ndraunikau*. The sorcerer makes a little fire and then, according to ritual, circles around
and around, reciting his incantations and throwing strange and horrid
objects upon it. "When I do that, the man dies," the witch doctor
says, and each Fijian believes implicitly that he himself can be so
willed to death.

Ndraunikau is a problem in the English colony of Fiji, where
witchcraft has to be denied officially, and where a man cannot be
jailed for a crime that does not exist on the statute books. But in
Australian Papua witchcraft is a criminal offense. Once when a work-
man on a Papuan plantation announced he had had a spell put upon
him and was about to die, the skeptical owner, who would stand no
such nonsense, said, "Well, maybe so, but you'll die from this first,"
and he took a whip to him, and when the man ran, he chased him.
The man did not die; the white man's magic was stronger.

The Australian Commonwealth had an economic interest in the

diseases of those living along the coast, because of the rapid development of rubber and cocoanut plantations there. When it appeared evident that the natives were heavily infected with hookworm, the Rockefeller Foundation was invited to make a survey.

The Melanesian aversion to labor was not so strong as the Polynesian, but in order to keep a force of eight thousand steadily at work the year round, three times that number had to be held in readiness; on the average the Papuans would not stay on a plantation more than a year at a time. This disturbing habit of theirs caused considerable hardship to the planters, but was an advantage from our point of view, because the larger the number employed, the larger would be the number receiving instruction in anti-hookworm propaganda.

Dr. Lambert carried out a remarkable demonstration of what could be done with savages who had no communication with neighboring tribes. Papuan dialects could be numbered by the hundreds; in some regions he found as many as three language groups in five miles. Along the coast, however, pidgin English offered a common speech. This idiom had been introduced in the early Nineteenth Century by the sandal-wood traders, in order to facilitate their commercial dealings.

Dr. Lambert learned pidgin English.

Wherever a superstition would serve his purpose, he was prompt to utilize this also. The snake, which played so large a part in Papuan life, was, among other things, believed to cause disease by taking up its abode inside the bodies of the sick. The sorcerer who, to give him his due, worked harder at curing than at killing, with incantations pretended to suck the ghost of the snake from the mouth, ear, or umbilicus of the patient. Afterwards he gave ocular demonstration of his power by spitting a small snake from his mouth. If the sick man happened to be suffering from a fear malady, naturally he would often get better.

This snake theory gave Dr. Lambert his opportunity. Holding in his hand a little bottle of hookworms, which his audience accepted as snakes, he would begin the story of the hookworm cycle:

"You altogedda boy. You listen good 'long dis story. One big fella sick he stop 'long bell' b'long altogedda boy. Name b'long dis sick him he hookworm. You look 'long dis bottle. Gottem plenty small fella snake he stop. Dis fella he stop 'long in bell' b'long boy. Tooth he gottem. Him he kai kai bell' b'long boy. Blood he come. Him he kai kai blood b'long boy. S'pose boy he kai kai. Kai kai he no b'long boy. Snake he catchem fust time. Now dis fella snake he allee same pidgin. He gottem hegg. S'pose boy he go 'long bush. Now hegg he come out 'long ground. Now rain he come down. Sun he cook him dis fella hegg. Bimeby one small fella pickaninny snake. Him he come up inside 'long hegg. Now hegg he broke him. Now him he walk about ground quick fella too much. Boy he come 'long. He put him foot 'long dis small fella pickaninny. Quick fella he come up inside foot b'long boy. Now he go, he go, he go. Bimeby he come up 'long heart b'long boy. Now he come 'long wind. Now he come 'long t'roat b'long boy. Now he scratch him t'roat. Boy he swallow him. He go down 'long bell' b'long boy. Now dis long time dis fella pickaninny he stop inside bell' b'long boy. He come in fust time he small fella too much. You no sabe look him 'long eye b'long you. He small fella too much. You sabe look him 'long big fella glass. Now he stop 'long time in bell' b'long boy. He more big. Now he come 'long bell' b'long boy. He gottem tooth. He sabe kai kai bell' b'long boy. He sabe kai kai blood. Boy him he lose him blood. He weak fella too much. Him he sick too much. Close up he die."

Although the Papuan had accepted the explanation of snakes as perfectly natural, he had to be constantly reassured that he was not putting himself in jeopardy by allowing examination of stools. His unquestioning acceptance of the superstition that the body excreta, as well as the paring of his fingernail or a dropped hair, might expose him to his enemy's vengeance made it doubly difficult to win his confidence.

The work was, as usual, started on the plantations. But prisoners in the Central Jail at Port Moresby, none of whom could very well protest, also made excellent subjects. The prisoners were not merely under complete supervision, but, due to the peculiar system of promotion effective in prison circles, they also offered an excellent means of spreading health education in the districts we could not reach.

The Australians have tempered their own severe ideas of justice to the mores of their subject people. Murder has to be treated in the light of the Papuan conception that taking human life was no crime, because a man was not a man, native style, until he had killed. The police query, "Did you kill this man?" directed to the culprit, always elicited a boastful, "Oh, yes." Only at rare intervals was a gallows set up for a public hanging, and then almost always to serve as a warning to leave white men alone. In the ordinary course of affairs the guilty ones were let off with a short jail term, and, after having learned the rudiments of civilization, they graduated and were sent back to their own villages as constables. Badges were hung on their naked chests to distinguish them from their fellow tribesmen, and they became the sole representatives of law and order in their own neighborhoods, where they usually performed their duties with vigor and determination.

In Papua as well as other places in the South Seas the Rockefeller Foundation made a demonstration in hookworm control, but it concentrated its efforts in Fiji, a British crown colony which to all intents and purposes represented the center of the South Sea Islands. Of the more than two hundred islands in the Fiji group, only Viti Levu and Vanua Levu are of any size; many of them are mere atolls almost awash at high tide.

In spite of the inviting verdure, the cooling breezes, and the pleasant prospects, Captain Cook had sailed straight through the middle of the group, not risking a landing because of the fierce aspect of the natives. The sandal-wood traders began timorously frequenting Fijian shores at the beginning of the Nineteenth Century, but not until 1826 did the missionaries first arrive. During our Civil War British commercial interests had seen an opportunity for profit, and the fields in harvest time were white with bursting cotton bolls. This industry died a natural death in the seventies when the United States again captured the markets. Then in the eighties the Colonial Sugar Refining Company brought renewed prosperity. Sugar and bananas were exported by the energetic planters.

Travelers sailing eastward from the coast of Asia have often noted that the variety of vegetable and animal life steadily diminished with each successive landfall. Apparently the Archipelagos of the South Seas, like Australia, had been cut off from the mainland before the development of mammals; the ubiquitous pig was introduced by Captain Cook. Fiji does not even possess bedbugs, white ants, leeches, snakes, or crocodiles. But it has a few native marsupials, among them a species of rat which gnawed down so many canes in the plantations of the Colonial Sugar Refining Company that the mongoose was imported from India to get rid of it. This little animal, which at home put up so brave a fight against snakes and rodents, when transplanted to its new environment promptly began to multiply beyond all reason and, far from warring with the rats, made friends with them and hunted zealously for birds. Similarly, the myna bird, cousin of the starling, was introduced to pick off the cane borers, and now its incessant and clamorous conversation is heard throughout the land.

Fiji has had a number of economic setbacks in recent years. The cocoanut palm was destroyed so completely on Viti Levu that many grown Fijians today have never seen a cocoanut, elsewhere the staple product of the South Seas. Another blow was the barring of Fijian bananas by Australia, which wished to develop the industry in her own state of Queensland. But the government of Fiji, in spite of the depression, continued to spend about twelve percent of its entire revenue on the care, cure, and prevention of disease. I was constantly astonished that so few people could maintain a government that could accomplish so much, even under these conditions of storm and stress.

The cultivation of sugar requires monotonous sustained labor. The Fijians possessed a physical endurance consonant with their great stature, partly due at least to freedom from malaria, but they refused steady jobs. They were willing to labor temporarily at loading ships or being boatmen, draymen, or house builders, or would toil spasmodically in the gold mines, because miners were fed well and housed well. But even when working in company with others for short periods it was important to employ a jester to amuse them. Fijians cared nothing for money; a full belly and simple recreation were their sole essentials. Their personal needs were simple and easily come by. The Fijians' economic nonchalance was assured, because the British government managed and rented out their public lands at good prices to the plantation owners, returning the income to them.

The planters, in despair over the amiable obstinacy of the Fijians, decided that if production were to be put on a profitable basis Tamils would have to be imported, even though their working capacity was only half that of the Fijians. The first influx of Tamils brought the question of health to the fore. The planting interests could not protest against health measures, because the government was the more powerful and they were afraid of losing their indentured labor.

The Darling Commission in 1915 determined that hookworm had not been started by the Indian coolies as at first assumed, but was endemic among the native population. The survey was simplified because no mixture of blood had taken place between Tamil and Fijian; hence the two could be examined separately. It was found that, although the Tamil coolie was almost one hundred percent infected, his was the ancylostoma whereas the Fijian harbored the necator. Curiously enough, half-caste and European children were almost free of worms, although they ran barefooted throughout the year.

Nobody knows how the Fijians would get along if a paternalistic government should force them to compete on equal terms with the Tamils, who have a monopoly on industriousness. Few of the Tamils imported to work on the plantations now return to India. They like the Fiji Islands, and it is a long way home. After they work out their indenture the Colonial Sugar Refining Company sets them up on small plots of land, where they can have their own fields of sugar cane. Now half the population of Fiji is Tamil.

When I first saw these Indians in Fiji in 1916 they lived in miserable houses and filthy villages and seemed to have no desire for anything better. I was much interested in 1934 to see the changes one generation had wrought. Everything was in vast contrast to the conditions which still exist in India. The Tamil had dropped many of the handicaps of his religion, and much of the caste system had been abolished. Lately a movement among the older Indians and their holy men to induce the new generation to return to the ways of their fathers met with little success. They were happy where and as they were.

They had been miraculously transformed from a dejected, downcast, docile, uninterested people, who could not even play, into one which was healthy, alert, sport loving, and mentally so progressive that they were agitating for schools and the vote. They owned fine fat cattle and rich lands, and had, on their own initiative, built a superior type of house, each with its neat latrine. They had well earned their reputation for industry and thrift.

This regeneration had been accomplished by mass treatment for

369

hookworm. Nothing like it has ever happened in history. At last the Tamil smiles.

Carnegie with his libraries had been before us in the Fiji Islands, and his donations had been well publicized. The local newspapers, confusing the two philanthropies, announced that I had come to Fiji to study the habits of the bookworm, assuming perhaps that the Carnegie volumes had somehow become infested. The school children, anxious to show respect to the newly-arrived bookworm investigator, entered a competition, and one inspired Fijian young lady turned in an essay entitled "Parasites Lost and Parasites Regained." I have always believed that no more fitting title could, by any fortuitous circumstance, have been chosen.

Hookworm prevention was the primer used in teaching the peoples of the South Seas that it was possible for them all to have sound bodies. But because of the prevalence of yaws, which all the Islanders had heretofore taken for granted, neo-salvarsan injections provided an open sesame to their hearts, although they were at first timorous of treatment for fear of "driving them in." Many of the children were being entirely deprived of the physical exuberance which is the inalienable right of childhood. Some, with the aid of canes, had to hop on their heels because of the ulcers on their toes, or walk on their toes because of the ulcers on their heels. Others could not walk at all, but would hitch themselves along in a sitting position. One of the times when I have been proudest of being a member of the medical profession was when I saw the cures wrought among the children of the South Seas by the practitioners, who gave them back their childhood, so that they were able to laugh and run and play once more.

The second great curse of the South Seas was filariasis, or elephantiasis. Patrick Manson, a Scotch physician in Amoy, made the brilliant discovery in 1879 that the filaria bloodworm was conveyed from one human being to another through the agency of the mosquito.

When I was traveling about with Dr. Lambert through Fijian and Samoan villages I often slept in native grass huts and, though we both carried nets, I was frequently bitten by the vicious mosquitoes which swarmed everywhere. The knowledge that almost half the people around me had filariasis made me feel distinctly uncomfortable, because any one of these mosquitoes which were biting me might already have dined on one of the nearby sufferers. Dr. Lambert, whose skin had apparently become immune, could sit around in his pajamas and apparently not be bitten, while I would be complaining and scratching incessantly at the huge welts.

After Manson's original observation it was later discovered that the filaria is a white thread-like worm which, after being deposited by the mosquito on the skin, bores its way into the lymphatics and blocks them. Due to this blockage, a tremendous enlargement of the tissues may take place. A leg, for instance, may attain the size of that of an elephant, hence the name.

Filariasis, which is fortunately not painful, takes years to develop. Although the presence of embryos can be detected at an early stage by blood examination, no cure has yet been found. Unless the victim can be removed to a temperate climate soon after infection, the progress of the disease cannot be arrested. Surgical operations give only mechanical relief, but any surgeon who could cut out one hundred and twenty-five pounds of excess tissue naturally found favor in the eyes of the Islanders, and many such operations were performed. If the adult filaria could be tracked to its hiding place, a patient could be cured, but it is often so securely concealed that even the most thorough autopsy, sometimes lasting for days, in which every organ is dissected, fails to reveal its presence.

Not until something was learned about the breeding habits of the filaria-bearing mosquitoes was any effective measure possible against this disease. Only a few years ago it was determined that discarded cocoanut shells which were filled with water by every tropical shower furnished ideal breeding places. With this information in its hands, the Samoan government passed a law compelling cocoanut shells to be broken up, burned, or piled upside down. The incidence of filariasis in Samoa has been declining since then.

Unlike the French, whose interest in their colonies did not seem to include much humanitarianism, the British were greatly concerned over the progressive depopulation of the South Sea Islands. Scientists generally believe that the main cause of the diminishing numbers is the lack of immunity to introduced diseases. It has been generally held that British nationals had been largely responsible for the high death rate from this cause, although the Chinese trader must also bear a portion of the blame. Much evidence, however, has been accumulated to prove that infant mortality is largely due to diet deficiency, as well as the difficulties in inducing Polynesian mothers adequately to care for their young.

The fostering of communications caused these newly introduced diseases to run through the populations like wildfire. Tuberculosis, measles, and pneumonia took a terrible toll. Waves of bacillary dysentery swept over the Archipelagos. The measles epidemic in Fiji was the major catastrophe of its history; over a third of the population died. More recently, influenza was imported, causing an estimated loss of ten to twenty percent in the districts affected.

It is interesting to speculate upon the physical changes which must take place in a people during the process of acquiring immunity. Those who have not been exposed to such diseases as measles and tuberculosis will probably have certain characteristics which are lost to the world by their death, and the survivors will have certain physical qualities which will make for a different line of evolution in later generations.

Recently an airplane bound for the goldfields of New Guinea discovered in the interior a strange people as yet unknown, lighter in skin, who lived in villages, had streets and neat fields, carefully fenced. A doctor could experience no more exciting adventure than to explore some such community, hitherto completely isolated from all contact with civilization, to tabulate the indigenous diseases, and also to experiment with methods of providing against the ravages of disease when the communication barriers are broken down.

Nothing definite was known in 1915 about the relative importance of the causes of depopulation in the South Seas, except that the process was going on at a rapid rate and something should be done about it. The Polynesians were very desirable residents for British colonies. They were such delightful, charming people, and their culture so perfectly conformed to many amenities of life that practically everyone became immediately friendly to them. They got on well with white people. Their high degree of intelligence qualified them to rank equally with the British in education and in privileges, and, as they disappeared, the unassimilable Japanese and Chinese were taking their places.

It had always been difficult to get doctors from home for service in the South Seas because of the extremely isolated life. This isolation caused many who did make the journey to become addicted to alcohol or drugs. Furthermore, such efforts as had already been made to give medical instruction to South Sea Islanders had been inadequate. I have visited hospitals where I found untrained natives handling dangerous medicines of which they scarcely knew the dosage, and making diagnoses such as "feverish," "bad food," and "bad blood."

Australia, New Zealand, and Great Britain were all endeavoring to find some solution. The Australians proposed to balance the birth and the death rates by a system of hospital ships traveling from port to port. The utilization of the waterways for this purpose sounded as reasonable to them as it had to me when we had first tried it out among the Moros in the Philippines. However, I had learned then that hospital ships were not feasible. The expense was heavy, and only relatively few people could be benefited; the sick could not be brought easily to the ports.

The British had first sought the cooperation of the League of Nations and then had approached the Rockefeller Foundation. We, as interested spectators of the varied efforts, were delighted at the chance to offer suggestions. Teaching the people to take an interest in their own health problems was one of our fundamental tenets. In this case we were encouraged by the sanguine expectation that a school for training Polynesians and Melanesians in medical practice had a better chance for success than those erected in many Oriental or Latin countries where the experiment had been tested out previously.

"Why don't you provide a suitable medical education for these people?" we asked. "British doctors—white men on high salaries requiring long vacations—cannot be depended upon for any certain tenure. Furthermore, you should have medical representatives who already know the customs, languages, and superstitions of their own people, who can live among them permanently, who have the interest of the country at heart, and who could do the job at a cost the government could sustain. You have a unique opportunity here, because

373

you have a people intelligent enough to absorb the necessary knowledge."

A small, primitive school was already operating at Suva, the centrally located capital of the Fiji Islands. With a population of about five thousand, more than a quarter white, it was already a thriving port of call for many steamship lines. Several three-story concrete buildings gave an air of commercial prosperity to the main street, and a trio of moving picture houses, an Otis elevator, and other fleshpots of civilization catered to the universal desire to be amused.

The hospital ship idea was abandoned and, without any great enthusiasm, a plan was agreed to whereby the Rockefeller Foundation would assist in reorganizing the Suva school and turning it into an institution to serve the whole South Seas. Ultimately seven Island administrations—American Samoa, New Zealand Samoa, Tonga, Fiji, the Solomons, Cook Islands, and one of the French islands—sent students and helped to support the school.

Dr. Lambert, Deputy Central Medical Authority of the Western Pacific High Commission, with amazing good nature and tact, has been able to conciliate the various Island administrations and settle their differences. His most notable achievement has been to induce them all to join in the support of a central leper colony at Mokogai, Fiji. His latest proposed development is a Western Pacific Health Service for the entire South Seas, in which a system of promotion by merit will spur white health officers to ambition through the knowledge that they will have an opportunity to advance from remote posts to more active ones.

When the Central Medical School was first started no more than a three-year course for training medical practitioners was contemplated. Although I already had great faith in the mental capacity of the Polynesians, even I was astounded at the facility with which the students forged ahead. Nor was it mere rote learning which would enable them to pass examinations; it became obvious they were entitled to further education, and the three-year course was lengthened to four, in preparation for turning out regularly qualified physicians.

The most striking aspect of the school was the spirit of vitality which infused it, and the eagerness for learning evident in every classroom. In the course of one of my routine inspections, the Professor of Anatomy suggested, "Would you like to ask any question?"

I feared that, according to the time-honored custom, some prize pupil had been groomed to impress the visiting examiner. "May I ask anyone I wish?"

"Oh, yes, anyone."

I looked around and selected a student who I was sure could not have been a brilliant Samoan strategically placed for my attention, and requested him to describe the brachial plexus. To his query, "Would you mind if I demonstrated on the blackboard because I can do it better in that way?" I said of course not. He thereupon took up some red, blue, and white crayons, and made a drawing superior to any such extemporaneous art I had ever seen, all the while commenting fluently on the complicated nerve network. Fortunately, I had been handed a textbook, or I should have been completely lost in trying to follow him.

The practitioners from the School went back to their native villages dressed in the tribal style except for the formal addition of a coat, so indivisible from the idea of British caste. But they were thinking along new lines, and bearing neo-salvarsan and hookworm demonstration paraphernalia. Their health propaganda, so enthusiastically supported by the people, brought about a larger percentage of latrine installations and use than any other country has achieved in a similar space of time. Depopulation stopped where health work was well established, and the numbers of Polynesians and Melanesians in the South Seas, with the introduction of modern preventive medicine, are apparently increasing year by year.

Our task was not finished when we graduated medical practitioners; we had to make sure no slip-up should occur after they had been back in their own environment for some time. It was inconceivable that young men, straight from their grass-roofed huts, bred to the terrors of spells and charms, and with only a relatively slight amount of training, would not occasionally sink back to the level of the community.

Even in the classroom the face of every Fijian student became like a carven image when *ndraunikau* was mentioned. Not one of them

375

could be induced even to discuss it. No Westerner can comprehend the degree of courage displayed by Malakai, the best medical practitioner turned out by the School, who once dared to challenge the power of the chief of the witch doctors, although he well knew many had died at the time appointed for them by the curse. "Why don't you kill me? You say you can *ndraunikau* me. Go ahead! I defy you! It's all nonsense! If your system of medicine will work, show me what you can do!"

Malakai proved his faith in what he had been taught, and his bold defiance brought him no harm.

Part of our plan was to have traveling officers—men who would go in a friendly, helpful spirit and not one of criticism—inspect these medical practitioners after they had been at work for some time on their islands. I also wanted to see how they were applying their knowledge. Samoa, the home of the most intelligent of the Polynesian strain, was naturally expected to show the best results. In company with Dr. Lambert I made several interesting trips there, the more pleasant because of his popularity; his avoirdupois coincided with Samoan ideas of beauty and this, added to his talent for speech-making, made him irresistible to them.

Almost at the outset of the War New Zealand had seized German Samoa, but found that these reputedly most gentle of the pure Polynesians did not greet the change in masters with the expected rejoicings. Insurrection has been in progress ever since. The Samoans resent bitterly being a colony of a dependency; they would not have minded so much being directly subject to Great Britain. Moreover, color intolerance, so conspicuously absent in the case of the Maori, is said to have had much to do with their sense of grievance.

The Samoans have been rebelling over something or other for a hundred years or more, usually as to which was the ranking house, that of Mataafa or Malietoa, and by this time have had so much practice that they have attained a high degree of efficiency. The rebellion against New Zealand, or Mau movement, has taken the form of non-cooperation; for example, the Samoans blandly refuse to pay their taxes. At one time New Zealand tried to exact compliance by troops, but it was out of the question to shoot a man simply because he would not pay. Samoans were adept at thinking up schemes to annoy. Before the rebellion they had, to a great extent, used latrines but, because the New Zealand Health Department approved this practice, they promptly abandoned it, and, in derision, even polluted the doorsteps of the officials.

On the whole New Zealand was lavish with money and attention, and used force only to assert her sovereignty. But finally, her patience near exhaustion, she withdrew the medical practitioners, and in remote districts closed hospitals and dispensaries. At the time of my visit with Dr. Lambert, the people in some rural areas had had only herbalists on whom to depend, and many sick were brought to us for our ministrations.

I interviewed many of the chiefs. The most powerful among them was Fau Mui Na, weighing three hundred and nine pounds, fisherman and philosopher. It was said that but for his intervention, the Europeans in Apia would have been wiped out at the beginning of the Mau movement. I also met Mataafa, a descendant of the former King of that name, who had been educated for the priesthood and spoke beautiful English, German, and French. His daughters entertained us with sitting, knee, and standing dances.

Near Foa (pronounced, "Fona," because the early missionaries' printing outfits had been deficient in certain letters) we had an important public meeting with thirty-four chiefs and orators. At times it looked as though we might become involved in Island politics, but finally we made them understand that in all civilized countries neutrality exists in medical affairs; even between people who are at war.

The Samoans were afflicted with much illness. Filariasis was common there as elsewhere in the South Seas. Blindness, due to ophthalmia and also trachoma, was frequent. But out of the population of fifty thousand only twelve insane were in confinement, and no others were known that required restraint. This may have been due to the absence of syphilis, which in turn was due to the high incidence of yaws; we conducted three successive campaigns in Samoa for the treatment of yaws. Yaws is a horrible disease, but it has this virtue that to its presence may be due the absence of syphilis, which commonly makes its appearance with the white man's advent.

Samoa impressed me primarily as being a land of unfinished churches. Every one of seven villages had one or more, usually concrete, with a capacity far in excess of any conceivable use. In some villages of four or five hundred a Catholic, a Seventh Day Adventist, a Methodist, and a Mormon Church would vie for favor. It often happened that while one was under construction, another village would erect a larger one, and the first village then had to cease building, tear down what it had already constructed, and start over again on an even larger scale. It was said that each year when the time for raising funds for new churches drew near, prostitution and burglary increased commensurately.

Certain formalities had to be observed on visiting a Samoan village. Dr. Lambert, because of his long sojourn in the South Seas, was able to guide my steps so that I would not offend our kindly hosts. They appreciated being informed in advance of our arrival because they had certain preparations to make for the welcome of foreign guests. A delegation of villagers would don their best clothes of tapa, a cloth of hammered bark, soft as silk and artistically decorated. Thus attired they would meet us at the outskirts of the town or, if we came by sea, would paddle out to greet us.

We were usually welcomed in the great oval *fale*, the community house, held up by big round posts, beautifully carved timbers, and marvelous trussing in the interior which I have never seen outdone by European or American engineers. The *fale* was open to every breeze; if a sudden squall swept down, a mere pull of a cord released the protecting fibre curtains on the windward side, which shut out the lashing rain while the ceremony proceeded without interruption.

The ceremonial surrounding even the lives of the humble in Samoa compared with that of a royal family in Europe. The head of the table had always to sit with the long axis of the house and the ranking guest sat on the sea side with his back to it. All guests were announced, in order of precedence, by a special official in a loud voice. When a roast pig was served, the head had to go to the chief, the part under the belly to the *taupo*.

No woman was permitted entrance into the *fale* save the *taupo*, the village virgin and its most guarded treasure. She was usually the handsomest daughter of the chief; if he had none, he would adopt a young girl worthy of carrying on the tradition. The entire village saw to it that she remained a virgin until the chief decided the time had come for a political union with a neighboring tribe and a new *taupo* took her place. When she slept, four women surrounded her, one at either side, one at her head and one at her feet. She was the center of all life in the community—entertained visitors and officiated at the mixing of the *kava*.

Kava, the universal South Sea drink, might be considered semisacred; two people never met for conversation without the bowl between them, and no welcome was complete without it. The degree of ceremonial varied with the importance of the occasion. Any visitor who could not play his part in the highly formalized and set ritual was branded as a barbarian. The government encouraged *kava* because its elaborate preparation fulfilled all convivial needs without the inebriating effects of alcohol. In my experience every Oriental country had indulged in a native alcohol made from cocoanut, sugar, or rice. The absence of such a beverage among the South Sea Islanders must have had a profound influence upon their history, and especially their sex life.

At the first *kava* ceremony I attended, the *taupo* placed a small quantity of the pounded, shredded, and dried root of the piper methysticum into a huge iron sugar kettle, added a little water, then swooshed the spongy mass up and down time after time, wringing it out as though it were laundry and tossing it aside for her helpers to shake. With this and new root constantly added, the process was repeated again and again until the *kava* reached the proper strength.

The serving of the *kava* was tremendously important. The *taupo* filled a half cocoanut shell and handed it to the cupbearer who, gorgeously arrayed, taking so many steps this way and so many steps that, finally, with a deep bow and a genuflection, presented it to the guest of honor. Before I put it to my lips, I spilled a few propitiatory drops on the ground. This libation stamped me as someone who was familiar with local customs, and won approval. As I drank the *kava*, which had a flavor reminiscent of root beer, everybody sang and clapped. In some villages etiquette demanded that each gulp should be attuned to the rhythmic beat of hand on hand and I was conscious that my Adam's apple was the focus of attention. When I had drained the cup, I sent it spinning with a twist of the wrist into the center of the *fale*. Not until it stopped its gyrations did the cup-bearer pick it up and present it to the *taupo* for refilling.

Simultaneously with the *kava* preparation, speaking was going forward. Samoans look upon oratory as an art for which there should be special training, and, unlike ourselves, they endeavor to discourage amateurs from engaging in after dinner speeches. The position of tribal orator is hereditary, and he is next in rank to the chief. In some places he is prime minister; in others he is more powerful than the chief himself. I never heard the Rockefeller Foundation acclaimed in such glowing terms as a great humanitarian force which exercised its beneficence in the furthermost recesses of the globe, even extending to this poor little island. I must admit I was flattered to hear extolled so eloquently virtues I had never before known I possessed. Where the orator had obtained the romantic story of my past I do not know, but even more amazing was his discriminatory use of the English language.

I was no such master of my native tongue. I was contemplating with dismay the prospect of having to reply in kind, or at least try to explain gracefully away my elocutionary shortcomings, when my apprehensions were allayed by being informed that another orator would take my place.

My mouthpiece replied to the praise of the Rockefeller Foundation with praise of the virtues of the tribal chief and his queen in well-rounded, beautiful phrases such as I could never have uttered. The words of the virtuoso sparkled so entertainingly that the chief's speaker was spurred to emulation. Fortunately, the competition did not become so keen as at some *kava* ceremonies where these verbal tourneys sometimes took hours.

After the *kava* cup had proceeded down the line in strict order of rank, and after the last oration had been made, the dances began, endless in their variety. Both men and women engaged in these, although they rarely touched each other, usually sitting cross-legged, twisting their bodies and arms, swaying to the accompaniment of strings and drums, sometimes moving silently, sometimes singing melodies of surpassing beauty based on hymns learned from the missionaries, and more poignant even than those of our own South. At evening entertainments the dances often continued from nine until four in the morning. The spectators at this late hour were exhausted, but the performers would have kept on with unabated zest as long as any audience remained.

The missionaries have discouraged many native dances. The hula is seen no more either in Samoa or Fiji, although it is beginning to reappear in the Cook Islands, where the government has not discouraged it.

In Fiji, as in Samoa, I was able to visit many of the remote islands. The Governor kindly lent us his yacht, the *Adi Beti*. The friendly Fijian people also expressed by ritual and symbolism the courtesy which was part of their daily lives. As soon as the native canoes drew within hailing distance of the yacht, a great shout of *"Sabua!"* (sambula) would greet us. We would call back the correct reply of *"Moli!"* which meant literally "orange juice," or, "your words are sweeter than oranges." Then would follow the impressive ceremony of presenting the whale tooth *tabua* (tambua), a compliment bestowed upon those whom the Fijians esteem their friends. The original *tabuas* were of wood, and probably had some phallic significance. Their exchange was an affair among chiefs, and acceptance obligated the recipient to grant any request the donor might choose to make. The whalers had left in their wake the teeth of the great cetaceans, and the bulk of the *tabuas* in use today still date from the days of Moby Dick. Any additions to the floating supply have to be gleaned from dead whales washed up on the beach.

The Fijians also had their *kava* ceremony which they called *yaqona* (yanggona). This was held in the *mbure*, or assemblage place, but in Fiji each person had to make his own speeches, with the aid of an interpreter if necessary. Here, too, we were entertained afterwards. I remember in particular one occasion at Masi, where Nitavua, chief of the Curomoce tribe of firewalkers, set before us an elaborate repast of five kinds of root vegetables, excellent crabs, shrimp, duck, chicken, roast pig, and oysters. But even the *yaqona* and the feast did not satisfy Nitavua's sense of hospitality. He arranged a firewalking ceremony for our benefit.

The secret of firewalking, supposedly the exclusive property of this tribe, had been handed down for many generations. It seems that once, many years ago, a *ratu*, or chief, caught a devil devil in the form of an eel. The devil devil began to tempt the *ratu* in exchange for his freedom.

"I'll make you the richest man in the Island," it promised.

"I'm already the richest man."

"I'll make you the biggest chief."

"I'm already the biggest chief."

"I'll get you the most beautiful women."

"I have them already."

Finally the devil devil said, "I'll confer upon you the ability to walk through fire without being hurt." The extreme form of punishment among the Fijians was to drive an unfortunate victim through hot pits so that he died, and the promise of immunity from this torture was powerful enough to win the *ratu*. The devil devil whispered the secret to him, receiving freedom in return, and thereafter the initiates could walk unharmed through fire.

In preparation for our arrival at Masi a fire had been kept burning for days in a pit some four feet deep and fifteen feet in diameter; the layer of limestone boulders above and below had become red hot. Even after all the embers were raked out and the stones had paled to grey, they still radiated such intense heat as to set fire to the clothes of anyone who stood too near the edge of the pit. Just before the firewalking was to take place, I tied a folded handkerchief over the end of a long pole and touched about a dozen stones, one after the other, with the weight and speed which I estimated would approximate that of a man walking quickly and lightly over them.

At a given signal about a dozen barefoot Curomoce rushed into the pit and stepped rapidly across its diameter. I was amazed to find when they emerged from the pit that their feet gave no evidence of burning or reddening.

My handkerchief also, after being washed clean of soot, showed no evidence of having been burned or even scorched. One explanation, though it does not quite satisfy me, was that each performer curled his feet to form an insulating air cup. Before this could be heated to an intolerable temperature, he had stepped to another stone.

PARASITES LOST AND PARASITES REGAINED

As soon as the last man was out of the pit, *massawe*, a sugary vine, and earth, were thrown in to make a bed on which taro and yams were left to bake for several hours. While one of the firewalkers was arranging the tubers, the heat was still so intense as to set his grass skirt on fire, and rapid action had to be taken to save him from burning.

I sometimes found it difficult to reconcile the friendly hospitality and good fellowship of the Fijians whom I encountered with the tales of their former cruel practices. Heavy war canoes, sometimes a hundred feet long, were for good luck launched over the live bodies of men used as rollers. It was also the custom to put a live slave in each posthole of a chief's house before setting in the post. Far from objecting to this sacrifice, the slaves esteemed it a great honor; they would ask to be so buried and grasped the post with both hands as it was put on top of them, thus assuring their future happiness.

The Fijian habit of which everyone has heard was cannibalism; a prisoner was thrown into an oven similar to but larger than that used for firewalking. Cannibalism, shocking as it is, served two purposes for the Islanders. It prevented the spread of disease, because the inhabitants of one village never dared stray far beyond their own boundaries, and it also satisfied a meat hunger. In the back countries there was no game, and sea food was carried up with much effort. This does not explain cannibalism on the seacoast, where fish were abundant. Long before we were acquainted with vitamins, the Islanders knew the value of fish livers.

In the old days the *ratu* used to have his prisoners brought out early in the morning for an inspection, to see on which he and his warriors would dine that day. Eating human flesh was a ceremony —the heart for courage, the liver for wisdom, the genitals for virility. A prisoner's only chance to escape being roasted was to sneeze, because thereby he showed himself lacking in fortitude, and no self-respecting cannibal would eat any but a brave man. "I will give you life," the chief would scornfully say, and the prisoner would humbly reply, *"Moli."* But after this craven action he could never for the rest of his days associate with his fellows.

Cannibalism is supposed to be extinct in the South Seas, but occasionally in Papua, and doubtless other places, "boys" still disappear from the plantations, and little doubt remains in the minds of those familiar with native ways that they have been eaten.

The last official record of a cannibal feast was in 1867. Missionary Baker had been afflicted with more than the usual martyr's zeal. Against the advice of those experienced in Fijian conduct, he went with a companion into the dark interior, protected only with high leathern boots against the jungle dangers. A certain *ratu* on the coast disliked the missionary intensely and wanted to get rid of him. Since the *ratu's* village was under the strict eye of Great Britain, he was afraid to resort to the simple expedient of his forefathers. He fell back, therefore, upon the ancient rite of the *tabua* whereby the recipient must grant any request he might make. Along with Baker the wily *ratu* sent a runner who, at each village where the party stopped, was to offer the *tabua* to the head man. But in each case, as soon as the messenger attempted to present his gift, the sight of Baker was sufficient warning to bring about a courteous but firm refusal to accept it. The *ratu* could readily divine the nature of the request, and he had a wholesome dread of British retribution.

Finally, the clever runner darted ahead of his party and proffered the *tabua* to an unsuspecting *ratu*, who graciously received it. But gratification rapidly evaporated when Baker put in his belated appearance. "Now I know what you want me to do," he said sadly to the runner. "I would never have taken the *tabua* if I had been warned."

But his tribal sense of what was due and fitting compelled him to accede to the expected request, and Missionary Baker went into the pit, boots and all. According to custom, the choicest bits were sent around to neighboring villages, and the story, which has become apocryphal in the telling, relates that one *ratu*, who received a delicacy in the form of a roasted foot and leg, encased in well-seasoned leather, commented, "Don't these missionaries have tough hides?"

I remember once on a remote island meeting an ancient chieftain whose son was then in the Central Medical School at Suva. He was reputed to have been a cannibal in the good old days, but seemed to resent the term extremely. He informed me ingenuously that when he was young and his warriors had beaten a tribe thoroughly, and that tribe again made war on them, they would capture a man and eat him—not for food, but as an extreme form of punishment.

Then the missionaries came along. The chief had not invited them and had not been at all interested in what they had to offer. But the missionaries would not go away, even though he kept asking them to depart. Finally, the tribe had to eat a few to make them understand they were not wanted. The old gentleman assured me earnestly and with conviction in his eye it was no pleasure to eat the missionaries; he found them extremely tough.

CHAPTER 22.   FISH STORIES

THE beauties of tropic nights on moon-bright waters have been sung by poets for centuries. But even a poet can convey no more than an impression. A scientist finds the reason behind this magic effect equally full of wonder. He knows that when the oars of his boat drip silver and gold, and the wake is like molten metal, this enchantment is caused by certain minute organisms at breeding time.

I have often been traveling at night in a launch, and from the bow watched the startled fish, like luminous arrows, flash right and left. If we were speeding fast enough, the phosphorescence set up by our passage, red and green or white and blue, would send so bright a glow into the air that a newspaper, held near the water, could be easily read. A Japanese discovered that, after being dried, these tiny bodies still retained their radiancy. I once saw a professor of chemistry rub some over his face which, when the light was extinguished, shone pale and eerie as a ghost.

This was not the only natural reading lamp which I chanced upon. One black night I was coming down the Butuan River in Mindanao, and saw ahead a reflection so brilliant that I wondered what traveler might have built his campfire there. As the boat swung round the bend, I saw it was a tree all illuminated with the flickering lights of a myriad giant fireflies, brightening and dimming in unison.

The flying fish of the Philippines, which seemed bigger than those in other waters, were never ending sources of interest. We used to spend hours hanging over the rail of the *Basilan*, watching the gossamer winged fish leap, skim, and dive. My cabin was close to the water, and the electric light by which I read shone out over the waves. Many times these cold and clammy visitors from the deep would come shooting on to my bed. I would revenge myself for the shock by sending them to the galley, and the next morning would enjoy a tasty fish breakfast.

In the early days in the Philippines Governor General Forbes was an enthusiastic fisherman, and I learned about fishing from him. There were no bright trolling spoons then, and, although we fished industriously, we caught comparatively little. Governor Forbes later brought out the first modern trolling outfit, and most of us soon had similar ones. Immediately we began pulling in the most beautiful fish—tremendous fighting pompano which grew in Island waters to eighty pounds, Spanish mackerel, bonito, barracuda, and the lapu lapu, a species of grouper blue with red dots, or bright red with blue dots. Governor Forbes, who displayed the same vim and energy in his play as in his work, had a neat trim boat built with a square stern in order to have free play with the rods.

I remember once in clear, deep water, when Governor Forbes had a good strike, I looked over the side and said, "You've hooked a sea bass."

He also leaned over, and replied, "You're wrong, that's a red snapper."

I peered more intently, "It's a sea bass or I never saw one."

Meanwhile he was slowly reeling in his tackle, and when it came to the surface, we looked triumphantly at one another. One hook had a sea bass and the other a red snapper.

In the course of my inter-island voyages I had discovered many good fishing waters, and was able to introduce General Wood to them. One morning in 1924 we were cruising off Apo Reef on the West Coast of Mindoro. After a fairly good morning, a lull came. Finally the General's line began to run out slowly. I sank back on the cushions, saying, "General, it's hardly worth drawing in. That can't be much of a fish. There isn't enough pull to it."

"Oh, I don't know. It may be a long thin one swimming toward us," he replied defensively, "and that's why it doesn't offer much resistance."

But just as he had reeled the fish almost alongside and I had my gaff ready, the line started off furiously and quite a length was out before the tension slackened.

"I've a bigger fish than you think," exclaimed the General triumphantly.

"Oh, it's not so much," I retorted.

He began taking up the slack, winding and winding until the spool was almost filled and we were expecting the fish to break the surface any second. Suddenly the reel started zing-g-g-g, and the line cut through the water like the bow of a ship. It curled up spray a foot or more as it boiled out.

"Now you'll have to admit I have a big fish," boasted General Wood as he applied the brake ineffectually. The line ran out to within a few feet of its four-hundred-yard length. The General, with a jubilant glance in my direction, began his labors once more. The reel spun and whirred as he lost all that he had gained. He battled with his catch for an hour before it was exhausted enough to bring within gaffing distance.

Looking down into the transparent water I saw an eight-foot shark still lashing around. I gaffed it and we hauled it in. "General, that was never the fish that was on your line when you had the first strike," I said firmly.

"It may have been," he insisted.

"No, never," I repeated, and turning to a sailor I said, "Hand me a knife."

I ripped open the shark and inside found a three-foot Spanish mackerel. The General showed some surprise, but the smirk of satisfaction did not leave his face.

"What's more, you never had that Spanish mackerel on the first time," I asserted.

"Go as far as you like."

I cut open the mackerel and found inside a little ten-inch, polka-dotted lapu lapu, Jonah's dinner, with the hook through its lip.

Baron Munchausen would have had difficulty in improving on this story. I took the precaution of having General Wood sign an official affidavit testifying to its truth, and seal it with the Great Seal of the Philippine Islands.

FISH STORIES

The South Sea Islanders had perfected methods of catching fish which surpassed anything developed by Westerners. "You think you Americans are sportsmen," they would say to me. "You don't even know what sort of fish you're going to catch. We're choice in our tastes. We like only certain kinds."

The young men proved their contention unmistakably by showing me how they did it. In the late afternoon several of us would paddle toward the reef. When fish were seen swimming below, one of the youths would put on water goggles, which fitted tightly into the eye sockets and fastened with a strong cord around his head. With clear underwater vision thus assured, he would dive over the side and glide so quietly down among the fish that they did not seem to become alarmed. The water was translucent, and I could readily watch from the side of the canoe what was going on. The Islander would select a likely fish and, stroking it gently on the belly, gradually work his hand toward its head. Then, with a quick movement, he would slip a finger into its gills and bring his prize to the surface. If it met approval, it would be hauled in; if not, he would descend again for another. The less skilled fishermen used a pole with a barbed end on which the fish was hooked.

Going fishing for bonito in Samoa with Chief Fau Mui Na was a pleasant experience. We paddled out in his special bonito canoe, built sturdily to hold his enormous weight. He was very proud of it; the woodwork was all lashed, and the joints were sealed with lead and tar. Fore and aft it was decked over, and raised pegs indicated his rank as chief. The paddles were heirlooms from his grandfather. He trolled for bonito from a flexible bamboo pole set upright in the canoe, and used a barbless hook of tortoise shell tied to a piece of mother of pearl.

While at Beqa (Bengga) I saw an entire Fijian community join in their remarkable fish dive. At low tide, when about a foot of water covered the selected mile-long reef, a party of fifteen was stationed at each end. All were spaced equally across the reef along a vine rope, tied together, which must have been a half mile in length. Gradually the two parties approached one another, each man holding the vine with one hand and beating the bottom with a pole as he moved forward. Curiously enough, the fish, which were swarming in

389

with the rising tide, never attempted to escape under the slack vine. By the end of about two hours of this slow motion, the gap between the two parties had become no more than a few hundred yards across. About a hundred more villagers now rushed in and grabbing the vine with shouts and laughter, helped to herd the fish toward the V-shaped aperture which was being formed and where others were holding a huge net in readiness.

By this time the water had come up almost to the shoulders of the participants, who whooped and danced and beat the surface with their paddles until the leaping, churning fish were driven into the net. Then still others sailed a boat to the outer edge of the reef, and the net was heaved on board, laden with a ton of finny prizes.

Each island group in the South Seas has its own fishing customs. In Papua nets of tremendous strength are made from the webs of giant spiders, which indefatigably spin their geometrical patterns from tree to tree. The Santa Crucians use spider webs in an even stranger manner. Out of cocoanut fronds they construct an octagonal kite, the tail of which serves as a fish line. The lure is merely a mass of cobweb, trailing along the water. When the garfish leaps for it, he entangles his recurved teeth inextricably in the sticky substance and is easily retrieved.

In Australia the fishermen of the Great Barrier Reef use dynamite in a special way. Ordinarily the detonation bursts the bladder of the fish so that they sink and must be gathered up by diving. But the bright Antipodeans have discovered that if the dynamite is placed near tree coral, this phenomenon apparently does not take place, and the stunned fish float on the surface.

The Cook Islands are great lumps of coral into which the ebbing and flowing tides have eaten caverns, and there the sharks, replete with food, love to lie. But the semi-amphibian natives are equally familiar with these lagoons and know also the favorite resting places of the somnolent sharks. A Cook Islander, according to report, will dive until he finds one that pleases him, and then "talk to it." His right hand strokes its throat while his left, with forgivable duplicity, slips a noose around the body of the great fish, which is then hauled, ignominiously, tail first to the surface. It is also said that an old woman in Samoa was on even greater terms of familiarity with sharks.

She would stand on the foreshore and call until the vicious brutes came silently to her.

Fishing for sharks is great sport as long as the fisherman himself is not the bait. In 1923 I was inspecting health progress in Central America where there were no roads from one country to another and, as yet, no airplane service. Because the capitals of these countries are all far inland, I had to make the long journey around by sea. The hot, humid, and dusty journey from Guatemala City to San José was especially tedious and trying. I left at six in the morning, and it was not until late afternoon that I arrived at San José.

From my hotel window I could see the gentle swell of the broad, empty Pacific purling on a fine sandy beach. The cool-looking water was so alluring that I changed quickly into my bathing suit and hurried down to the deserted pier.

As I gathered speed for a running jump off the end, I was faintly conscious of shouts and yells behind me, but the water called me irresistibly, and I dived in. I swam slowly and steadily until I began to tire, and then rolled lazily over. My gaze was idly wandering when it was suddenly arrested by the pierhead, which had miraculously become black with people. Faint cries of *"Tiburon! Tiburon!"* came to my ears.

Almost at the same moment huge, dim shapes loomed through the crystal-clear sea. The water seemed suddenly icy. I was entirely surrounded by enormous sharks, their yellow-green eyes all fixed unwinkingly upon me.

My first startled impulse was to frighten them away by splashing and making a noise; but my reason checked this rash action. I had swum out leisurely with long, steady strokes, never moving fast. The sharks had not yet attacked me, and perhaps would not so long as I made no violent move. I resumed, therefore, my studied, rhythmic motion, turning quietly toward shore. Playfully the sharks swung around with me. Occasionally one would come so close that I could almost feel the clammy brush of his tail, and imagined I could see the ominous white of his belly. Nobody who has not looked into the cold, glassy eye of a shark swimming beside him in the water can ever realize what a horrible experience it was.

I began the long swim back, the longest swim, I believed, that anybody ever had, and, stroke for stroke, the sharks kept pace with me. I steeled my muscles to their deliberate mechanical task. Using a side stroke I swam like a slow-motion picture, with hardly a ripple or splash.

After what seemed hours, I was off the end of the pier, and could see the agonized expressions of the people, who were momentarily expecting to see me devoured. But when I reached the little iron ladder I did not obey my impulse to leap for it. I grasped one rung cautiously. Nothing happened. Then I lifted the other hand with equal deliberation. I put one foot on the ladder. Still nothing happened. Another foot. Nothing.

Once free of the water I swarmed up the ladder without pausing to wave farewell to my late companions. Not until then had I dared to take a full-sized breath.

The next day the steamer I was to take came into the harbor and anchored just where I had met the sharks. The sailors began fishing for them with salt pork. As soon as one was hooked, they let down over the line a rope with a noose on its end, and eased it along until it reached the shark's tail. Then they tightened it suddenly, so that the shark was firmly caught, and the ship's winch could lift him. One of the sharks weighed more than a ton, and could have swallowed me easily, with room to spare.

I was thankful over my escape, but puzzled as to why I had not been attacked.

Later when I became acquainted with Fau Mui Na I told him that I had heard of his expertness in lassoing sharks, and I asked him whether he would show me how he did it.

"We'll go out this very afternoon," he promised.

Accordingly, we embarked from his private fishing island in a precariously balanced outrigger canoe, accompanied by a mother ship.

"We don't catch our sharks with salt pork bait," the chief said. "We really fish for the fun of it. Catching sharks with a hook isn't considered sporting here. We use our hands as bait."

"Don't people ever lose their hands?"

"Practically never."

"How do you do it?"

392

"I'll show you."

We paddled just outside a barrier reef. The chief put his hand in the water, and trailed it slowly. Soon a shark drifted up and moved as gradually after his hand. As the fish drew alongside the canoe, a noose was gently dropped between it and the hand; the shark, unheeding, followed through. When the rope had passed back of the first fin, it was cautiously pulled tight. If it were to slip over the tail, the shark would struggle and the boat might be upset.

The moment the noose was taut, Fau Mui Na withdrew his fingers. "It's all in knowing how," he said. "If you move your hand slowly, the shark will also move slowly. If you move it quickly, off will come your hand."

The shark was allowed to swim off lazily for about fifty yards, and then was eased around and pulled near the boat. A member of the crew was standing ready with a long-handled mallet, and, as it came within reach, stunned it. The line was then passed to the mother ship, and the great fish was hauled aboard. In two and a half hours we caught more than a dozen specimens, each from six to ten feet long.

This exhibition may afford an explanation as to why I had escaped unscathed at San José. My instinct had been right, and slow-motion was probably the secret.

The report has often been spread about that a South Sea Islander with no other weapon than a knife will engage a shark in submarine combat. Dr. Lambert made the offer of twenty-five dollars in many islands to anyone who would perform this feat. Even though such a sum of money represented a fair-sized fortune in those latitudes, no one volunteered.

There has been much controversy as to whether sharks bite human beings. But Manley Beach at Sydney, Australia, has to be surrounded with iron fences behind which swimmers are supposed to stay. Airplanes patrol the air above and, when a shark is sighted, an alarm is sounded and the bathers flee to safety. Even so the papers almost weekly carry stories of reckless people who have disregarded the warnings and been mangled by sharks.

In my hospital experience I have treated patients whose legs had been bitten off by sharks. A crocodile may also bite off a man's leg, but its canine teeth tear and crush; a shark's curved razor-like teeth shear cleanly through the bone, leaving an unmistakable mark.

I was anxious to do my part in quashing the fallacy that sharks do not bite human beings. A cocksure English magazine had long offered a reward to anybody who would send in an authentic account of a shark bite. I watched as the years went by, and no case apparently was submitted; the reward was continued. Finally, I carefully photographed a femur showing the easily identifiable toothmarks, and claimed the money. My letter was unacknowledged. I wrote again, and, after a third communication, I received a notice that the reward had been withdrawn.

CHAPTER 23.   A GREAT LITTLE PEOPLE

"WE ARE spending seventy-five million yen a year on health," said the Japanese when, in 1924, they requested that a general survey be made. "We are not accomplishing as good results as other countries in our class. Either it is useless to spend money on health, or we are not doing it in the right way. Every ministry has been instructed to receive you and give you all the information you want. We have provided you with an interpreter. Use him or not as you wish. Everything is wide open to you. We want to know what is wrong."

By boat, by train, by motor, and by rickshaw I traveled up and down Japan in search of the difficulties. To ride in an automobile in Japan was a harrowing experience. The chauffeurs drove like mad through streets so narrow that pedestrians had to flatten themselves against the walls to avoid our headlong rush. From one end of the Archipelago to the other all roads were a moving mass of humanity, where no one seemed to give precedence, and bicycles and rickshaws and handcarts darted here and there, all in the greatest confusion. Every street was filled with color, sound, and motion. Smiling butterfly girls in gay kimonos clop-clopped on wooden *getas* over uneven pavements. From little handcarts or dangerously swinging poles men sold their wares.

The appearance of the landscape of the Island Empire was as fragile and delicate as a print by Sesshu. This country where every tillable acre was in cultivation, and where tillable acres were so few, presented an endless panorama of mountain and valley, of cherished views of sacred Fujiyama, of the torii of the Inland Sea, of red lacquer bridges connecting islet with islet, of dancing paper lanterns and glittering fireflies on beautiful winding streams, of giant lacy cryptomerias, twisted dwarf pines, and gorgeous chrysanthemums, of flowering cherry and plum in the spring and blazing maples in the fall.

I found the perfection of this formal fairyland, designed with such variety of charm, had been sadly marred since I had last seen it. The road to the incomparable summer resort of Miyanoshita, so beautiful with its gardens and pools, had been almost completely destroyed in the great earthquake of the year before, and, after the rains, was little more than paste upon the sides of the precipitous slopes. Huge slides had stripped the steep mountain of its loose volcanic material. The journey up along the road, which was scarcely wide enough for the car, reminded me of my hazardous days with the Italian army in the Dolomites.

In Japan, vehicles follow the English fashion of driving on the left hand side of the road. Because we were circling up the mountain on the left, we had to take the outside whenever we met vehicles coming toward us. Usually we had to back down the curving dangerous road to a place which we hoped would be wide enough for passage. Below us was a gorge thousands of feet deep, and on the inner side of the road a big, heavy oxcart that at any moment might topple us over the brink as it ground ponderously past.

In the towns the completeness of the demolition by earthquake and fire was much greater than anything I had anticipated. In one open square at Yokohama the fleeing inhabitants had sought refuge, dragging their household goods with them. But sparks had fallen on the bedding and, in the resultant conflagration, fifteen hundred people had died. I sadly viewed the ruins, where I could find no vestige of the homes in which I had been so many times lavishly entertained, and for all my searching could not trace my former hosts. My friends had disappeared and nobody knew what had become of them.

Nine months after the shock, Yokohama was still as depressing as the waste lands of the Johnstown flood, or the vicinity of Arras after the German bombardment. Twisted iron, brick, and non-inflammable débris were piled high. Only a few of the streets had been shoveled clean.

At Tokyo, only seventeen miles away, the damage had also been considerable. Only properly erected, reinforced concrete buildings had withstood the shocks and the fire. The escape of the Imperial Hotel, that fantastic structure designed by Frank Lloyd Wright of Chicago, whose contract was said to have called for making it earthquake proof, was most astonishing. Its enormous size and its immense, unsupported ceilings had marked it for destruction. That it stood intact in the midst of falling ruins was a great triumph for American design and construction.

Rebuilding was going forward rapidly, but well-informed foreign residents told me that the Japanese did not fully realize the far-reaching financial effect of the tremendous disaster, and that, had they done so, they would not have continued to create a bad impression by attempting to maneuver the foreign insurance companies, especially the British, into paying fire losses. Common opinion seemed to be that the Japanese, officially and privately, were trying to exploit foreigners. In the effort to prevent them from owning land, the government was prohibiting permanent reconstruction in the city or port areas, claiming time was needed to permit the earth to settle before making a survey for a new town plan.

Any Japanese in a foreign country was apt to be a spy, usually self-appointed. I was told that the government had received literally thousands of unsolicited notebooks and photographs made by its nationals in other countries. Examples of amateur spying had frequently occurred in my Philippine experiences. Japanese fishermen, who had virtually controlled the industry around Manila, had surreptitiously but meticulously sounded the entire Bay, although the information could do their country no possible good; for twenty-five cents a Geodetic Survey chart of those waters, scientifically accurate in every detail, might have been purchased by anybody. Apparently the Japanese could not believe the charts were accurate.

This was no isolated instance. At another time a Filipino with a broken leg had been carried to the nearest doctor, who happened to be a Japanese. But the "doctor," to everybody's consternation, after fumbling for some time, had finally confessed he did not have the faintest idea how to set the bone. His admission had naturally been reported to the Constabulary who, in searching his office, had found, instead of pills and instruments, plans of the United States Naval Station at Olongapo.

Because of their counter fear that foreigners might discover their military secrets and thereby gain some foothold in their country, the Japanese had enacted all sorts of protective rules, including a provision that no foreign warship might enter Tokyo. A week after the earthquake, however, an American Naval vessel, in defiance of regulations, is said to have steamed straight to the city and made fast to a government pier. The Japanese folded their hands; in a few hours they expected to see the American flag flying over Parliament House. But, to their bewilderment, instead of manning the guns, the middies were panting and sweating over unloading rice, medicines, bandages, splints, even building materials hastily despatched from Manila.

The Japanese lacked a sporting instinct in the Anglo-Saxon sense, and could not understand it in others. We were among the first upon the scene with assistance, and they looked upon our action with amazement; it was not only compassionate but startlingly efficient. "How could we have been so mistaken?" they asked. "We have sent all our young men to Germany to be educated. What a blunder! If we had trusted to American ideas, what progress we should have made!"

For a short time thereafter no country stood higher in Japanese estimation than the United States; we were regarded as true friends, and could have had anything we wanted. Japan, always avid for learning, showed her admiration by deflecting hundreds of her students to this country.

We rebuffed this gesture with scant courtesy. By our Japanese immigration legislation, California inspired, we immediately and loudly proclaimed that no Japanese should enter the United States. Although this prohibition did not include students, visitors, merchants, or those who were classed as temporary residents, the bill was regarded as a national affront. The goodwill which had come as a result of our generous action was lost almost overnight.

Resentment against America was extremely bitter in all quarters.

A GREAT LITTLE PEOPLE

The subject was on the lips of everyone in government circles with whom I talked. The American Ambassador, Cyrus Wood, in a conversation with me, stated that his previous relations with the government had been so pleasant that the merest suggestion on his part of a course of action had been followed. This had been particularly helpful whenever Japan's actions to close the Open Door in China, in accordance with her Twenty-One Demands, had seemed inimical to the United States.

An American adviser to the Ministry of Foreign Affairs, with whom I talked, was well qualified to interpret the Japanese point of view because he spent half his time in Tokyo and the other half in the Japanese Embassy at Washington. He told me that after the first unofficial intimation that an Exclusion Bill was under consideration, Prime Minister Hanihara had despatched a "grave consequences" note which Secretary of State Hughes had seen and with which he had apparently sympathized. Japan had been awaiting the negotiations customary to abrogating treaties, even one so nebulous as President Roosevelt's Gentlemen's Agreement by which, if we passed no Exclusion Act, Japan would prevent all emigration. The Japanese claimed they had kept the pact, but California claimed that could not be true since there had been a huge increase in the number of Japanese coming into the country.

It was the opinion of many persons that a satisfactory solution of the problem could have been reached by putting the Japanese on the quota, but it was contended on the other hand that this could not have been reconciled with our general policy of excluding all aliens who were unassimilable.

In this connection it seems only fair to mention that it is seldom brought out that Japan for perhaps similar reasons excludes other races, and even those of her own color, from her country.

One morning when I was calling on Foreign Minister Shidehara, an intelligent gentleman who had been educated in the United States, he lamented, "It's too bad this should have happened. I'm afraid public resentment is going to last for years. If Washington had only let us know before taking this step we might have prepared our people, and it would have been so much better."

"I don't see how that could have helped."

"It would have been simple. If your government had informed us in advance that it intended to pass a bill excluding all Japanese labor, we would then have had an opportunity to announce it to our people in the form of an agreement that no American labor could come to Japan. Since you don't send any labor here anyhow, this would have accomplished your object and at the same time have saved our face."

I myself could verify the state of animosity in the attitude of the daily press. When I came to breakfast one morning at Kobe, I was greeted with flaring headlines stating that rioters, in protest against America's action, had broken up the Saturday night dance at the Tokyo Imperial Hotel. The article claimed it was part of a larger movement to evict all Americans. Some papers expressed it one way, some another, but all featured the story, because it showed how high feeling was running. *Mainichi* of Osaka said it was nothing but a five-year-old boy dancing around with a paper stage sword and the Americans had become frightened and run away. The *Japan Chronicle* of Kobe gave a conservative statement of what appeared to be the facts; the dance had been broken up by members of Japanese patriotic clubs who had distributed handbills requesting that Americans be expelled and their goods boycotted.

The press was only reflecting popular sentiment. Signs in the Kobe stores read, "No goods sold to Americans." At a huge mass meeting a demand was made for the expulsion of American missionaries, the boycott of American goods, and a law to prevent Americans coming to Japan until Congress should modify the Exclusion Bill. Ships' officers complained that the hatred was shared by stevedores, who were delaying the unloading of American vessels by wrecking the winches. On returning to Tokyo, the center of anti-American agitation, I found the entire city under the spell. The Imperial Hotel, instead of being gay with the weekly dance, was shrouded in darkness.

I always suspected that I was guarded by government secret service agents. Whenever I would start to light a cigarette, a match would be all too hastily proffered me by a stranger. Even the omnipresent politeness of the race would not seem to account for the fact that I suffered unpleasantness only once. On this occasion I had boarded a tram already well filled with Japanese and had hardly seated myself when the gentleman beside me rose, bowed, and with a sweep of his hand indicating the other passengers, asked coldly in English, "Shall we leave the car at the next corner, or will you?"

Since it was their country I replied, "If my presence is objectionable to you, I'll leave," and accordingly I alighted at the next corner.

The intensity of feeling thus expressed eventually died down, but the hurt and the slight remained in the backs of the Japanese minds. John D. Rockefeller, Jr., always sympathized with the Japanese sensitiveness, and, to show that all America did not feel hostile, he gave a million dollars personally to rebuild their once fine library. They accepted this gift, even though, I fear, they privately looked upon it with suspicion, lest some string might be attached to it. We might, for instance, try to impose an American style of architecture. Nevertheless, the gift helped to create, in academic circles at least, a more favorable attitude toward the United States.

The Rockefeller Foundation had no cause for personal complaint in making the survey; cooperation was complete and full. Every office was open, every request was granted, every record was available, even to the accounting systems. It was hard to determine whether these apparently open facilities were being offered frankly or only as a means to an end. I sometimes gained the impression the Japanese were merely tolerating the presence of our men in order to have their own trained.

On all my Japanese trips I took with me Dr. John B. Grant, Professor of Hygiene at the Peiping Union Medical College, an extremely able young man whose popularity in China and Japan was unparalleled. He was one of the best administrators developed by the Rockefeller Foundation and was of inestimable aid on this survey. When Dr. Grant discovered what he took to be a discrepancy in the Japanese accounts, the greatest distress was aroused. As I was going out of the hotel one day I noticed a truck unloading huge volumes borne by a staggering line of porters. The sight was, to say the least, unusual, and in curiosity I followed them, to find the tomes being deposited in Dr. Grant's room. Although the Finance Department had merely changed its fiscal year, it was going to prove that nothing had been falsified.

The Japanese are the most hospitable people in the world, and entertained me as I have rarely been entertained elsewhere. I shall never forget my first dinner at the Maple Club, given by the Japanese Cabinet, at which Dr. Grant and I were the only Americans. Because I had been a bachelor for many years, a hole in my sock below the water line made little impression upon me. But, since shoes are not worn in Japanese houses, such nonchalance would not do; I had, as a precaution, provided myself with a supply of new black silk socks so that I would have a new pair available for each function. For this particular dinner I garbed myself in morning clothes, the accepted attire for evening wear in Japan, and one of my new pairs of socks.

Thus confidently fortified I entered the limousine which had been sent for me. The Japanese realize that the difficulties a stranger experiences in any foreign country are increased in theirs because he cannot even read the signs. Therefore they always thoughtfully provide means of transportation.

We arrived a little before six. My shoes were whisked away but, instead of being conducted directly to the reception room, I was regaled with the beauties of the Maple Club's rock garden, reputedly the finest in the country. It was a perfect late afternoon in June, the height of the iris season, as the summer months are characterized in Japan. My guide conducted me down winding paths and over little bridges, and past fern grottos where goldfish twinkled, rippling little waterfalls, shrubs, and flowering plants. Everywhere bloomed gorgeous iris, the most lovely I have ever seen, shading from purest white to deepest purple. Posed here and there among the rocks were geisha girls in brilliantly embroidered kimonos of the latest summer style. Feasting my eyes upon the attractions of the scene, animate and inanimate, I did not notice that the many steps I had taken along this maze of gravel paths, tortuous as the dwarf tree trunks, had had their effect upon my frail silk socks. Not until I reached the reception room did I suddenly realize that one of my toes was peeping shyly forth.

Instead of bending over as was my wont in Japan, I drew myself up to my full height, so that the short Japanese with whom I was conversing would have to tilt their heads up at me. By the use of this subterfuge, I trusted the disgraceful condition of my toe might escape unnoticed. I carefully covered the exposure with my other foot, and congratulated myself that nobody had apparently remarked it.

After a round of courteous conversational exchanges, the paper doors were slipped aside, and we entered the dining room. I was unable to hide my foot discreetly under the table, because there was none. The seating was on the floor in the shape of a horseshoe, and I, as guest of honor, sat in the depth of the curve. I tried unsuccessfully to fold my legs under me in the approved fashion. I imagined I could see dotted lines from the guests' eyes focused upon me, and then I noted with unbounded horror that there had been a hernia of the big toe and it had popped through the sock. Tightly constricted as it was, it had become as fiery red as the tail light of an automobile. I hastily concealed it under my leg, but try as I might it would slip out and the burning gazes were renewed.

Japanese dinners last a long time. A geisha sits before each guest, entertaining him with song and sprightly talk; if he is English she speaks to him in his own language. Sometimes she drinks *sake* with him. As the waitresses patter in with each course, she prepares his food, and, realizing that taking a bird apart with chopsticks is no easy feat, she assists him. Between courses all the geishas join in a ballet. But even the delightful witticisms of my charming geisha failed to make me oblivious of my toe, and the *sake* in this instance proved no Lethe.

For at least two hours I struggled with the recalcitrant digit, but when at last the dinner was over and the signal was given to rise, another embarrassment was in store for me. At Japanese banquets hot *sake* is always served in tiny porcelain cups, and courtesy demands that each diner approach the guests of the evening and with a profound bow drink a cup of *sake* with them. Although this is not a particularly strong drink, if there are forty diners the odds are heavily against the guests and considerable alcohol is consumed. Dr. Grant, who was sitting some distance down the horseshoe, failed to rise with the rest of us. A horrible thought struck me. Mr. Rockefeller was the premier prohibitionist of the world, and one of his officers was so drunk at a Japanese banquet that he could not rise to his feet!

403

I approached Dr. Grant with a firm tread and whispered severely, "You've got to get up!"

He looked up at me appealingly but made no effort to rise. I took him by the arms and lifted him; he sank limply back again to the floor. In even sterner tones I said, "You've simply got to stand up!"

I lifted him again; again he sank back. "Are you drunk?" I demanded.

"No!" he replied indignantly, "certainly not!"

"Then why don't you stand up?"

By this time our whispers had risen to audible tones and our Japanese hosts were hovering solicitously about. "I can't. My legs are paralyzed."

Immediately the Japanese bent over him concernedly, massaged his legs vigorously, and Grant was soon on his feet.

Probably my contortionary efforts to hide my toe had alone been responsible for saving me from the same cramps. I realized also that in my efforts to conform to the customs of the country I had erred on the side of elegance. Thereafter, at all functions, instead of silk socks I wore stout cotton ones similar to those with which the Japanese protected themselves from such predicaments.

Because of the universal politeness and courtesy of the Japanese, many situations that might otherwise have proved awkward were smoothed over. Courtesy is extended even to that stronghold of rudeness, the customs service. If a customs officer discovered tobacco in my baggage, he would say with a bow, "You probably won't need this in Japan. We'll keep it for you and return it to you when you leave." Any attempt to bribe them would probably be followed by a jail sentence. The honesty of the Japanese public services contrasts strikingly with conditions elsewhere in the East.

One of the national handicaps was the Japanese inability to learn foreign languages well. I sometimes found it extremely difficult to discourse with men who supposedly were educated in English. German helped me enormously, but, even so, conversation was disconnected. It seemed very difficult for them to grasp the spirit of a question, and their abbreviated vocabularies were distressing. When

I came to know them better, they would often confess their humiliation. A great part of their bowing and scraping was due to embarrassment; it also gave them time to formulate their answers.

Another obstacle to mutual comprehension was the lack of a sense of humor as Americans understand it. Our oral fun-making was readily intelligible to the Chinese—which may in part account for the greater ease with which we get along together. But the Japanese found cause for laughter chiefly in the vulgar joke.

The people are, nevertheless, at heart merry, and sometimes, to my own amusement also, played pranks upon me. In this country of small people, nothing is built for tall men. The berths on the sleepers, some of which are compartment trains, are only five foot ten, and are so narrow that when I lay on my side my doubled-up knees protruded. One hot night I had been twisting and bumping this way and that in acute discomfort when a brilliant idea struck me. I adopted the simple expedient of stretching out full length and letting my feet stick through the window. With a sigh of relief I sank into deep slumber.

I do not know how long I had been thus happily occupied when I returned to consciousness with a convulsive start which jerked my feet back into my compartment. The train was no longer moving. To see who or what had so disrespectfully tickled my toes, I peered out, and found my window surrounded by a group of adult Japanese, convulsed with laughter, to whom my large, bare, white feet had proved an irresistible lure.

Only a tall person knows what another tall person suffers. Heads are always being bumped under low doorways, feet or shoulders protrude from blankets. But in New York hotels, at least, his feet will not stick out. The Constitution of the State, due to the efforts of the Six Foot Association to alleviate his agonies, provides that no hotel bed shall have a sheet shorter than eight feet. In my Eastern travels I was happiest in Java, where appurtenances are built to fit the tall Dutch; I was apt to become stoop-shouldered in Japan.

The Japanese were very sensitive about their size. Newspaper reporters used to come daily to my hotel for a story. I had early developed a method of sidetracking them. "Gentlemen," I would say,

"I'm a guest of the government. Whatever you wish to know must be obtained from official sources."

This shunting device worked beautifully; medical officials, always inclined to be jealous of outside interference, were disarmed because they realized I was not trying to steal their thunder.

After I had made my excuses to the reporters for some time, one of them said, "Look here, we've been around day after day and you always put us off. Come on now, give us at least one story."

"All right," I said. "I can't give you one, but, if you'll keep my name out of it, I'll tell you where you can get one. You've a scientist here in Tokyo who has made a certain fish extract which possesses the property of stimulating growth tremendously. The children to whom he is giving it are growing larger and larger. If you see Dr. ——, he'll give you the details of his experiments."

The next morning the story of the magic growth powder appeared in all Tokyo newspapers. Because this was such important news to the Japanese, the Associated Press and Reuter correspondents picked it up, and, to give it more than local interest, sent it out over their wires under my name. When I reached the United States I found awaiting me bundles of newspaper clippings and letters by the hundreds from little short people all over the world. The tenor of the latter was, "I saw in —— paper that you said a Japanese had invented a growth powder. I am five feet tall. I want to be six. How much of the powder would I have to take to grow this extra foot? How much would it cost?"

The volume of letters was so great that it taxed the office force considerably to answer them and express my regrets at being unable to help. I never saw a story persist as long as that of the magic growth powder. Finally, it was put into plate and syndicated throughout the world. My name was inextricably linked with it, and hardly a voyage passed that somebody did not ask for further information about it.

The members of the Japanese press are as pertinacious and resourceful as their brothers of the fourth estate elsewhere. One warm June morning, worn out after the long night's train ride and the many courtesies tendered me, I stepped off the train at Tokyo to face a camera squad ready for action.

"Have you seen Dr. Heiser?" one of the photographers asked me.

"Oh, yes," I replied mendaciously. "He's just behind me on the train. He'll be off in a minute."

I had no desire to answer questions, and certainly not to pose for photographs, an ordeal which I have never faced with composure. I was hot and tired, and aspired solely to a refreshing bath. I betook myself quietly to the Hotel Imperial, and soon was merrily sloshing around in the sunken tub provided for captious foreigners.

No locks safeguard doors in Japan; the Japanese have never felt the need of them because, unlike Christians, they do not indulge in petty pilfering and have no sense of personal privacy. Having finished my bath, I walked unconcernedly toward the outer room, but just as I was framed in the doorway my startled glance fell upon several cameras in position. With one bound I knocked aside a hand, poised to set off the flash. "Even in Japan," I protested, "you wouldn't run a photograph like that—of a man without any clothes on."

"Oh, no," one of them replied. "We'd cut off the bottom and nobody would know the difference."

The picture of a bald-headed man in this décolleté pleased me little more than the idea of the full-length nude. I had prevented a major catastrophe by my prompt action, but I was still unclothed, and there is something about such a state that produces a distinct feeling of helplessness. In the ensuing argument I found myself at a great disadvantage. The photographers had been sent on an assignment, and were determined not to return to their papers without pictures. Nevertheless, while keeping up my end of the controversy, I was slipping on a garment here and there, and, as my self-confidence returned, my arguments increased relatively in potency. Once safe inside my clothes, I was a match for them, and was able to persuade them to retire.

Everything had to be done strictly according to rule in Japan; no deviation was allowed. At the smaller hotels in the interior the ritual of bathing was an experience to remember. Although the people were unbelievably clean, the result was accomplished by means of a little two-quart receptacle of water, not much bigger than a washbasin. But, because they suspected that the Anglo-Saxon might be up to his well-known trick of plunging, before he had washed himself, into the big tub which had to serve for everybody, diligent maids constantly pattered in and out to see that bathing customs were not violated. Only after I was supposedly cleansed was I given an opportunity to sit in the extremely hot water of the tub and rest, relax, and contemplate. When the time came to emerge, I was as red as the proverbial boiled lobster.

The hotel maids were equally determined that I should get no fresh air at night. I wanted the panels between my room and the out-of-doors left open, but this was contrary to Japanese custom. After retiring I soon heard light footsteps, and the panels were noiselessly slid shut. When all was quiet, I would steal catlike to open them again, but would soon awaken to find them once more closed. Such battles often continued through the night.

In the morning the constant entrance of the same smiling maids, regardless of the state of my attire, was embarrassing to me but apparently not to them. Shaving seemed to afford particular amusement. At one hotel the entire staff gathered eagerly to watch the operation. The departure from this same hostelry was rather touching. From manager to porter all seemed to be as sincere in their farewells as in their greetings. They did, however, expect the traveler's tip to equal the hotel bill; if he were a real gentleman he would double it.

The clean and sociable Japanese made pleasant fellow travelers, although their hospitality on occasion was carried to excess. Whenever a new passenger entered a compartment on a train, he passed around a box of laxative pills. Courtesy demanded that one be accepted and swallowed. I did not mind taking one, but the Japanese were constantly getting off and on, and each newcomer would inevitably produce his little box. On long journeys I had to resort to sleight of hand.

But in spite of their embarrassingly frank customs and their strict observance of tradition, the Japanese were enamored of Western ideas. It seemed to me they copied everything American, even to the numbering of their sleeping cars, and the rubber-tired electric baggage motors were reproduced to the last screw.

I became much impressed with the efficiency of this people. The trains were run on time. I could set my watch to the minute by comparing their scheduled arrival with the time-table. All waste motion was eliminated in loading ships or freight cars, and the muscular coordination of the coolies, notwithstanding their handicap in size, was admirable.

The Japanese showed the same efficiency in all their operations outside the country. When I first went to Manchuria in 1916, in the days when it still belonged to China, the Japanese-owned South Manchurian Railroad was the acme of perfection, with beautiful roadbed and American-type Pullman cars. The railroad had a fine hospital and maintained a medical school.

It is extraordinary to observe that the Japanese are the only Orientals who have been able to rise above their own self-satisfaction and have, furthermore, disturbed the mass inertia of other Orientals with whom they have come in contact.

In Korea also, which Japan was endeavoring to pull up to Western standards, a good job had been done from a machine standpoint, and much more money was being spent than was collected in revenues. Enormous public works had been undertaken, agriculture developed, schools introduced, and hospitals built. The Japanese did not seem favorably disposed to the efforts of the missionaries, and hence taxed their property heavily. Apparently in an effort to ease them out entirely, the Japanese would build bigger and better hospitals of their own near missionary dispensaries, and thus greatly aided in elevating the standards of medical practice.

In 1916 I saw the border Japanese town of Antung, planned along the best lines, with wide streets and proper drainage, in the making, but it seemed to cause no emulation in the Chinese town across the Yalu River. Korea was hilly and full of huge loose surface rocks. Even so, the valleys were intensively cultivated, mostly with rice. Oxen were apparent in large numbers, carrying great loads on their backs. The countryside was brown and sere and heavy in frost. Everyone was dressed in white cotton cloth and this, in the prevailing freezing weather, gave me a chilly sensation. The stiff, silly, black horsehair headgear worn by the Koreans to protect their topknots looked like silk hats several sizes too small, and contrasted grotesquely and startlingly with the whiteness of their other clothing.

In spite of the Japanese improvements over Korean ancient customs, the Koreans were extremely hostile to their overlords, and often assassinated them. Supervision was so rigid in Korea that tyrannicide was practised mostly outside the country. I once happened to be at Government House in Singapore when the present Mikado, then Crown Prince, was touring the East. He was naturally invited to an official dinner, and a guard of honor was sent to the pier to escort him. Fifteen minutes before the appointed dinner hour the telephone rang, and the request was made that identical arrangements for receiving the Prince be made at another pier, but to leave the first guard of honor where it was. Government aides scurried around in mad haste, and a second guard of honor was made up and despatched. The hour came and went without a Prince. Twenty minutes later he put in an appearance with no guard at all. After his official guardians had been satisfied with their complex preparations to throw off any possible assassins, they had sent him ashore in a sampan, and he arrived at Government House in a rickshaw.

I had an extremely interesting interview with Viscount Goto, former Home Minister and generally regarded as one of Japan's ablest statesmen. He was a fine looking old gentleman, with a goatee, and had charming, courtly manners. He was at first exceedingly cautious, but in the end my frank treatment of the situation called forth an equal frankness from him. He greatly deplored the Japanese tendency to analysis rather than to synthesis and admitted this tendency stood in the way of their progress. He said the Japanese regarded Burbank as being unscientific and only successful accidentally. He himself conceded that Burbank had made important discoveries despite his crude methods, and ventured the belief that many of America's achievements were due to her backing people who were following unproved "hunches" not verified by logical reasoning.

I told Viscount Goto I was learning many things; Japanese laboratories, in both numbers and equipment, were a source of constant amazement to me, and were superior to ours in their distribution. Good bacteriological examinations could be made in almost every nook and corner of the country. But I also pointed out that Japan, on account of the modern civilization she had adopted, had greatly increased her health hazards, and if she were to keep her place in the sun she must avail herself of health control measures. She had to take cognizance of her diseases caused by faulty nutrition and soil pollution, and also her rising typhoid and high infant mortality rates.

The thoroughness of the Japanese was by no means extended to all branches of medicine. Curiously enough, dentistry was not held in high regard, because their German teachers had not believed in focal infections. The Japanese medical profession itself had the worst teeth I have ever seen.

Leprosy was apparently on the wane, although only the most advanced cases, and these relatively few in number, were segregated. Those at large were under the ever-watchful eye of the police, who saw to it they used only their own utensils and did not come in close contact with well persons.

The increased cost of living had caused more and more crowding and poorer diet in the homes of working people. The most serious disease menace, therefore, was tuberculosis, which had fastened itself upon the country; the incidence was almost twice as high as in the United States or England, and the rates approached the worst slum centers of the world.

Japanese scientists concerned themselves little with the practical application of existing knowledge. It was their constant dream to discover a specific for tuberculosis or some other disease. In their zeal they often made unreliable reports. To prevent these reaching the outside world, a small committee in Tokyo took upon itself the task of suppressing them.

I have never felt more strongly about what is being done in the name of preventive medicine than after visiting a Japanese hospital. It was an arbitrary use of power in a futile endeavor to control things that would never happen. Such force and insistence were placed upon non-essentials that as much effort was wasted in making the machinery run as though a hundred horsepower motor were hitched to a lawn-mower.

Japanese hospital rules and regulations made any visitor feel bacteria were going to rise up and bite him. When I once visited a tuberculosis sanitarium, I was put through a most amazing rite. First I was encased in a pair of boots which came to my hips, and then the regulation hospital gown, which was so short on me that a portion of my booted legs was exposed. This caused the attending staff much concern, lest some possible infection might make its way through the area not protected by the gown. Only after a gauze face mask and a hood had been adjusted was I allowed to enter the presence of the patients.

On emerging, I had to wade through a huge tank of bichloride solution, after which an attendant, striving vainly on tiptoe to reach my throat with his atomizer, pulled up a little stepladder beside me, stood on it, and carefully sprayed my respiratory passages to kill any possible tubercles which might be lurking there. Finally, I was requested to gargle, and, feeling thoroughly purified, I was allowed to depart.

In the cholera hospital, the wheels of the ambulance which carried in the patients had to run through troughs of disinfecting solution. The same type of rules had been imposed in Korea during cholera epidemics. At the gateway to public buildings, horses and people were obliged to tramp through similar solutions, and, before any letter could be mailed, the correspondent had to wash his hands in a germicidal basin placed by each mailbox. In the light of modern knowledge their precautions were ridiculous.

In the application of maritime quarantine regulations the Japanese were strict. When an American Assistant Secretary of State was once traveling in the East, he was put in quarantine, because a case of plague had occurred on his ship. In high dudgeon he cabled Washington to get him out, but the Japanese health officers were adamant to all representations. He protested indignantly that this was an unheard of humiliation. His humorless jailers, a careful people, searched the records and found that the King of Sweden had once been in quarantine. Since royalty obviously outranked a mere Assistant Secretary of State, the latter continued to languish until the incubation period was over.

The German-trained men in charge of Japanese medicine adhered to the procedure of the age of bacteriology; they developed knowledge along the lines of Koch, Pasteur, and Lister, but had an entire lack of appreciation of the need to have it used in the lives of the people. Shibasaburo Kitasato was the outstanding medical scientist. The concentration on bacteriology rather than health was largely due to the power of his personality and ability.

A GREAT LITTLE PEOPLE

After Kitasato's memorable achievement in tracking down the plague bacillus, he was loaded with honors. But, unfortunately for the progress of medicine in Japan, he became involved in a dispute with the government, and resigned indignantly from his position as head of the Imperial Institute for Infectious Diseases. Nevertheless, his prestige was so great that by public subscription a laboratory was built especially for him.

Kitasato's action led to a disastrous schism in the medical profession. He not only took the majority of his staff with him but also the leaders in bacteriology, including Shiga, who had discovered a dysentery bacillus and was a most important figure in the Japanese medical world. The government had to build a new organization from the ground up. What one faction wanted, the other fought, although the government, which had no other source of supply, had to buy the various sera and vaccines manufactured by the Kitasato laboratory. The problem was complicated further by the fact that the government owned all the universities, with the major exception of the Keio, which set the pace for the rest. When the Kitasato group threw its weight behind the Keio, the government medical school languished and the rift grew wider.

Because of this cleavage among Japanese scientists, which had lasted for thirty years, all professional dealings with them had to be conducted with delicacy and caution. The jealousy was so intense that when Doctors Flexner and Welch went to Japan, they were received by one group and ignored by the other. They actually had to leave the country and return, so that they might be officially welcomed by the opposite faction.

Through the exercise of care the Rockefeller Foundation had always been able to maintain friendly relations with all parties to the dispute.

I would never compromise with their petty animosities although, since our survey came at a time when anti-American feeling was running so high, I had to allow it to be made more or less under cover; the politicians were afraid if they accepted help openly from America it might interfere with their political future.

Dealing with the Japanese government had one great advantage. Once an arrangement was agreed upon we could be sure it would be

413

faithfully carried out, no matter how the balance of power in politics might shift. German influence in government medical circles was on the wane, and there seemed to be hope that the authorities would subscribe to the concept of applying knowledge to prevent disease and realize that Germany had not progressed so far as America in this respect. As an indication of the change, it was also astounding to see to what extent English was coming into general use, and how rapidly German was declining.

Gradually I came to be accepted as a neutral and could go freely from one group to another. I told them both frankly that, if they could not agree, there was no hope of getting the Rockefeller Foundation to aid them. Eventually I worked them up to a point where they jointly petitioned for us to help them start a Health Institute in which they would both cooperate.

When the Far Eastern Association of Tropical Medicine met in 1926 at Tokyo, Kitasato was still all-powerful. Each time the great man spoke, the awed delegates from all over the Orient were silent. He was chairman, and it was amusing to see that no vote was ever taken; any motion put by him was accepted as unanimously passed. Everything was most amicable. At the first formal meeting the toastmaster made a happy address, quoting from some ancient Japanese writings the impression made upon the Japanese who had first dissected a white man. They had been astounded to find that underneath his skin he was constructed in exactly the same way as themselves.

A great to-do took place over which country's delegate should preside at the banquet to be given by the foreign guests to their Japanese hosts. Finally, unable to reach a conclusion, they compromised on me, who represented no country, and was known to be equally well disposed to all.

Over seven hundred persons assembled in the huge banquet hall of the Imperial Hotel for one of the largest international dinners ever held in Japan. Kitasato, who was sitting on my right, told me much about his early days with Koch, and, to my surprise, admitted that bacteriology now had its back to the wall; further development would probably be along the lines of bio-chemistry. I could not interest him in nutrition as an important factor in disease, although the Japanese themselves, in their own laboratories, had proved the importance of diet by producing stones in the bladders or kidneys of white rats with a diet deficiency, and had dissolved them again with proper diet. But Kitasato, like so many other research scientists, saw no further than the discovery, and, assuming it would immediately be adopted by the people, did not realize that usually more effort is required to bring a discovery into use than has gone into the original research.

After our survey was completed it was obvious that the didactic teaching should be largely supplemented by the inculcation of methods to bring modern scientific knowledge into the lives of the people. To accomplish this a modern school of hygiene and public health for Japan was recommended, and this was finally agreed to by the Japanese government. The development of new knowledge was to be encouraged in every way, but equal importance was to be attached to its practical application.

The chief difficulty in founding a Health Institute in Japan lay with the stubborn elder groups, still headed by Kitasato. He had no faith in it, because he had spent his life in the cloistered seclusion of the laboratory. He did not believe in his heart in what we were recommending, but, because he realized I was above the battle and had no personal objectives in my long persuasive efforts, he finally acquiesced. We inveigled a group of these elder scientists to come to the United States to observe the friendly cooperation in American scientific circles, and see how research workers in bacteriology and the men who applied their discoveries could work in harmony together. The ancients were still dubious after their expedition to America, but they could be counted upon at least not to oppose the venture.

Once the Health Institute had been decided upon, the great problem was how to apportion the control. Admittedly the elders had to be put in charge, but it was very hard for them to change the guiding principles they had acquired in their youth, and the reverence for age was so great that, although the younger men might know better, they were still apt to bow respectfully before the older wisdom. Determined to have a body of younger men with progressive ideas to serve as a check, we stipulated, "You'll have to have an advisory committee."

During the many years required to establish the Health Institute, we brought many of these young men to America on fellowships, selecting the applicants carefully from both government and Kitasato groups, so that by the time the Health Institute should be ready to open its doors, there would be a staff of young men who would have lost to some extent their ancestor worship and would champion their own ideals even against the elders. After this new school has a sufficient number of graduates it is the hope that personal idiosyncrasies, habits of mind, and the old German concept of hygiene, which is still strong, will be overcome, and that the application of preventive medicine will become a reality.

CHAPTER 24. PICKING UP BROKEN THREADS

THE Harrison bonfire which had blazed so merrily for many
years and around which the Filipinos had danced so blithely,
finally flickered and went out, leaving only dead ashes. They were
still warm when General Wood and former Governor General
Forbes came to poke among the ruins to see what of value remained.
I was on my 1921 trip and saw a paper with American news only
occasionally. I was cognizant that President Harding had appointed
these two old friends of mine to report on the condition of the
Philippines, but did not know precisely where they were.

In the course of my travels I arrived at Sandakan, Borneo, just in
time to see the *S.S. Eastern,* which I had expected to take to Manila,
steaming out. I had a choice of waiting in Sandakan several weeks
for the regular sailing, or of taking an extra week to retrace my steps
to Singapore, and going thence by another line to Manila.

The following morning, still perplexed as to what I ought to do,
I was walking along the harbor front. Low down on the horizon I
saw faint trails of smoke. "What ships are those?" I asked the Captain of the Port.

"Haven't you heard?" he replied. "Early this morning we received word the Wood-Forbes party was to pay an unexpected visit
to the Governor of Borneo."

My gloom lifted as the gossamer wisps grew into black smudges.
Just at that moment the Governor's aide came along, and I saw a

launch making ready to leave. "Could I go out with you?" I asked him.

"Of course, if you would like to, but I think the Governor is expecting you to accompany him."

"If you don't mind, I'd rather join you."

As we gradually drew near, I recognized the old *General Alava*, an inheritance from the Spanish, and the *Polillo*, the despatch boat of the previous Governor Generals. I could see through my glasses that we also were objects of scrutiny. I was, of course, in civilian clothes, but my face was well concealed by my huge helmet; the arriving party was scurrying about. I could hear the bugle sounding and see sailors lined up stiffly on the deck. At the top of the gangway, the officer saluted smartly.

"Where's the General?" I asked.

"On the quarterdeck, sir."

"Lead the way."

"Aye aye, sir."

General Wood and his staff, former Governor Forbes, Major General Frank McCoy, Colonel Gordon Johnston, Major Edward Bowditch, and other old friends among the members of the Mission were all standing strictly at attention. General Wood was the first to recognize me. I could see him blink. Just then Forbes relaxed his official attitude and ejaculated, "You damned old scoundrel, we're not drawn up at attention to meet you. You're not the Governor."

As we pumped each other's hands enthusiastically, General Wood exclaimed, "This is the most extraordinary coincidence. I've cabled all over the East trying to find you. Imagine running across you in Borneo. You may not know it but you're joining the Mission, and you're going on with us to the Philippines."

Nothing could have pleased me better. Bag and baggage I was transferred to the *General Alava*, and that evening we sailed.

This was a particularly happy occasion. I was back in the midst of many friends whom I had not seen for years, with whom I could reminisce over old battles, old triumphs, and pleasant and amusing experiences we had shared together. Once more we were in harness at the old job of hauling the Filipinos out of the slough. My friends seemed to be equally divided between the two ships, and, since it was impossible for me to be in both places at once, we talked by wireless. I even carried on an animated chess game by wireless with General McCoy.

Seven years dropped away as we inspected island after island which I had so often visited as Director of Health. At each stop we heard the same old charges and countercharges, discovered shocking examples of delayed justice, and heard the same addresses of welcome pitched in the same old florid vein. The independence leaders had agitated well; the keynote of many of these orations was independence, though many Filipinos themselves realized that the time was not yet ripe for independence without a protectorate.

A warm welcome awaited me in Manila. My old associate and prize cholera fighter, Dr. Vicente Jesus, who was now Director of Health, seemed overjoyed at my return to share his responsibilities. He had already had a desk placed beside his, and offered to retire temporarily while I was there. I was never more touched than by this demonstration of trust.

General Wood asked me to stay with him at Malacañan during my visit. My acquaintance with him dated from 1903 when he had been in command at Mindanao. Then and later, when he had been head of the Philippine Division of the Army, we had often consulted together on problems of health. He was a delightful man to be with, urbane, courteous, and full of interesting anecdotes. Like Theodore Roosevelt, his close friend, he surrounded himself with unusual people, and had the gift of setting them at their ease and drawing them out.

One evening when we were alone at Malacañan, coffee and cigars were brought out on the veranda, which overlooked the Pasig River. Between the palm trees the native life could be seen hurrying up and down this artery of trade and traffic in endless procession. The General had been offered the position of head of the University of Pennsylvania, which was clamoring for his return to take up his post there. President Harding had just offered him the Governor Generalship of the Philippines and he was obviously pondering the problem. I obtruded upon his thoughts.

"I don't know your ambitions," I said, "and, of course, it's none of my affair, but I suppose you still would like to be President of the United States. If you stay here I believe you might as well abandon any such idea. If you do a hundred percent job as Governor General, it will be taken for granted. Here you have a political and economic crisis to deal with; some of the things you attempt to do under such conditions will inevitably be failures. These will be seized upon by your opponents, who will make political capital out of them in the United States. You will be too far away to answer any of these slanders. Furthermore, your salary here will barely pay your expenses, whereas at the University of Pennsylvania you will be better off."

"That's quite true," he replied.

"But what's more important," I went on, "in Philadelphia you will be close to affairs. You will be in a strategic position politically, because you can put in an appearance whenever the weather is propitious, and stay in academic retirement when it isn't. After four years here you will be forgotten, especially if things are running well. Obviously, it will be much to your personal advantage to go to Pennsylvania."

General Wood took a long pull on his cigar, and then said slowly but with complete finality, "I believe I can serve my country best in the Philippines. What effect this may have on my career is immaterial."

Though I regretted the benefits he was to lose, I could only admire his decision, particularly in the face of the burden he was assuming.

The Philippines had changed sadly for the worse since I had last seen them. As General Wood remarked to me at Sandakan, "Only here and there could I find a few rusty streaks where the rails had been." Governor Harrison had carried out to the limit his theory of the Philippines for the Filipinos; he had let them ruin themselves. A wise governor general would have tried to prevent this. A small group, surfeited with power, managed to bring about the resignation of Americans against whom they had a grievance, and it so happened that in the normal exercise of duty most of those formerly in control had found it impossible to avoid giving offense in some quarter or other.

The Wood-Forbes Mission found that the government-owned projects had incurred tremendous deficits. Among other things, thou-

420

sands of railway passes had been issued. Sugar companies had started up on a shoe string and then borrowed government funds without adequate security. One hundred million pesos had been lost in banking schemes. To cap the climax, the silver metal reserve behind the currency had been sold to India, so that the peso had fallen to thirty-eight cents. General Wood had to get an emergency loan authorized by the United States Congress to put the Islands on their feet financially.

The report of the Mission concluded that an immediate grant of independence would be "a betrayal of the Philippine people," and that "under no circumstances should the American government permit to be established in the Philippines a situation which would leave the United States in a position of responsibility without authority."

As soon as General Wood had reestablished financial credit, he turned his attention to the Bureau of Health, which had fallen hopelessly into politics; its ramifications were so extensive that innumerable plums were to be had for the plucking. Since I had built it up originally, he believed I was the one best qualified to resurrect it. The Rockefeller Foundation concurred, and I spent several months making a survey and offering suggestions for its regeneration. The Foundation furnished funds and expert advisers and placed its resources at my disposal.

In order to ensure the fulfilment of my survey I talked to Manuel Quezon, pointing out on a chart how the death rate had risen steadily since I had left, and how the whole future of the Islands depended on getting the Health Service out of politics. He agreed with me completely, and induced the principal leaders of the Legislature to sign a document that they would support me loyally. This they continued to do, even through the thick of their contest with General Wood.

The Health Service was overloaded with old fossil men, educated in past epochs, who had no conception of modern hygiene in its scientific aspects, and who were too old to learn. Improvement was impossible until younger men were trained. Filipino students were sent on fellowships to take post-graduate courses in American schools. As they returned, the standards of the Medical School were gradually raised to their former excellence. Eventually they formed the staff of a new School of Hygiene—with the exception of India the only one East of Suez. The nursing schools were also restored with the aid of imported experts. The slow business of education had to be started all over again to convince the Filipinos of the value of the Health Service. Not until then would the Legislature vote money of its own volition.

The Bureau of Science presented a more difficult problem. Only with adequate guarantees of a certain tenure of office for a number of years could a desirable set of men be induced to accept positions again. The *Philippine Journal of Science* had also lost its standing, but in time its former reputation was to a great extent regained.

The state of the lepers and the steps taken by General Wood to remedy their deplorable situation have already been described. Equally distressing was the condition of the insane. Those under confinement were existing almost like animals and receiving inadequate attention from the authorities. More were roaming the country at will; many insane women were becoming pregnant as fast as nature would allow.

General Wood was horrified to find the extent to which the care of the insane had deteriorated. I was motoring with him one noon on our way to lunch when he happened to spy on the street one of the principal Filipino doctors of Manila. The General, who was always a man of action, stopping his car, hailed the doctor. "I'm going to the insane hospital," he said. "Won't you come along?"

"But I'm just on my way to lunch."

"Skip lunch and come with me."

Such a request from the Governor General could not be disregarded. The doctor perforce joined us. General Wood spent two hours meticulously pointing out every harrowing detail. He had missed lunch but made a convert. The doctor became one of the ardent supporters of appropriations for the large modern asylum which was ultimately erected.

Apparently there was always a genuine desire and willingness on the part of the local people to cooperate with the Rockefeller Foundation cordially and openly. But they were sometimes timid owing to the fear that they might lose prestige and influence among their own people. It was difficult to make much advance, but we did prevent further retrogression and dissolution during this trying period of reconstruction.

On the morning of May 13, 1922, in the midst of our busiest days, the British cruiser *Renown*, bearing the Prince of Wales, now King Edward VIII, dropped anchor in Manila Bay. The Prince landed at noon, but before he could have any lunch he had to review the crack Ninth Cavalry on the Luneta, and the crack Constabulary company at Malacañan. Although he must have already experienced similar demonstrations of local pride hundreds of times, he had to school his countenance to pleasant appreciation. To my mind his charm of manner was much heightened by his apparent embarrassment. Instead of a prince of twenty-eight, he gave the impression of a young boy of eighteen who had never performed such a function in his life.

The Prince had obviously been brought up in the true British traditions of the dangers of the noonday sun. His amazement was manifest when he observed the Governor General essay bareheaded the short journey from the government offices where he had been received to the palace where he was finally to have lunch. He was apparently of two minds over donning his helmet but after a few moments' hesitation concluded to be on the safe side and wear it.

By way of further entertainment, General Wood had arranged a polo match for the afternoon. He and I were watching from the grandstand when by accident our royal guest was struck on the head with a ball. The game was stopped and the Prince was carried off the field.

General Wood exclaimed, "Come on, Heiser! We'd better go over." We jumped into his automobile and dashed across the field to the stable, where we found the Prince lying on a bench with an inch and a half cut in his forehead. A severed artery was spurting a stream of blood with each heart beat.

The Prince, still conscious, blinked up at me with his one good eye and said, "Won't you look after me, Doctor, and have my surgeon help you?"

I clapped a compress on the wound at once, and said, "We'd better do the rest of the dressing at Malacañan. The stable's not a good place."

Tetanus germs may always be lurking about a stable; consequently the recognized practice was to give an anti-tetanus injection for any wound received in the vicinity of one. But I knew that the only serum in town at the moment had been causing the most violent reactions.

I was in a quandary. I retired to meditate. "If the Prince dies of tetanus, I shall be condemned by the entire world for not having given him the injection. On the other hand, if I give him the serum, and he dies of that, the result will be equally bad." I had in my care the most valuable asset possessed by the British Empire; his life might be in my keeping.

I went myself for the serum to the hospital where I received dubious assurance that it was safe. Hoping I was doing the right thing, I ordered the injection made. A cable was immediately despatched to King George V, informing him the injury was slight and that the Prince expected to keep his full program the next day, and a similar message was sent to President Harding.

The Prince was able to attend a luncheon at Malacañan the following noon. I found that he was, as so often described, truly a Prince Charming, but he also had an astounding grasp of the problems of his country. He was quite serious, discussed world events with great judgment, was well-informed on names and places, and seemed to have an extraordinary memory for his experiences in France and for what he had learned on his long journeys in behalf of the Empire.

The Prince and I talked over in detail the Indian situation, with which we both were familiar. I described the hookworm survey in Madras, and suggested that the elimination of hookworm alone would go far toward building up the stamina of the Indians. He asked particularly about the difficulties encountered over caste, race, and religious prejudices.

That night the Prince himself gave a dinner on the *Renown*, at which it was imperative that he appear. Although it was time for the anti-toxin to show a reaction, he succeeded in taking his place at the head of the table. I noticed he was surreptitiously scratching all the time, and suspected what was wrong with him. As soon as the dinner was over, I approached him. "Are you feeling comfortable?" I asked in a professional tone.

He playfully hit me a tremendous punch in the chest. "You know perfectly well I'm feeling miserable. I hardly slept last night at all. Look!" And he displayed the most beautiful case of hives I have ever seen. Fortunately he suffered no other ill effects from the injection.

The Prince's fondness for dancing was common knowledge, and also his idiosyncrasy that his partners should preferably alternate between blonde and brunette, and that none should be as tall as he unless, of course, she happened to be his hostess. His choice of partners, which seemed so spontaneous, was often managed. He would privately have the best dancers pointed out to him and would then ask them to do him the honor; they would sparkle with delight under the exhilarating thought that he had selected them out of all the beautiful bevy.

The publicity attendant on the goings and comings of the Prince caused him much concern. Amusing anecdotes are told about his attempts to attain a measure of privacy. In Japan, where privacy is at a premium, it is said he staged one of his greatest successes. The Japanese were determined that he must be entertained every moment. Once when he came from an officially escorted inspection into the anteroom of the quarters provided for him, he excused himself to the Japanese general detailed to accompany him, walked into his own apartment, and hopped through the French window into his Rolls Royce which his chauffeur, accustomed to these escapes, was driving slowly past, according to instructions. He crouched in the bottom of the car as it passed the sentries and nobody saw him. No sooner was he outside than he quickly changed into the street clothes waiting in the limousine, and immediately abandoned it for a rickshaw.

The general in the anteroom first grew tired of waiting and then alarmed; finally he instituted inquiries. When the news leaked out that the Prince had vanished, the tocsin was sounded. The Japanese pride themselves on being able to locate any foreigner within their gates in a few hours, but they could not find the most conspicuous figure in the world. The Prince frequently changed rickshaws, wandered about, shopped, and when he grew tired returned to the palace and walked coolly into the bedlam of police and detectives.

While the Prince was in Manila we had several sets of tennis together. When, once or twice, he suspected I was not exerting myself, he was much annoyed. He disliked excessively the fanfare and acclaim which greeted his every appearance. When he would walk in from the court everybody would rise. "Look here!" he would say, "I'm just a tennis player."

Although the Prince was able to assume with startling rapidity whatever public attitude fitted the moment, he was fundamentally a sober-minded person. He would often inject a serious note in a frivolous conversation, as when he said self-deprecatingly that he had been able to accomplish very little in the world beyond appearing as the model for "what the well-dressed man will wear." The terrible discomforts of men's dress as decreed by convention in the East seemed to cause him much distress. As soon as he was East of Suez he made it a point never to wear a waistcoat, and to replace the hot black dinner coat with a cool and comfortable white mess jacket. "You travel through the Orient a great deal," he said to me. "Why don't you set the fashion of wearing mess jackets?"

"I'm afraid my influence wouldn't carry very far," I smiled.

"Yes, it would. We'd get the thing started, and think what a boon it would be to men all through the tropics."

Because I was so thoroughly in accord with the Prince's sentiments I agreed to do my bit. When I arrived in Calcutta a few months later I was invited to a formal dinner at the Bengal Club, at which I knew a black dinner coat would be *de rigueur*. But it was so steamy and unpleasant that the mere thought of broadcloth was abhorrent. I decided that I could follow no better sartorial example than that of His Royal Highness, and appeared, therefore, in a mess jacket.

My host was obviously most uncomfortable, but I remained serene. "I see that mess jackets aren't being worn," I remarked affably. "I'll go back and change if you like. It's only a few blocks. But, perhaps I'd better say first that H.R.H. has requested me to wear a mess jacket wherever I go in British territory. If you gentlemen in Calcutta—"

This put a different aspect on the matter. The news that I had been acting as personal physician to the Prince had been cabled all over the British world. A meeting of the House Committee was

426

called at once to discuss this upheaval in all accepted social canons. After weighty deliberation it was agreed that under the circumstances exception should be made in my case. All during the banquet I could see the news going around from mouth to mouth. "H.R.H.—mess jackets." And then they would look intently at me as I sat cool and complacent, a white beacon against the background of oppressive black.

When I attended a second banquet only a few nights later every man in the room was attired in a mess jacket.

Just before the Prince left the Philippines I paid my official farewell call on the *Renown*. He asked me into his quarters and presented me with a silver cigarette case, thanking me for my services, both official and unofficial, and saying, "Doctor, do come and see me in London."

"That would be very pleasant."

"Just let me know in advance. I want you to come down to my farm. I'll show you I sometimes work too."

The visit of His Highness had provided a pleasant interlude in the midst of our labors which, as he had observed, were heavy indeed. Immediately after General Wood's appointment as Governor General, October 5, 1921, the Filipino leaders had been meek as children who had broken their toys through disobedience and wanted them mended. Like a kind father he repaired some of their favorite playthings but others, which had been given them under the mistaken impression they knew how to use them, he removed until such time as they should prove their maturity. If he were to rehabilitate the Islands he must take back the executive powers Governor General Harrison had allowed to lapse. The Legislature's submission was short-lived. After the first year he had to face a terrific political agitation organized against him by Quezon, who consistently opposed every measure General Wood proposed, and accused him of autocratic methods, even going as far as to demand his recall.

In rooting out the graft and corruption which had permeated the government service, General Wood had to make many removals, but even the most justifiable one would cause the most frightful abuse in the Filipino press. The General paid no attention to the clamor, but held to his appointed course. He knew that he had the administration at home behind him.

General Wood was always held up by his opponents as an extreme example of militarism, but in reality he was directly the opposite. I remember one particular occasion when he had a matter he wanted approved by a group of leaders. He invited them to the government office for a discussion. The conference began at nine-thirty in the morning. He set forth his views in great detail. His auditors were not in accord with them, but because of Filipino aversion to joining issue with someone in authority, they remained silent.

General Wood was extremely patient. He expounded everything over again. And a third time. The whole morning went by and the lunch hour arrived. The Governor said, "I suppose you gentlemen are hungry. Won't you take lunch with me?"

The silent opposition became vocal and accepted politely; an agreeable hour was passed in amicable conversation. Afterwards all adjourned once more to the office, and Wood resumed his unruffled round of argument. He talked at the Committee members all the afternoon. They had practically nothing to say—certainly not "yes."

When seven o'clock came, General Wood said, "You gentlemen must be starved. Won't you have dinner with me?"

The session lasted until late in the evening and was begun again the next morning. The second day followed the pattern of the first until finally, worn down by the Governor's unwearying calm, and replete with good food, they capitulated.

Filipino legislators were only silent when it served their purposes. More often, though, they conducted their business with formality, dignity, and decorum, they talked, and talked, always with waving arms and grandiloquent gestures.

General Wood attempted to win his victories by pacific means, but unfortunately he was often forced to use his veto power. As he explained to me, the bills which he vetoed and for which he was being criticized so much in the press had practically all been rejected after consultation with the Filipino leaders. Many of these bills were of a frivolous nature and designed to force any conscientious administrator into exercising his prerogative. Eighty-seven of them were passed the closing night of one Legislature, and it was humanly impossible for any member to know what they all contained. Even Quezon and his co-agitator Osmeña were astounded when they later saw the contents of the bills they had approved.

It was assumed by observers that these bills had been railroaded through with the full understanding of their worthless character and for the express purpose of forcing the General to use his veto power. The charge of tyranny was duly made by the Filipinos.

Even in the United States General Wood was branded as a militarist, and it was said constantly that he was dominated by the sabre and the spur and his methods were anything but pacific. His detractors pointed accusingly at his ex-officio cabinet which was composed of Army officers, sometimes called the cavalry, kitchen, or muchacho cabinet. But the explanation was simple. The Legislature was trying to curtail his activities by their oft-repeated and effective method of cutting down appropriations. These had been so reduced that no money was available to pay for any advisers, and General Wood had been forced to borrow from the Army, which gladly lent its best men.

Fortunately, the character of these officers was such that no accusation could stand the light of investigation. Major General Frank McCoy had had a long and distinguished career as General Wood's aide-de-camp in Cuba and, because of his gift of diplomacy, was to be appointed by President Coolidge to serve as peacemaker in the first presidential election in Nicaragua after the insurrection.

The chief fame of Colonel Gordon Johnston also rests upon his peace time activities. He was doing fine work in connection with the Guardian Society. The quartering of any army upon a people is followed by many illegitimate births. The military occupation had lasted so long in the Islands that the numbers of these children had reached the appalling figure of eighteen thousand. The mestizos of other races—Spanish, Chinese, and English—ranked high socially because their fathers saw to it that they were provided for materially. But the casual American soldier had generally evaded responsibility for his left-handed offspring. Many of the Filipina mothers, poor Cho-cho-sans abandoned by their Pinkertons, were forced to form new connections in which the children of the former alliances played no part. They usually sank to the lowest social strata; many of them were kept by the warmhearted but impoverished Filipina taos. No career was open to the pretty girls as they grew up except that of mistress to prominent Filipinos.

General Wood realized that these Army waifs should quite properly be wards of the country whose soldiers were responsible for their sad plight. We had until this time disgracefully shut our eyes to the situation. The Governor General delegated Colonel Johnston to organize the Guardian Society to take care of them. Many of the fathers who had returned to the United States were traced and made to contribute to their support. The aid of Catholic and Protestant organizations was enlisted, and they were persuaded to provide proper homes and arrange marriages. What had been a tragic situation was ameliorated. Colonel Johnston became foster-father to thousands of *café-au-lait* American orphans.

The loyalty of General Wood's personal following, who were intimately familiar with his daily life, was intense; they bitterly resented all criticism of him, and he, in turn, placed absolute reliance upon their honesty and judgment, and had the gift of eliciting the best in them. He had an original method of keeping associates and subordinates on their toes. On inspection trips in the government despatch boat *Apo*, his traveling office, he would have as his guests representatives of the railroads, the public works, the non-Christian Bureau, or the Health Department, depending on his particular interest of the moment—generally enough to make up a table of twelve to fifteen. At every stop all would go ashore, and, during the first meal afterwards, General Wood would ask each in turn to describe something unusual or particularly interesting he had seen. If anyone were caught napping the first time, he was sure to keep his eyes open the next so that he could contribute.

The real significance of the American work in the Islands had been to protect the masses against the classes. A constant struggle had been waged against the old order of things which tended to give additional privileges to an already privileged class. Because of their illiteracy, the great body of ignorant Filipinos had always been unable to make themselves heard, and for generations had remained in ignorance of their rights.

PICKING UP BROKEN THREADS

Though the politicos' campaign against General Wood was fierce, he retained the admiration and affection of the masses. Certain safeguards had been placed around all the preceding governor generals, but no need of these was ever felt in General Wood's case. Several times I have been riding through the provinces with him in his automobile when an old tao who had heretofore hardly dared lift his eyes to the cacique, now held up his gnarled hand, confident that he would not be rebuffed. General Wood never failed to stop. The tao, with patient eyes and shy smile, would approach in a respectful way, and say he wished to thank the General for all the fine things he was doing for the Filipinos.

As the years went by, one after another, they told more and more upon General Wood's strength. He often admitted to me he felt exhausted after struggling with Filipino officials in the effort to push them to some constructive action. We had all experienced this fatigue, but we did not somehow look for it in a man of General Wood's abundant energy and robust physique.

The Governor had more reason for exhaustion than any of us fully realized at the time. When he had been in Cuba as Governor General years before, he had one day risen suddenly from his desk and his head had come in contact with great force against an old-fashioned oil counter weight lamp, hung low from the ceiling. The triangular iron handle had penetrated his skull, and the injury had been followed by a tumor of the brain and a certain amount of paralysis of the left side. The tumor had twice been removed before he had gone to the Philippines. He should have returned to Dr. Harvey Cushing at the end of his first two years, but had been at that time in the thick of the fight and would not let go.

Because General Wood was an international figure, he was frequently photographed for news reels; often he was shown pre-views. I noted how stoically he looked at them, but it was apparent that it hurt him terribly to watch how painfully he lifted himself in and out of boats or automobiles; he had been so proud of his physical strength.

Only after six years, when he believed his work was nearly finished, would he consent to go home long enough to have the operation performed. But by then the tumor had grown to enormous size.

I happened to see moving pictures of the General's landing at Seattle, and was shocked to observe how one of the finest specimens of manhood I had ever known had changed; his entire side had become paralyzed. But even then he insisted on reporting in person and consulting over the best method of winding up his work in the Philippines, which he expected to do as soon as the operation was over. When finally he went to Boston for his long-delayed ordeal the blood vessels in the tumor had become so large that the hemorrhage could not be stopped and he died almost immediately. He had given his life as truly as any soldier on the firing line.

After General Wood's death, even the Filipino leaders who had fought him so bitterly admitted their animosity had been of a political nature only. They realized that, although they had not seen eye to eye with him, he had labored long and well in their behalf.

Henry L. Stimson, formerly Secretary of War in President Taft's cabinet, was appointed General Wood's successor. He had paid a visit to the General in the Philippines some six months earlier, had become conversant with affairs at that time, had approved the Wood policies wholeheartedly, and was prepared to continue them. The fight for the restoration of the powers of the executive had been already won, and Governor Stimson continued to exercise them. No acute question arose during his term; Coolidge prosperity ruled in the Islands as well as at home, and Governor Stimson's main objective was to set about the development of material resources so that the country might rest on a sound economic foundation.

Governor Stimson asked me to be his adviser, and the Rockefeller Foundation made it possible for me to remain longer than usual in the Islands. President Hoover shortly recalled him in 1929 to enter the cabinet as Secretary of State and in his place was selected Dwight F. Davis, D.S.C., donor of the Davis Cup for the international tennis championships, and public-spirited patron of art and culture in St. Louis. As Governor General he continued to be one of the most retiring of men, and consistently avoided publicity. Nothing was attempted which might have caused trouble during those years when the Filipinos were shouting louder than ever for independence. He told me privately he was not satisfied with his accomplishments, but that as long as the United States would not declare a definite policy toward the Philippines it was useless to attempt anything beyond keeping the situation peaceful.

Theodore Roosevelt, Jr., took office upon Governor Davis' resignation. He had inherited to a conspicuous degree his father's charm of manner, and became tremendously popular among the Filipinos. He came from the Governor Generalship of Puerto Rico speaking Spanish, was hail-fellow-well-met with one and all, radiated cheerful enthusiasm, and played upon the heartstrings of the emotional Filipinos who vibrated to his masterly touch. He devoted himself to them and made much of them socially. Not even former Governor Harrison in his heyday had won greater plaudits. I discussed with him, among other things, the anomalies of malaria in the Islands. Like his father he talked so continuously it was difficult to make a point with him, and his conversation was peppered with quotations from Kipling and the Bible in support of his theses.

The last Governor General of the Philippines was Frank Murphy, now representing the authority of the United States in the new Commonwealth. Although many believed his former public services as Mayor of Detroit were not sufficiently broad, by his acts he proved an exceedingly able administrator in a difficult situation, and became well liked by the Filipinos, who admire those who know how to play the political game.

We were morally bound to give the Filipinos their independence. President McKinley made the first commitment, and in the Jones Bill we again assured them they should have independence when they had a stable government. The moot point has always been the definition of a stable government. Does it rest upon the maintenance of law and order? Or upon self-sustaining power economically?

The heart of the question at the moment is indubitably one of economics. The Filipinos have been raised by means of the tariff privileges we have granted them to a standard of living formerly unheard of among Orientals. If we shut them out completely it is hard to see how they can exist.

I have a great deal of confidence in the Filipinos. They in return have a real liking for us, and feel their destiny is with us. Thousands volunteered for service in the World War, although it was too late for them to go to France. They want to retain our goodwill, but we are handicapped because we spend no money to support our views, while opponents are active in propaganda.

Once more the Filipinos are given an opportunity to show their capacity for conducting their affairs in a manner which will be conducive to the general good. Their fate lies, to a great extent, in the hands of Manuel Quezon who of all Filipinos has had most political experience and has made the best use of it. President Quezon of the Philippine Commonwealth is not the same man as Resident Commissioner Quezon who used to play poker with Uncle Joe Cannon backstage in Washington, using an Independence Bill as stakes, and hoping for a lucky break.

Naturally I saw Quezon whenever I went to the Philippines, and visited him at Baguio during his long illnesses. As the years went by I found him increasingly frank.

In the fall of 1935 my telephone rang, and when I answered it a voice said, "I'll bet you don't know who this is."

"You're Manuel Quezon, the coming President of the Philippine Commonwealth," I replied.

"Yes, Doctor, you're right. I'm in the hospital. Will you come down and see me? I want to talk to you."

I went to the hospital. "What a big fool I am," he greeted me. "I let a newspaper friend of mine pick out a doctor. Why didn't I call you up in the first place? Now I want you to tell me whether I should let them operate on me."

"What's wrong with you?"

"Pepino," he called to his man. "Bring me the X-ray plates."

The briefest examination of them showed he had a stone in the kidney.

"The doctors want to take it out. What do you think of these New York surgeons anyhow?"

"They have excellent ones here," I assured him.

"But suppose this were your kidney and your stone. What would you do yourself?"

"I'd go to Dr. Hugh Young at Baltimore. He's been very successful."

"Pepino! Bring me my clothes. Get me a limousine. I'm going to Baltimore."

Then turning again to me, he spoke impulsively, "I want to talk to you on the way to the station. After your long experience in the Islands you know them from a health standpoint better than anybody else. I want you and General MacArthur and General Harbord to come out and advise me. Think it over and let me know whether you'll accept."

I told him honestly that I had little inclination to do so; that I had given many years of my life to establish a Health Service which he had allowed to decay. "See what's been done to the Bureau of Science which is so badly needed by your people," I reminded him.

"Oh, we'll fix that up again all right."

"How are you going to do it?" I inquired. "I've just been talking to Theodore Roosevelt. He says you used to have a revenue of sixty million. Now you have forty; once you are outside the United States tariff wall, you won't have more than twenty. That will barely cover the absolute necessities of government. How's there going to be anything left for the Health Department?"

"I have that all solved," he confidently asserted.

"How?"

"I've just been in Ireland, and have been studying the workings of the lottery there. We can have much better ones in the Philippines, and we'll sell most of the tickets to you Americans. The lottery will be under state control, and directed under the best auspices. It will bring in several million dollars a year anyhow, and perhaps as much as ten million. You can have it all for the Department of Health. I want you to be the only one to say how it is to be spent."

I had no doubt of the sincerity of his intentions. Quezon had admitted once to General Wood that he was swayed by his white blood in one direction and by his Oriental in another, but in spite of himself the predominant sway was toward the white. He has much force, energy, and moral courage. He may have a successful career as well as a tempestuous one. In spite of the many attempts on his life made by his political opponents, he has no physical fear. An automobile salesman once informed him an armored car could be manufactured to protect him against cranks for not much more than the price of the model used by ordinary citizens.

"No, sir, I'll have a landaulet, an open car. A statesman should know how to die in the performance of his duty."

CHAPTER 25.   AN OUNCE OF
PREVENTION

AMONG all tropical diseases malaria is supreme. In my experience it is the most persistent, the most destructive, the most widespread, and the most difficult of them all to control. Plague is terrible, but the precise method of its transmission is known, and rats can be eliminated. Cholera, smallpox, and beriberi have no excuse for being. Dysentery and typhoid could be wiped out. Though leprosy creates horror it seldom interferes with the march of progress; the poor and lowly are the principal sufferers. But for malaria there is no specific and the problem of prophylaxis is enormous in its complexity and expensiveness. The method of its widespread control is not yet out of its swaddling clothes.

Those races touched by the shaking finger of malaria have undergone a progressive decadence. The "glory that was Greece" faded out before its onslaughts and will not shine again until the minute pools in her broad rocky river beds cease to be a threat. The "grandeur that was Rome" paled centuries ago and only recently has the light flared up. The Campagna, the fertile farmland region around Rome from which the early Republic derived both its food and the men for its conquering peasant armies, has been the scene of recurrent waves of malaria. The drainage operations of the Etruscans had kept it healthy, but under Rome the population steadily declined. When fever and chills swept over the marshlands, the terrified populace sacrificed to the Goddess Mephitis, who, with her bald head, great paunch, swollen veins, and emaciated limbs, typified

437

the essence of horror. The city itself remained free because of the Cloaca Maxima and its communicating system of interlocking porous earthen pipes, which antedated our modern subsoil drainage installations by several centuries.

The barbarians lost army after army of their non-immunes; Alaric himself is said to have died of malaria. Pope after Pope tried to reclaim these Pontine marshes in vain. Not until "Il Duce" led the stagnant waters in huge canals to the sea did the land once more become fertile and the cities once more spring into life. It is magnificent and also startling to see Sabaudia and Littoria, modernistically designed from church to peasant dwelling, rising renascent from the desolation that was.

Whether malaria was endemic in the New World before the arrival of the discoverers and explorers is a matter of dispute. Certainly *calenturas* were mentioned early and often in contemporary accounts. The first Spanish venture of Columbus in Hispaniola had to be abandoned because of the "fevers." Half the inhabitants of Jamestown, encircled by the miasmic Virginia marshes, died within six months of their arrival. Up and down the coast the first settlements were established by the water courses, and even after the pioneers had moved into the primeval forest, in clearing it they left pools and standing water. Moreover, power to saw the lumber and grind the grist to house and feed those who, all unaware, were inviting malaria into their midst, was furnished by innumerable millponds.

From earliest times the connection of marshland and malaria had made itself apparent. Miasmas or mephitic airs arising, particularly at night, from these moist regions, were blamed for the disease, and the neighboring inhabitants believed safety could be assured only by closing every door and window against their entrance. When men began to apply scientific words to their observations of natural phenomena, they claimed malaria was due to the "decomposition of organic matter in low areas which thereby freed poisonous gases." This theory that disease was air borne had been, from time immemorial, accepted as a reason for epidemics. Malaria, especially, was subject to this plausible explanation.

Malaria, "bad air," was first so called by an Italian, Torti, in

1753, and introduced into England in 1827 as a specific name for the malady known variously and vaguely as marsh miasma, paludal poison, ague, jungle fever, hill fever, tropical fever, intermittent and remittent fever, or, simply, fever of the country.

The chills and fever so often described by the ancients were undoubtedly malaria, because the symptoms are so distinctive that there was little chance for confusion. Hippocrates, a native of Aegean Cos, had studied the disease in Asia Minor, where it was prevalent in the Fifth Century B. C., although it had not yet extended to Attica. The Father of Medicine had divided these fevers into quotidian, tertian, and quartan. This same differentiation of types is still retained; in the quotidian form the attack recurs daily, in the tertian every other day, and in the quartan every three days.

The chills, which last perhaps fifteen minutes, are usually accompanied by the most violent paroxysms. I have seen the malaria ward in a hospital actually tremble from the violence of the shivering; a single bed would move on the floor. The initial stage is followed by burning fever which rises to a peak, after which profuse perspiration breaks out and the patient gradually returns to normal temperature, and remains so until the next attack.

The Tenth Century Arabian poet, Al Mutanabbi, described in the following verses the disease which had become his companion.

> "I watch for her time of arrival without desire,
> Yet with the watchfulness of an eager lover,
> And she is ever faithful to her appointed time;
> But faithfulness is an evil
> When it casts thee into grievous suffering."

Malaria is often deadly in its action. In the cerebral form, parasites become so thick in the blood that they clog the capillaries of the brain and cause almost immediate death, and the same may be true if they lodge in the kidneys.

But a far larger number of cases are chronic; the parasites gradually destroy so many red blood corpuscles that extreme anemia results. The patient's liver does not function properly, he has frightful headaches, cannot eat, and takes no interest in anything. The most indicative symptom in the diagnosis of malaria is the enlargement of the spleen "which often makes the belly protrude mightily." I have seen many a child so badly afflicted that his spleen bumped against his side as he walked, rather like a box showing through a bag. This condition is colloquially called ague cake.

Because malaria is age-old, physicians of every period have made attempts at cures. One of the Roman methods was to place under the head of a patient with quartan fever a copy of Homer, opened to the fourth book where the healing of wounded Menelaus is described.

In the Middle Ages treatment was little more efficacious. Patients were bled, were advised to change the air, fed wormwood, lettuce, crocus, linseed, given warm water to make them perspire. At times when an epidemic raged, huge bonfires were lit to purify the bad air.

But long before the disease was given its present name, its remedy was known in South America. In 1600, Spanish missionaries used the bark *quina quina* in Loxa, Peru. Don Francisco Lopez Canazares, Corregidor of Loxa, was himself cured in 1683, and thoughtfully sent a supply of the bark to Lima, six hundred miles away, for the use of Francesca de Rivera, second wife of Don Luis Geronimo Fernandez de Carera, Viceroy of Peru, stricken with tertian fever. She recovered and took a supply back with her to Spain. Her physician, Juan del Vego, followed her with more of the bark, which he disposed of at Seville for one hundred reales a pound.

In 1742 that industrious Swedish naturalist, Linnaeus, who dedicated his life to classifying and naming botanical specimens, made a slight error. He gave this bark the name of cinchona, after the deceased first wife of the Viceroy, Anna, Countess of Chinchon, who had never been to Peru, had never been ill of malaria, and had never taken the medicine. Before that it had been known as Jesuit's Powder or Bark, because the Jesuit order, as the power behind the throne in Peru, had a monopoly of quinine sales. The priests received its weight in gold from those who could afford to pay; to the poor it was free. The supply was never equal to the demand, and in the effort to adjust the balance, the trees of South America were stripped of their bark and largely destroyed.

The failure of the South American governments to protect the source of supply from this destruction brought efforts to cultivate cinchona elsewhere. In 1852 seeds and plants were introduced into the Buitenzorg Botanical Garden in Java, where the Dutch tended them carefully. Four hundred and fifty live plants were transported to India by Sir Clements Markham with great difficulty. Soon the Ceylon planters had the monopoly on production. But then Charles Ledger, in 1865, made it possible for the industry to take a great forward stride by grafting a Brazilian variety on another wild variety which had a strong root system and would flourish in less fertile soil. Until that time cinchona production had not been successful in Java. But the Dutch found they had ideal conditions for the cultivation of this grafted cinchona. The Ceylon planters had to cut down their trees and set tea shrubs in their places.

With perfected technique, the Dutch no longer killed the tree by stripping the bark. They kept the supply perpetual by constant thinning and pruning. Now, only the young twigs, which have the largest percentage of alkaloid, are used for bark. With the monopoly thus secured, the price was kept so high that thousands died because they could not afford to buy. The Dutch always insisted it cost them a great deal to produce quinine, but skeptics suspected that, since the expense of extracting the alkaloid was known to be relatively small, the profits must be unduly large.

The task of breaking the Dutch monopoly seemed for a long time utterly hopeless, but, because the price of quinine was a matter of world-wide importance, I suggested to the Health Section of the League of Nations that this was a type of activity admirably suited to its purposes. The League fell in with this idea and began from Geneva a campaign of "pitiless publicity," subtly planned and beautifully carried out. Its effectiveness lay in its simplicity. The figures of quinine production appeared at stated intervals in League bulletins. "Over nine hundred tons out of a thousand were produced in the Dutch East Indies. The price in 1890 was such and such; now in 1917 it has risen to such and such." The great difference between the early low cost and the later high one told its own story.

Years were spent in bringing down the price. But on each of my European trips I visited Geneva, and each time I talked cheaper quinine. If the officials evidenced a lessening of interest in it, I would spur them on by relating some of the harassing tales I had heard of fellow human beings who were afflicted with malaria and lacked the means for relief. The campaign continued with renewed vigor. Nothing was said directly; no attack was made. But the Dutch found the shoe fitted and began to be sensitive.

The campaign had been progressing for some time when I happened to visit a prominent Dutch gentleman in the Netherlands who owned many shares in a Javanese quinine estate. Unaware of my interest in the subject, he said, "It's terrible! We're gouging the whole world. I'm going to get rid of my stock and wash my hands of the whole business!"

This feeling was shared by so many people and in time the opprobrium became so great that gradually the cost of quinine was voluntarily reduced.

The citizens of the United States can with difficulty comprehend the poverty of the races which are most scourged with malaria, or the blessing which a cheaper drug conveys upon them. We had depended upon quinine exclusively in the Philippines, and had struggled constantly with Chinese druggists who found it profitable to make pills out of lime and sell them at a high price. The credulous Filipinos had been deceived by the similarly bitter taste. We had put the genuine drug on sale at the office of every municipal and township treasurer throughout the Islands at a cost of nine cents for a dozen five-grain tablets. Instead of arresting and fining the Chinese druggist, we had found it far more effective to put him out of the quinine business by offering the drug at a price lower than his bogus lime tablets.

An extract of all the alkaloids in cinchona barks called totaquina, the great advantage of which is its cheapness, is now being recommended by the League of Nations Malaria Commission. The average Filipino, for example, cannot even afford the two and a half pesos for two hundred and fifty grains of quinine, an average treatment, but can usually find the necessary thirty-five centavos for totaquina.

I had naturally suggested to various laboratories throughout the world the possibility of manufacturing quinine synthetically, but had met with little enthusiasm for the idea. I was always assured it would be extremely difficult and costly; the research would be long, and the result problematic. But the indefatigable Germans were undeterred by these considerations. They began experimenting, and have recently produced two synthetic drugs, plasmochin and atebrin. However, they are apparently not yet entirely satisfied with results, because they have made no attempt to capture the world market. In a number of respects, plasmochin and atebrin are more effective than quinine, particularly in treating the malignant types of malaria, but many drugs that seem so good in the first trials prove to have deleterious after effects. Until more is known about these drugs they should only be administered by a physician. Quinine, on the other hand, can be taken by anybody, and seldom more than temporary deafness results from overdosing. Until recently the belief was firmly established that quinine was a specific for malaria, and had a lethal action on the malaria parasite. Later research throws doubt on this sweeping conclusion, but, nevertheless, quinine cannot be dispensed with in malarial treatment.

Nor is quinine a prophylactic for malaria. The drug has not yet been found which will kill all forms and stages of the parasite promptly. Although as long as quinine is taken there will be no attack, the parasites are ever lying in wait, ready to appear, if, as too often happens, the patient wearies at the long and tedious treatment, and stops it too soon.

"The Roman fevers are faithful according to an imprescriptable right. Whom once they have touched they do not abandon as long as he lives."

Thus despairingly wrote Peter Damian in 1060 from his malaria-ridden bishopric of Ostia, the ancient port of Rome.

It is true malaria may recur in one year, or two years, or after many years. The parasites hide away in the deep recesses of the body, such as the spleen and the bone marrow. One of the paradoxes with which the subject of malaria abounds is that often when latent cases are removed to cold climates the disease recurs; it is also true that the colder the climate, the greater the hope for a complete cure.

It had been obvious for a long time that water played an important part, but no one was able to bridge the hiatus between cause and effect until the end of the Nineteenth Century. Then Sir Patrick Manson, who, after his successful demonstrations in filaria, was still eagerly interested in research on the theory of insect transmission of diseases, stimulated Major Ronald Ross, a former pupil, to try various experiments with mosquitoes. Many of these failed but after each disappointment Manson would write Ross letters of encouragement, and would suggest some new method of attacking the problem of malaria transmission.

The hundreds of known varieties of mosquitoes are divided broadly into the culex and anopheles groups. Little was known of their habits except that the male lived on fruit and was quite harmless; only the female bit. Ross had naturally picked upon Culex fatigans, the common tiger mosquito, as the villain. This was readily understandable, because of all the hundreds of varieties it was the most common and annoying in its numbers, its buzz, and its bite.

After laboring for many years Ross finally in 1897 found the same type of cell in a dapple-winged anopheles mosquito that the Frenchman, Laveran, in 1880 had discovered in Algeria in the blood of a human being suffering from malaria.

In this connection it seems only fair to mention that in the beginning Manson believed filariasis was transmitted by water or its emanations, previously contaminated by mosquitoes which had bitten persons with filariasis. It was not until after the American, Dr. Theobald Smith, in 1889 had shown that cattle fever was transmitted by the *bite* of a tick that transmission of filariasis by the *bite* of mosquitoes was proved. In 1894–95 Bruce demonstrated the transmission of trypanosomes by means of the fly, glossina. These discoveries helped clear the path and established the method by which malaria was transmitted.

An anopheline is usually distinguishable because of the little black dots on her wings, which other mosquitoes do not have, and because she looks as though she were standing on her head when biting. A tremendous number of enemies are ready to destroy her; she cannot even stand wind or bright sunshine. Her life history occupies only about one month, but as long as she lives, she has a meal every two to three nights. The swelling from her bite is not large, nor is the itch particularly annoying—sometimes a person does not even know he has been bitten—yet one bite is enough to cause malaria.

Malaria can only be contracted from a mosquito which has previously fed on someone who had malaria parasites in his blood. Years of study were devoted to discovering the complex and almost improbable life cycle of this tiny animal organism called the plasmodium. Many lacunae in our knowledge still remain. But when an infected anopheline bites a human being, with its saliva are introduced a number of rod-like objects, pointed at each end, called sporozoites, which, with graceful undulating movement go swimming off into the blood stream. For eight or nine days they disappear completely from view. Repeated examination of the blood reveals no trace of them, and nobody as yet knows what is taking place. When they next come into view, they have changed their shape completely. Tiny little rings, called schizonts or trophozoites, much smaller than the rods, now are discoverable inside the red corpuscles. These increase rapidly in number and size, some becoming sexual and others non-sexual. Each cell of the latter type at regular intervals divides itself into as many as fourteen smaller ones, and whenever this segmentation takes place, toxins are freed—thus accounting for the periodicity of the disease—and the human host suffers chills and fever.

The sexual forms, the gametocytes, go circulating in the blood stream and do no harm. But if some of that blood happens to be sucked up by an anopheline mosquito of the right variety, then the sexual life of the plasmodium begins. The female cell is fertilized inside the mosquito, and then elongates, penetrates the wall of the mosquito's stomach, and attaches itself to the outside of the gut in the peritoneal cavity. There it begins to grow, and forms a cyst which eventually bursts and frees a vast number of sporozoites. These penetrate all parts of the mosquito's body, some of them lodging inevitably in the salivary glands, ready to be deposited in a human with the mosquito's next meal. During the twelve days required for this process, she cannot infect a human being. At no time, apparently, does she receive any injury from incubating the plasmodia.

Malaria flourishes in a broad zone on both sides of the Equator, where it assumes vast proportions, creating great economic loss and taking a high toll of human lives. It is also endemic for some distance into the temperate zones, diminishing, however, in frequency and severity. Poor old Africa, from which the slave trade broadcast so much disease, is, as usual, assumed to have been the seed bed. But the largest centers are in Asia. In India it is the arch-destroyer; half the three hundred and fifty million population are estimated to suffer from it, and one million die annually. Th figures. Turkey, Syria, Palestine, Malaya, Siam, Indo-China, Java, Sumatra, the Philippines, and China are all intensely malarial.

In Europe there have been outbreaks in the Netherlands and England until recent times. Huge epidemics occurred during and after the World War in Macedonia, Serbia, Rumania, and Russia. Greece and Italy are badly affected. But in Denmark and Norway malaria is practically unknown. Why some places are exempt or why the seeming immunity of others is suddenly broken down is difficult to explain. Penang was healthy until occupied in 1786 by the British, and became malarious a few years later; clearing off the jungle and exposing the pools did not seem sufficient explanation. Chile and Barbados were free of it until 1927 when cases began to occur.

Though today largely confined to the hot countries, malaria does occur in the United States, at one time extending as far north as Wisconsin. At the first settling it was common in Connecticut, but disappeared, only to return when Italian immigrants, who swarmed in to occupy the abandoned farms, brought the infection in their veins. It was so prevalent in the nineties along the Sound that when the Cambridge crew came over from malaria-free England to compete in the races, during the course of the final training near New London some of the oarsmen caught malaria and subsequently lost to Yale. They claimed it was just another of those damn Yankee tricks.

Year by year the malaria line in this country is receding. The disease was once bad enough in Washington to interfere with the sittings of Congress. But draining and improving the surrounding land has gradually eliminated the anopheles there. In the South, broadly speaking, malaria is largely man-made. Railroad embankments and the more recently built automobile roads were thrown up across the country, and the drainage culverts were often a little higher than the level of the water in the trenches or ditches. These created perfect artificial breeding places for mosquitoes, which added to the ever-present danger from swamps.

Since the aim of the International Health Board was to promote public health so that local health departments could get a legitimate share of appropriations, and as hookworm demonstrations gradually began to achieve this object, the subject of malaria grew more and more important. Accordingly, we embarked on a program which included both a study of the incidence of the disease, and the type and breeding habits of the mosquito responsible, so that control could be attempted at the larvae stage. Our hope was finally to devise means whereby poor communities might effect control at a price they could afford.

In 1916 the International Health Board made a demonstration at Crossett, Arkansas, that a community could be freed of malaria by freeing it of mosquitoes, and within a reasonable cost. When this was successful the work was gradually extended until in 1921 a general attack upon the disease was being made.

The perplexing questions raised from the entomological angle proved malaria to be a paradox of paradoxes. Many ideas and theories were completely upset; even the nomenclature of mosquitoes had to be changed as our knowledge of types was extended. All progress in malaria control is accomplished by a narrowing process. It was a tremendously complex study in itself to determine which mosquitoes caused what disease and where. Yellow fever and dengue, or breakbone fever, as well as filaria and malaria, are transmitted by the bite of a mosquito.

There were over thirty species of anopheles in the Philippines and twenty-two on the Island of Luzon alone, but only one or two were an important factor in carrying malaria. Moreover, a given species might be dangerous in one country and not in another. In Batavia, Java, where the geographical and climatic conditions were practically identical with those of Manila, frightful malaria was transmitted by the same anopheles which was harmless in Manila. To complicate the problem in the South Seas, malaria was extremely severe in the New Hebrides, but was totally lacking in neighboring New Caledonia which was in constant communication with it, and where no quarantine precautions were observed by the French.

Malaria was extremely vicious in Asia, diminishing in intensity with the distance therefrom. The Rockefeller Foundation representative in Siam, Dr. Milford E. Barnes, found thirty-four varieties. There were not quite so many in the Dutch East Indies, only three or four in Dutch New Guinea, in Australian Papua only one, and Fiji, though it swarmed with culex, had no anopheles whatever.

For a long time it was believed in Europe that the maculipennis was the only malaria-carrying anopheles. But several factors seemed confusing. For example, in one section of Italy where the maculipennis was numerous there was no malaria, and in another where it was scarce, malaria was very bad. The larvae of mosquitoes from both regions appeared identical. Finally the simple idea of examining the eggs occurred to a retired sanitary inspector named Faleroni, and, instead of one maculipennis, he was able to distinguish five varieties. Further investigation showed some of these carried malaria and some did not.

Further progress in research in Italy was hampered by the difficulty of finding infected mosquitoes in bedrooms, their common and logical hiding places. Ordinarily not more than four percent of the anopheles in a given region are infected, but if the bedroom is dark the anopheles, after biting, remains and hides there until it is time for another meal. If this bedroom is occupied by a person with malaria the percentage of hazard to others in the home is normally greater than the percentage of mosquito infection in the district. Dr. L. W. Hackett, the Foundation's malariologist in Italy, took one thousand mosquitoes from a bedroom in an Italian home where all the members had malaria, and found in every case the anopheles had fed on cows' blood. It had always been assumed they had been securing nourishment from the humans in the house, but actually they had only been taking shelter after their meal.

The anopheles is not usually found above the 3,000 foot level; 2,000 feet was the height in the Philippines, but under rare conditions it flew higher; 4,500 in Malaya, 6,000 in Mexico, 6,500 in Lebanon, and 8,000 in the Himalayas.

The horizontal flight of the anopheles was discovered to extend far beyond the hundred yards once set as the limit. Although the large sturdy-winged New Jersey culex has been known to travel forty miles, the average distance for the anopheles is about one mile. At Camp Stotsenberg in the Philippines individual mosquitoes would fly over two miles to get a feeding of blood, but the average was too low to do much harm at that distance.

Mosquitoes are most persistent in their search for a blood meal. In Georgia we selected for our experiment a certain swamp caused by one of the numerous limestone outcrops which, wherever they occur in low ground, bring about the accumulation of water, difficult to drain. In this marsh many anopheles were known to breed. The nearest house was a mile away over the crest of a hill, and between the swamp and the house were many pine trees which had been ringed by turpentine gatherers and later died, leaving the branches bare so that mosquitoes could not hide among them. One summer a group of college students was assembled, and each one stationed in a tree with a huge mosquito net. All the insects caught were sprayed with a carmine stain. When released, they invariably flew in the direction of the house, although it was out of their sight and had no lights. If the weather were windy, they might proceed no more than a tree or two, and remain sheltered on the lee side. If the weather were more favorable, they would make greater progress, but always at night. Sooner or later, if they survived, they arrived at the house, ready for the anticipated dinner.

In every survey which was made, the first task was to study the habits of the local mosquitoes. The culprits had to be run down, and then enough facts detected about them so that the proper offense measures might be taken.

In the Philippines malaria was widespread from the Bashi Channel in the North to the Sulu Sea in the South. The approximately two million cases a year resulted in from ten to twenty thousand deaths, although practically none of these occurred in the principal cities of Manila, Cebu, or Iloilo. Malaria interfered with every enterprise. In getting the lumber out of the forests and raising sugar cane in the fields, laborers died by the hundred. Because of malaria, Mindoro, a great and fertile island in sight of the mouth of Manila Bay, was supporting only a sparse population of semi-civilized people. Hundreds had died there under the Spanish régime in the effort to start sugar plantations, and the first American attempts fared little better. Although as a direct cause of death malaria ranked fourth in the Islands, as a humanitarian and economic problem it ranked among the first.

Outside of Manila we had to deal with extensive population shifts during the various harvest seasons. It was the rule that laborers went from their native towns to distant ones or to the mountains to collect forest products. On such occasions they frequently built lean-to shelters along ditches in which anopheles bred abundantly.

It was difficult for the lay mind to associate danger with anything which appeared as harmless as a mosquito. Many of the Filipinos adhered tenaciously to the bad air theory and absolved the mosquito from all blame while she went on with her deadly work. The simple-minded tao could see no direct cause and effect, particularly since the mosquito bite did not annoy him as much as it did a thicker-skinned race. He had sojourned on terms of a "live and let live" relationship all his days.

In Manila, if the innocent day mosquito, the stegomyia persistans, or the equally blameless night mosquito, the fatigans, were allowed to breed, the Bureau of Health was promptly accused of laxness. The fatigans bred in drain pipes, septic tanks, and cesspools, and the persistans chose rain barrels, house gutters, cans and bottles.

During the first year of the mosquito campaign the householder was given instructions by the mosquito squad of the Bureau of Health. Receptacles were emptied, other collections of water were covered with petroleum, and storm gutters were frequently flushed out by the Fire Department. If mosquitoes were thereafter found breeding on private premises, the occupants were listed on the roll of dishonor in the daily newspapers. This procedure had a very good effect. The culprits' names became bywords throughout the town. The few remaining delinquents were taken before the court, where fines for maintaining a nuisance were imposed. The enforcement of these measures resulted in eliminating practically all the mosquitoes which annoy man.

For years we could not account for the absence of malaria in Manila, which had so many anopheles mosquitoes. Furthermore, the great valleys of the Islands were also practically free of the disease. This too was a great puzzle.

Some progress had been made by oiling the surface, draining, and experimenting with larvae eating fish while I was Director of Health. The Bureau of Science had imported Texan gambusia—extraordinary minnows able to live equally well in salt, fresh, running, or stagnant water. But in the Philippines they were unable to fulfill their high purpose because of an even more extraordinary fish. The peripatetic dalag, or mudfish, pursued the tasty gambusia with avidity, and even hopped overland from pool to pool in quest of these delectable morsels. In the fountains and similar places the gambusia were able to keep the water free of larvae; in the ponds and esteros they were quickly eaten by the questing dalag, who himself often furnished food for Filipino appetites.

In spite of all our attempts at control, the problem was by no means near a solution. The campaign was given new impetus when I returned to the Islands in 1921. One evening after dinner Governor General Wood and I were sitting, as was our custom, on the veranda of Malacañan.

"I've a very pleasant surprise for you," the General said, "I've secured a million dollars for you to spend on malaria. According to the health reports, thirty thousand people are dying annually from it, and it's time we wiped it out."

"General," I replied, "I wouldn't know how to spend as much as that productively. From what I've learned about mosquitoes, the mere expenditure of money won't help toward the solution."

"Why not? That's the way they did it in Panama."

"But they never had to sanitate more than a few square miles in the Canal Zone while we have thousands."

"Of course you can get rid of it if you'll drain the swamps. That will cut malaria down right away."

"But, General, we're running into all sorts of contradictions in the study of malaria. Isn't it possible that swamps may not be responsible for malaria here?"

"They have everywhere else. Why not here?"

"Nobody's proved it, and it's not a scientific way of finding out."

"Well, that's the way I want it done!" was General Wood's categorical response.

I considered that the General, himself a medical man, should not have taken such an attitude. "In that case, General, I'd better stop," I said. "I can't proceed that way. It won't be difficult for you to find someone to work on the problem as you may direct, and your method may be right. I hope it is."

The subject was dropped on this uncompromising note. But the next morning, after a good night's sleep, the General, as was his wont, repented his gruffness and was extremely apologetic. "What do I know about malaria? Forget everything I said, and tell me your ideas."

"In the first place, I'd like to know whether all the deaths ascribed to malaria are really due to that cause. And, if they are, I'd like to find out why all the measures we've taken in the malarial districts have so far been practically ineffective. I suggest asking the International Health Board for help in getting a good malariologist here to make a survey."

Wood agreed to this program without a moment's hesitation, and as soon as possible Walter D. Tiedeman was brought to the Islands. He selected four towns, each representing a geographical type—one hill town, one lowland, one bordering a lake, and one lake village influenced by running water from nearby hillsides.

Fortunately the species of anopheles which carried malaria flew only late at night, the exact time depending somewhat on the moon. On dark nights, contrary to mosquito customs in the United States, where the flight begins at sundown, they did not put in an appearance until twelve-thirty or one. We knew that we could sit or move with perfect safety until bedtime—it was impossible to sit on a screened veranda in the Philippines in comfort because the screens shut off the breeze and made the heat intolerable—but must sleep under mosquito bars if we wished to avoid infection.

The Anopheles minimus was already convicted of guilt. But in the Philippines it was never found in the house during the daytime. Before any preventive measures could be taken, its home must be located.

All sorts of experiments were made. Among others, beds were arranged in trees so that biting habits at different elevations might be studied. The beds were baited with men and the sides of the mosquito bars left open. At about eleven the first minimus arrived for her meal, but the bars were not closed until enough had entered for experimental purposes. At two o'clock, after having fed, the insects were becoming distinctly uneasy, at three they were agitatedly seeking an exit, at four they were practically committing mass suicide, jamming their heads between the interstices of the nettings, and even breaking off their wings. They were obviously motivated by some tremendous homing instinct.

After having been sprayed with carmine, the prisoners were released and immediately a hunt was organized. Stones were overturned, blades of grass and leaves scrutinized, tree trunks examined. The search continued for two years and cost thousands of dollars but ultimately the hiding place of the minimus was ferreted out. In the Philippines the streams were always lined with bamboo, and where the current undercut the banks, the bamboo rootlets formed a tangled mass into which the elusive minimus would retreat during the daytime.

It was thus proved that malaria in the Islands was associated with the swift running waters of the foothills. Had Wood's million been spent in draining swamps, it would have been completely wasted.

This fundamental discovery gave us the information required for a fresh start in malaria control. Rice chaff was scattered on the surface of the stream, and as it floated along an observer noted where it stopped in the little eddies. In those places larvae or wrigglers were often found in abundance.

The eggs of the Anopheles minimus were laid among the bamboo rootlets on the surface of the water. Sometimes in the course of one day the larvae would form, and with the chisel-shaped egg breakers on the backs of their heads would cut their way through the shells. They would then lie on the surface to feed, breathing air with tiny tubes pushed up through the surface film, and brushing into their mouths any minute particles which might float their way. These wrigglers would take a week to develop into adult mosquitoes—if the water were cold, even longer.

The problem of eradicating the minimus would have been difficult of solution had we not been able to utilize the wonderful discovery made by Dr. Barber that the acetoarsenite of copper compound known commercially as Paris green, when mixed with ninety-nine parts of fine dry road dust, and released in clouds above the surface of the stream, would kill the larvae. The mixture is so effective that if larvae were living in a dish in a room, and somebody around the corner poured the mixture from one container to another, enough would sift through the air, drift through the open windows, and settle on the dish to kill the larvae.

Paris green had this additional advantage. Water treated with it could be used for bathing, washing clothes, or even be drunk with impunity, whereas pouring oil on water rendered it unfit for use. One of the latest developments is a machine run by a paddle wheel in the stream, which scatters the Paris green automatically over the surface of the water.

The discovery that malaria in the Philippines does not exist in the lowlands but only in the foothill country was turned to immediate use. The Army had established Camp Stotsenberg, with two thousand men, in the supposedly malaria-free foothills, and had employed all the anti-malarial devices effective at Panama. But in spite of every effort, the soldiers still contracted the disease, because the camp had been established in the one place where the Anopheles minimus was to be found in the greatest numbers. The disease was eliminated almost at once by spraying Paris green on the streams that ran down the two valleys leading to the reservation.

In almost every problem of malaria, the basic approach is to survey local conditions and then apply the remedy. It may be as simple as having carabao walk through a stream to disturb the larvae, or compelling natives to turn their discarded cocoanut shells upside down, or it may consist of the most elaborate and expensive engineering operations. In the course of the demonstrations we encountered many baffling problems in engineering. Even drainage operations, when not correctly planned, have sometimes done great damage by creating breeding places where none existed before.

The Rockefeller Foundation now has engineers who travel from country to country with the sole object of advising on malaria control. One of their more important jobs was in Palestine which, governed under mandate by Great Britain, had an efficient health service, but was still unable to cope successfully with malaria.

Palestine has never been self-sustaining; it has been maintained for centuries by the world's charity. Even the Jewish colonies established by the Rothschilds were economically unsuccessful. After the World War the Jews arrived in great numbers at their ancient but long deserted home with the intent of making it self-contained, and of establishing prosperity on a firm agricultural basis. Most of the Zionists were sentimental ancients or young enthusiasts with few children. In spite of all that can be done, no more than a quarter of them are in agriculture. They persist in drifting into shops; Tel-Aviv is a typical East Side New York.

The country as a whole is most desolate. Its series of steep hills and narrow valleys are covered by loose stones about the size of a fist. The few arable sections are found near the seacoast and in the Jordan Valley. In the former, citrus fruit is grown, but the climate is so dry that every orange tree must be surrounded by a dike through which water has to be pumped at frequent intervals, thus creating additional water hazards. The Jordan Valley is fertile, but, owing to the pernicious malaria which abounds there, cultivation has been almost impossible, and those who have made the attempt frequently paid with their health, if not their lives. It was for years impossible to determine the source of the malaria so prevalent in the district around Tiberias, because it was certain anopheles could not breed in the brackish waters of the Sea of Galilee, and no other possible breeding grounds could be located. Finally, some tiny springs were found in the hillside.

American engineers introduced expert methods of dynamiting and blasting to drain the stagnant pools and swamps. Strings of explosive were laid from these to the lowlands and then exploded, making channels instantaneously. Streams that could not be dealt with in this manner were treated with Paris green. The cultivation of the land made available by the irrigation project was in itself a deterrent to mosquito breeding.

Some years ago the All America Cables had a small station on the West Coast of Nicaragua, the staff of which was losing as high as fifty hours a week from sickness among its few employees. One of the Rockefeller engineers was despatched there, and found the station located in a dent in the high hills out of which water trickled and collected in the station. By digging a circular ditch around the back of the town, the weeping water was collected in one place, and there treated with Paris green. One thousand hours of time yearly were saved to that small group of cable employees by this simple device.

In Malaya the economic aspect of malaria was of supreme importance. Along the coast were thousands of miles of alluvial plain, bordered with mangrove swamps, and there was not a village which did not pay toll to malaria. In this vast, sparsely inhabited country, so newly opened to the rubber industry, no domestic animals were kept in the coolie lines, and human beings alone furnished blood for the mosquitoes. Death rates of over two hundred per thousand were not uncommon on some of the estates; nobody knew the answer.

There were three malaria-carrying anopheles in Malaya. The umbrosus dwelt in the jungle, the ludlowii in the brackish water along the coast, and the maculatus bred almost everywhere—in the bottom of a ditch, in a little water from a crack, amid spots of green algae where the water was no more than one-eighth of an inch deep. Because the maculatus is a seepage breeder it is extremely difficult to reach and control.

One of the great problems in Malaya was the constant silting which had occurred in the river beds that took drainage from the tin mine washings. Many of these river bottoms were raised so high that water from them wandered all over the country, forming innumerable pools, big and little.

Paris green had been of inestimable assistance in many places, but it was not all-encompassing. Some question had arisen of its effectiveness against a seepage breeder such as maculatus. On many estates and in many communities it was desired to get rid of culex also, but Paris green had no effect on culex larvae. To kill mosquito larvae Paris green must be eaten. The anopheles feeds at the surface, but the culex feeds with its head hanging below and consequently eats only particles in suspension, missing the Paris green, which floats on the surface.

A thin film of petroleum spread over the surface will kill all mosquito larvae by preventing them from obtaining air. But oil also had its advantages and disadvantages. In many places it was too expensive for use, and it was, of course, ineffective on running streams. From the point of view of supervision oil was favored. The health officer merely had to drive along the road and could see at a glance whether the coolie had done his job, whereas chemical analysis was required to discover whether water had been treated with Paris green.

The principal trouble on Malayan plantations, determined only after long search, was found to have come from cutting down the jungle, because maculatus larvae, which, unlike the adult mosquitoes, loved sunlight, would breed like mad as soon as the pools were exposed, while in the dark they would not multiply. If the planters refrained from felling the jungle, or if after felling they encouraged second growth, the anopheles could be kept under control.

Singapore in the old days was a veritable death trap. Gilbert Brooke, who held the office of Chief Health Officer of Rural Singapore, became so interested that he regarded mosquitoes as his avocation as well as his vocation. He made a hobby of these insects, and was writing a book about them, largely compiled from a huge mass of literature. Brooke read me a long poem from Vergil in the original, and then translated a passage which he interpreted as proving that the gnats therein described must have been culex mosquitoes.

The mosquito danger in Singapore came not only from maculatus but also from ludlowii, although the former was still the chief offender. The cost of dealing with them was high, but fortunately the Straits Settlements in those days of the rubber boom could afford it.

Every time the slightest excavation was made, the maculatus would breed plentifully. The site of the new city reservoir had been an old coffee plantation long abandoned because of its malaria rate. The huge granite boulders in the stream beds which fed it were flattened with dynamite, so that no pools could remain in the dry season. The crevices in rocks with pot holes, which gave rise to such intensive breeding, were filled with cement, making a smooth surface throughout. On the hillsides subsoil pipes were laid, covered with crushed stone and several feet of earth seeded with grass.

The ludlowii breeds in brackish water, Singapore lies right on the sea, and the spring tides always flooded the flats with salt water. Thereafter, when the daily rains diluted these residual pools to the right degree of salinity, the ludlowii flourished. Subsoil drainage was begun for their elimination when the Naval Base, which was to prove British power to the East, was started in 1923. But the short-lived pacifistic Labor government stopped the work, and it was not recommenced until 1925. The onrush of the jungle in tropical lands is so swift that the location of these pipes, laid eighteen months before, was lost and could not even be found. It was necessary to begin the work all over again.

In most of the countries to which I went, the health authorities were exceedingly anxious to secure help in their malaria problems. Pushed more or less by the native members, the Ceylon government was anxious to start an island-wide malaria control campaign, and intimated that large sums, possibly a million rupees, could be made available. But the firm policy of the Foundation was never to embark in any undertaking without a thoroughly competent survey having first been made. This survey revealed that, although there were eighteen types of anopheles on the Island, the only proved carrier was culicifacies. It had a wide range of breeding places— slow moving sandy rivers and pools, but also irrigation channels, quarries, open drains, clear fresh sunlit water, even hoofprints of cattle.

Special attention was paid to Anuradhapura, a section of Ceylon so arid that in the days of its magnificence water had been brought in by canals for storage and irrigation purposes, and thus had created its own malaria problem. We found that reservoirs and canals still leaked abundantly through crawfish holes and seepage along penetrating roots. The hazard of many years ago had been further increased by borrow pits beside the railroad and leaks from rice paddies. It was a question of efficient engineering to make the malaria disappear.

Malaria could be wiped out anywhere if enough money were spent, but the question of economically feasible control, particularly in rural areas, was constantly arising. In Ceylon the survey showed the average per capita cost would be six rupees, and no island-wide campaign would be practicable at this figure.

It is one of the paradoxes of malaria that in India it becomes epidemic with heavy rainfall, while in Ceylon the death rate soars with drought. The reason for this is clear upon analysis. In the

Punjab, the vast plain drained by the Indus, pools are left in the depressions of the land after the rains in July and August, and in these the mosquitoes breed. In Ceylon, the geography is quite different. The south central part of the island is a mass of hills and mountains whose peaks rise to seven thousand feet. From these flow numerous rivers and streams, many of which are only outlet channels for the storm water of the monsoon. Pools remain as drought shrinks the rivers.

In October, 1934, began the worst drought in the history of Ceylon, accompanied by one of the major malaria epidemics of history. In the ensuing seven months, out of a population in the affected district of three million, half had the disease. In some places the infection was one hundred percent. Eighty thousand lives were lost in the period, village life was paralyzed, agricultural operations ceased, trade and business stopped almost completely. The whole medical force was mobilized, the school houses were taken over as clinics, and everybody was supplied with free quinine. At the height of the epidemic, more than sixty thousand a day were treated.

An expert malariologist, supplied by the British government, was at once called into consultation. Hitherto such epidemics had been regarded as inevitable but after an exhaustive study he reported that, although epidemics could not be halted once under way, it should be possible, by combining all known methods and, especially, training the river beds to eradicate breeding places, to prevent their recurrence.

All over the world students, research workers, field and laboratory scientists are working on malaria. Until some method can be devised which is capable of general application, there is little hope of bringing the disease under complete control. The most that can be said today is that if enough money is spent, a malarial district can be made healthy; but it is a long and persistent task, and only unremitting care meets with success.

In the tropics there is no end to malaria control; as soon as antimalaria measures are stopped, the disease recurs. At one time Bombay was building a new port area, and nearly all crews of ships that anchored in that section of the Bay caught malaria. The situation became so serious that ships were short-handed. It was finally dis-

459

covered that rain had collected in half-completed basements nearby, and the mosquitoes had bred there, thus infecting the sailors. The work of ridding the port area of mosquitoes was so well done that the city fathers said, "We have no malaria"; and did away with the appropriation.

Malaria at once returned.

Even with the knowledge at our command, malaria control is not always possible. In the East religion sooner or later steps upon the scene. In Bombay the Parsees, who follow a strange cult, were dominant in the business affairs of the city. They are to be encountered everywhere in the city, readily distinguishable by their odd wooden hats, covered with yellowish and black oilcloth. They live in huge tenement-like structures built around a little courtyard in the middle of which is a well, sometimes thirty feet deep. On the roofs are vast cisterns. Both wells and cisterns are uncovered because all Parsees regard the four elements—earth, air, fire, and water—as sacred and uncontaminable.

In Bombay the malaria carrier is Anopheles stephensi, so perfectly urbanized that it will breed in almost any container, and is equally at home in deepest well or high-built cistern. Not until after years of persuasion and the exercise of constant unyielding pressure would the influential Parsees screen their cisterns and wells.

The Parsees ultimately withdrew their objections, but religion must still be dealt with in other parts of India. The recently powerful spokesman, Gandhi, flying in the face of all modern scientific knowledge and ignoring the tremendous number of humans being slain by such small insects, is reported as having stated in the *Times of India*, June, 1935, "We have no right to take the lives of mosquitoes, flies, lice, rats, or fleas. They have as much right to live as we."

CHAPTER 26.   AND MAKE
                PERSUASION DO THE
                     WORK OF FEAR

WHEN I first began traveling for the Rockefeller Foundation, the run from Singapore to Java was a bright spot in
the itinerary. The *Melchoir Treub* and the *Rumphius* were the
crack passenger liners of the K.P.M., the most powerful corporation in the Dutch East Indies. These boats, which resembled luxurious yachts, were built for comfort in the tropics. Passengers could
practically live on deck, taking refuge from the brief but daily showers in little shelters specially provided. The voyage was comfortable
and pleasant. Fat Dutch officials spent most of their time puffing
placidly on cabbagy cigars which glowed like red hot chimneys,
and, in the company of their equally fat Mevvrouws, gulping foaming
schooners of beer at the little deck tables.

With the low Sumatra coast on our right, never out of sight of
islands, we steamed the five hundred miles to broad and shallow
Batavia Bay. At dawn of the second day we approached the breakwater which protects Tandjong Priok. Neither at this modern port
nor at the old capital of Batavia, seven miles away, was there any
hint of the strange beauty hidden within the island. Low-lying Batavia itself looked like any town in Holland. Its stone-walled canals,
with gates to regulate the sluggish flow of the current, sometimes
traversed the centers of the enormously broad avenues, built on the
generous scale of the Dutch themselves.

The tidal flats of Batavia, more pestilential than those of Singapore, had offered no terrors to the Seventeenth Century colonists from the Zuyder Zee, who had come from a country in which malaria claimed then an annual tithe. In Batavia, which ironically enough means Fair Meadows, they clung intrepidly to the homes they had erected there. But the mortality was so overpowering—over a million died in twenty-two years of the Eighteenth Century—that the city ultimately was abandoned to natives and commerce; the burghers now come down to it only for working hours, and return as early as possible to Weltevreden (Well Content) where they live in their plastered tinted houses on ground only a little higher but far more healthful.

Even in Weltevreden—Batavia Centrum as it is now called—the heat is intense, and the mosquitoes, although not malaria carriers, made it impossible for me to work in my hotel room. The whole island swarmed with insect life, from butterflies to termites, and at sundown the air was resonant with their throbbing sounds. They were an omnipresent pest.

The Governor General found Weltevreden much too hot. He moved inland to Buitenzorg in the hills which, although not in sight from Batavia, are never much more than an hour from the coast. The world's most beautiful botanical gardens form a private park for his mansion. On the slope of Salak volcano, which through the centuries has fertilized its hillsides, grow specimens of every tree, shrub, plant, and vine known to the tropics. Throughout its spacious acres the Dutch experiment with tea, rubber, cinchona, sugar cane, rice, nutmegs, cloves, and pepper in order to develop them for commerce. Though the fundamental purpose is economic, the faithful botanists who have labored there have never sacrificed beauty to utility. Five thousand out of the six thousand known varieties of orchids open exotic blooms, and tree fuchsias of incomparable beauty are covered with dusky red and purple blossoms. Its primeval forest is watered by a river, and on its numerous ponds float the most marvelous water lilies I have ever seen.

Not many miles from the Botanical Gardens lies a mysterious plantation, encircled by a high stone wall. Within this enclosure, which no visitor ever enters, grow the cinchona trees of Java. The secrets of cultivation and extraction thus jealously guarded have made the Dutch supreme in the production of quinine.

This was by no means the only contribution of the Dutch to medicine. They introduced chenopodium for the cure of hookworm. In their laboratories they had developed the smallpox vaccine, sought vainly for so many years, that would remain effective for long periods under tropical temperature. They were the first to experiment with cholera vaccine on a large scale, testing it on the inhabitants of each alternate block in Batavia. Practically no cases occurred in the blocks protected by the vaccine. In Sumatra, where hundreds of laborers on rubber plantations used to die annually, administering the vaccine had cut the number down to one or two.

In the extremely difficult situations that confronted them, the Dutch seemed to possess to an unusual degree the ability to combine the scientific with the practical. They directed their efforts to finding specific remedies for treating tropical diseases and working out economical methods for dealing with health matters. It was a Netherlander in Java who invented the bored hole latrine, one of the greatest contributions to sanitation in the East. At last in dealing with the terrible problem of soil pollution a method was devised, the chief value of which lay in its simplicity. By boring a hole in the ground fourteen to sixteen inches in diameter and ten or twelve feet deep, preferably to ground water, a cheap, odorless latrine could be made available to all races and to suit all purses. The Americans, who are the well-drillers for the world, soon perfected drilling equipment, as easy to use as a carpenter's augur, which still further simplified installation.

The bored hole latrine has many advantages. Years of research conducted by the Rockefeller Foundation have shown that, under almost all conditions, such latrines constitute no danger to wells or other domestic water supplies.

Even the poorest peasants of Java can afford this safeguard and literally hundreds of thousands are being constructed annually.

Mrs. Marie D. Buck, a prominent teacher in Madras, states: "We expect every student to become a thorough convert to the B. H. L. and to leave us eager to install them in his home, school, and playground, as a disease controller and annihilator of the main reason for making outcastes untouchables. While we feel that control of hookworm and water borne diseases is a worthy ambition, even wider horizons open before us as we realize that if we can spread the B. H. L. all over India, human night soil ceases to become the concern of the outcastes. Then, though we shall not live to see its triumphant conclusion, we shall have struck a death blow at the reason for untouchability."

The Dutch handled ingeniously their peculiar malaria problem along the coast, which was a mass of ponds, artificially made. There fish had been raised for many decades in enormous quantities to help supply proteins for the teeming population. As many as three hundred and eighty varieties were cultivated, including the golden carp which grew to great size and made brilliant spots of color in the market places.

The fish ponds used to be profuse breeders of Anopheles ludlowii which hid in the masses of top algae where minnows could not reach them. To solve the problem thus introduced, deep trenches were dug encircling the bottoms of the ponds, and when the water was drained, as was periodically done, the level would sink so that water remained only in the trenches, where the fish could live temporarily. In this way the surface algae were destroyed and the larvae could be swallowed up by top minnows.

Few people realize what a vast population is under the control of the Netherlands in the Far East. That tiny little country, encompassing few more inhabitants than New York City, has a dependent population of over seventy-five million in Java, Sumatra, Borneo, and New Guinea, all Malayan save the latter. The average revenues from these Eastern subjects are so low that little is left over to meet the cost of modern health safeguards.

In practically all colonies the health departments are starved for funds. Only the crumbs and leavings come their way. But wherever the Rockefeller Foundation could stage a demonstration, with its attendant publicity and startling results, popular interest was directed toward health, and the appropriations for the health departments were almost immediately increased. One of the most valuable services we could render Java would be to bring prestige from the outside to the members of the local medical service, which paradoxically appeared to occupy the lowest status of officialdom. If we could get them to cooperate along our lines of preventive medicine, enormous numbers of people would be affected, but this was not easy of accomplishment because they were convinced of their ability to handle their health problems without outside aid.

I relied on the old familiar hookworm route to gain entrance to Java, and, following my rule to begin with the man at the top, interviewed Alexander W. Frederick Indenburg, the Governor General, a difficult undertaking, since high Dutch officials are not in the habit of seeing casual visitors. With the temperature at ninety, the humidity at saturation point, and not enough breeze to move a piece of tissue paper, I arrayed myself in redingote, heavy trousers, stiff shirt, patent leather shoes, and a silk hat and made my call.

I briefly described to the Governor General the development of the hookworm campaign in the United States; how it had gradually extended to foreign countries, and how it served as an entering wedge to make even the most lowly people acquainted with the good results that followed public health measures; I told him how our Board believed that a system of health could not be imposed upon a people from above, that it must come from below, and that it was only by patience rather than by force that permanent progress in health lines could be gained; I explained how hookworm was so simple that even the most ignorant could understand it, that our experience so far had been that through its treatment a desire was created in the masses for better health conditions, and that as soon as this was accomplished we believed the battle was half won; I laid special stress upon the improvement which might be expected in the economic efficiency of the people, and expressed our desire to make an infection survey in Java; and finally I suggested that, if suitable arrangements could be made, we would send a medical officer to cooperate with the medical officers of his own service.

The Governor General was very polite and affable. He would be happy to look into this, would advise me if anything were to be done, and gave me a letter to his Chief Health Officer, Dr. W. T. de Vogel, who would make the necessary arrangements for the Darling Commission's survey.

Dr. de Vogel intimated that when it came to control measures, his department was probably better able to handle them than our new organization. He agreed readily, however, to let the Darling

Commission make investigations, because pure research would not interfere with his department in any way.

The Dutch like formality and no great results are obtained if a mass of ideas is put to them too quickly. My only hope was to go slowly; caution and more caution was to become for years my motto in Java.

In all the countries I have ever visited, I have found no place where English did not suffice for travel purposes, though it might not always serve in scientific or polite conversation. In communicating with people generally I could usually find a short cut. *Pigi,* which means literally "bring," is a word combining a multitude of purposes in Java and Malaya. By consulting a list of common terms, and saying, "*pigi* this" and "*pigi* that," I could get what I wanted. When Dr. MacCallum was traveling with me, he would step up to a passerby and read a question from the Malay instruction book, but it was comical to watch his face when an unintelligible spatter of sounds piled up against his ear drums. Again and again it happened that after he had completed his contortions in Malay, I would put the question in English and get a perfectly good answer.

The Dutch realized that nobody could be expected to understand their language, and consequently learned English and either French or German as auxiliaries. Because the subtleties of the English language were often too much for them, and because German was more closely allied to their language and also more exact in itself, I frequently found that my German was more intelligible.

I had several amusing experiences with the Dutch inability to grasp the finer points of English. The morning after I had secured permission for the Darling Commission to work in Java, I sent a cable to the home office announcing my success. The girl in the telegraph office looked it over and apparently approved it. Since it was war time, all messages were eyed carefully lest they be in code. But that noon in the midst of a luncheon party I was giving at the Hôtel des Indes, a waiter bent over me and said, "Telephone for you, sir."

The only phone, unprotected by a booth, hung on the dining room wall. I took up the receiver, and above the hum of the many diners I heard a feminine voice, "Are you zee Doctaire Heisaire?"

"Yes."

"Zis morning you have sent one cablegram?"

"Yes, why?"

"Eet ees not zee Eengleesh. It must be zee Eengleesh."

"What's wrong with it?"

"Eet has zee word p-s-y-c-h-o-l-o-g-i-c-a-l. Zat ees not zee Eengleesh."

"Of course it is! It's a perfectly good word."

"No! Eet ees NOT zee Eengleesh."

"I cannot be responsible for your English education. I'll leave it to any English-speaking person."

That seemed to end her doubts, at least momentarily. She began on another tack. "You have anozzaire word. Eet ees also zee code."

"What's that one?"

"D-a-r-l-i-n-g. I have looked in zee dictionary and eet say 'one sweet zing.' "

"Darling is not one sweet thing. It's the name of a man," I assured the girl desperately, aware by this time that the whole dining room had ceased eating and was listening to this absorbing conversation.

"Oh, no-o-o, darling means 'one sweet zing.' It must be zee code. I cannot send eet."

"I insist on your sending it! It has to go through Singapore anyhow. Let them decide."

"Well," hesitatingly, "I don't zink I can send eet."

"You go ahead and send it," I adjured her, slammed down the telephone receiver, and passed through the length of the dining room to the accompaniment of knowing looks from the diners, all of whom were convinced that I had been communicating with "one sweet zing."

The Hôtel des Indes is a remarkable place. Javanese hotels are run on different principles from those of any elsewhere in the world. They are more like small villages, consisting of a series of cottages with two apartments, one above the other. For the time of the guest's occupancy, one of these, composed of veranda, sitting room, bedroom, bath, and cubby hole for the boy assigned to him as his personal servant by the hotel, is his private dwelling. This boy even accompanies him as he makes his way to the dining room in the central building, and waits upon him there.

It is not strange that the Dutch in Java seem to be ponderous with adipose tissue. On one of my subsequent trips I saw two Dutch women who were not fat, which I thought a great sight and scarcely credible. Too much alcohol, little exercise, and, in particular, overeating, are responsible.

I have never seen anything remotely resembling the Dutch meals. Possibly because of the heat, the men keep curious office hours—from seven to twelve, and from five to eight. Before embarking on the day's arduous duties, they breakfast sparingly on eggs, cold meat, several kinds of sausage, meat pudding, cheese, and coffee, the latter a concentrated syrup from a bottle to which scalding hot water is added. About ten in the morning they reinforce themselves further.

At lunch time comes the famous *rijstafel*. First the guest ladles rice into a soup plate the size of a washbasin. Then a line of waiters —sometimes as many as twenty—advances, every one with a tray containing two to five varieties of food; some of each is supposed to be taken. The many ingredients include chicken, duck, beef, Bombay duck—a form of dried fish tough as leather but with a delightful flavor—eggs, peanuts, shredded cocoanut, all imaginable vegetables from Occident and Orient, beets, beansprouts, water chestnuts, the extraordinary condiments of the East, chutneys and chillies, and curry which turns the mixture yellow and a cochineal red powder which, if taken in any quantity, burns like fire. With a large soup spoon in either hand the diners turn this mountain of food over and over as though they were putting it through a concrete mixer and then consume it to the last grain of rice.

Afterwards, the Dutch, thoroughly groggy, drag themselves groaning to their couches, where they repose until four-thirty. It is then time for tea, and so back to the office. Dinner, the real meal of the day, comes as a welcome finale at nine-thirty or ten, accompanied by a liberal supply of schnapps. Finally they retire exhausted to bed to repair the ravages of the day's toil.

To my astonishment, I several times heard Americans referred to as the heaviest eaters in the world. Since I had never seen anything that remotely resembled the Gargantuan repasts of the Dutch,

I was extremely curious. I puzzled until I discovered the answer. When they entered an American hotel or restaurant, believing it the local custom, they would mistakenly start at the top and eat their way through the à la carte bill of fare, a difficult feat, even for those in training.

The appearance of the Dutch, heavy and big-boned, was decidedly unattractive. Nor could the Javanese, with their wizened faces, be judged beautiful by Western standards. Only the mestizos, combining the best features of both races, were handsome. Fortunately there were many of these, because the Dutch and Javanese intermarried freely. Part of many Dutch women's lack of charm was due to the habit of sitting around in sarong and jacket until late in the afternoon. This could be excused on the grounds of the great heat, but not on those of esthetics.

The nights were so sticky and hot in the lowlands, especially since a mosquito net was indispensable, that it was the invariable custom to provide a long bolster called a Dutch wife. By placing one knee over this, the sleeper could expose a larger area of epidermis and receive the benefit of the maximum amount of air.

The Dutch were still far behind other countries in the fundamentals of tropical ventilation, so necessary in a country where the monsoon seldom blew. This seemed odd in the light of their many remarkable conquests of other tropical problems. The homes, scrupulously whitewashed and decorated with blooming plants in the tradition of the old country, had no jutting verandas. Instead, the middle of the front three rooms merely lacked an outer wall. Whatever breeze there might be could enter this open-air sitting room only from one direction.

Cholera was often severe in Batavia before the general application of vaccine. According to a Malay custom, when an epidemic was raging, in order to avoid registering their dead, they used to drag the bodies to the "particular lands" and abandon them there. These were private government grants, exempt from the Dutch health regulations, most of them located in the outlying district of Batavia called Meester Cornelis.

The danger of cholera was also present in rural communities, where villagers bathed their bodies and washed their rice in the same streams which they polluted. These *dessas*, as they were called, were surrounded by rice paddies and cane fields. Most of the houses were built flat on the ground, some made of *suale*, or woven bamboo, others of a substance resembling our adobe. In most cases they had heavily thatched roofs.

Although the Dutch conquered cholera, plague was still an unsolved problem in thickly populated Java. On one of my trips I learned there had been a hundred thousand cases, chiefly in the mountain districts. The authorities asked my opinion, and offered me every facility for visiting the plague area.

In the course of inspecting the districts affected I had a fine opportunity to see a great deal of Javanese village life. We rode in procession with a native official on horseback, and everywhere we stopped we were surrounded by curious multitudes. Even as we inspected the rat-proof houses, large numbers tramped after us. All the countryside came to make a holiday. At many points along the route we were greeted by the native gamelan or anklong bands. At Karangkobar a great show was staged for my benefit which was in many respects similar to the Ifugao fiestas in which I used to participate in the Philippines.

The Dutch method of dealing with plague was to demolish every house in any village in which the disease appeared. In putting the buildings together again, they cleverly split the bamboo poles in half, laying the ends of the semicircle of one section into the concave surface of the other so that no enclosed space for harboring rats was left. Naturally the plague disappeared in that town, but it was more than likely to appear in the one ahead.

After completing the inspection, I informed the Dutch frankly that first of all the primary sources of infection, the grain warehouses in the port cities, should be dealt with, and, since they had only about a million dollars to spend on plague, the method they were pursuing in the villages was not likely to be successful. In attempting to guard against the disease they waited until something happened, and then concentrated heavily on the infection itself. The idea of tearing down and reconstructing fifty thousand houses annually was a program which would have awed any but a determined Dutchman. My advice was to map the roads over which grain was accustomed to travel, because along those routes the plague would surely travel also. Instead of expending so much energy in a town already infected, I suggested taking a lesson from our enemy the fleas, and keeping one jump ahead of them. The wholesale destruction of a town was spectacular, but the otherwise efficient Dutch never caught up with the plague. Their plan was nothing more than a stern chase.

The Dutch, on the other hand, claimed the sectional method I had used so successfully in the Philippines was impossible in Java because rats could not be eliminated from the thickly thatched roofs. Furthermore, it was their duty to keep their population happy, and, since the Javanese never wanted anything done, they believed that in attacking infection after its appearance, they were interfering about as much with native habits and customs as circumstances warranted.

The Malay was not easy to work with. In his native state he was highly superstitious. When asked his name, rather than bring down upon his head the bad luck supposed to follow a direct answer, he would turn to a friend and ask, "What is my name?" Although nominally Mohammedan in Java, he still believed in *hantu*, evil spirits which lived in trees and lurked about the houses at night, and this *hantu* influence was believed to be sinister toward his family, animals, crops, and even his own person.

The Malay inability to stay awake was so serious that the Dutch would not trust the Javanese to operate trains in the darkness; consequently they did not run at night. Because prospective travelers had to be routed out of bed so early in the morning to catch trains, traveling was particularly tiresome. In spite of this inconvenience, however, the two-day trip along the mountain range which ran the length of Java was most scenic and impressive, particularly the section between Batavia and Djokjakarta.

At Djokjakarta the Dutch had compromised with the religion of their subjects, who fervently worshipped the Sultan as divine, by permitting him to keep up a shadow of his former rule. I had an odd feeling that it was, to say the least, unusual to find white Christian soldiers guarding a Mohammedan potentate in a country ruled by a European nation, especially when I recalled that this rule had now extended over a period of several centuries. For my interview with the Sultan I was conducted by a Dutch officer through his *kraton,* loosely called the palace, which, like those of all Eastern potentates, consisted of a series of buildings. Within the stone walls, which sheltered some ten thousand followers, was enclosure after enclosure. The private dwelling of the Sultan was located within the fourth enclosure, as were the harem apartments guarded by the princes, and a public reception room, ornately decorated with gilt carvings and scintillating with mirrors. Pictures of Queen Wilhelmina and the Netherlands royal family certified his loyalty to the source of his income.

The Sultan lived in colorful if not regal surroundings. Within the grounds paraded resplendent birds of paradise and peacocks. Many roosters were also being exercised, each with his special male attendant; cockfighting was one of the Sultan's principal diversions. Glistening shining carp, said to be very highly prized by the Sultan as articles of food, swam lazily in a pond into which drainage from the royal palace emptied.

Enormous pergolas dotted the lawns. In accordance with the tenets of the Mohammedan religion, worship could not be permitted under the clear sky. It was generally assumed that this meant services should be conducted in a mosque, but the Sultan had dodged both the issue and the heat by erecting these open-air structures which were cheap, provided shade, and at the same time might be interpreted as meeting the demands of his religion.

More attractive than the *kraton* were the fairly modern ruins of the nearby Water Palace, built by a Portuguese adventurer. Although when I first saw it, it had been abandoned for only five years, it was already in a state of great disrepair, and the jungle had crept over it. Many underground water-cooled chambers had been built to provide relief from the tropical heat, and from these in all directions led passages, apparently designed to afford ready means of escape.

Less than a hundred years ago was discovered the greatest of all Javanese ruins, which the jungle had swallowed up completely. The Dutch had been loyal to the antiquarian trust left in their hands, and had carefully removed the clinging tendrils from Boroboedoer. This magnificent relic, deserted with the Mohammedan conquest of the island, remained still to bear witness to the physical expres-

472

sion of the Buddhist faith. Tier on tier the huge lava blocks, fitted without mortar, held by no columns and no supporting arches, rose majestically above the plain. Each terrace was decorated with bas reliefs, representing the life of Buddha and symbolizing the spiritual development of man.

From the top of the temple the eye swept the countryside, fecund with rice, sugar, and cocoanuts. The pretty streams, the gentle people, the fertile country, and the harmonious landscape, impressed me with the thought that, after all, man did not defile all he touched, and even did much to make it more beautiful.

Boroboedoer stands as a cherished relic, but the ever-present volcanoes are still regarded with superstitious awe and reverence by the Javanese who live among them. The mild and kindly Tenggerese had a sort of religion, half Brahmin, half animistic, centered around the worship of Bromo, the most famous of Javanese craters, which reared itself from the Zand Zee not far from Soerabaja at the eastern end of the island. The morning I made the ascent the mists in the valleys at sunrise looked like great ocean billows, and the mountain tops stood out like islets here and there. At times I had the illusion that waves were being washed against the shore. Then the mists thinned, and the lowlands appeared dimly, as though seen through clear water.

At Moengal Pass, eleven hundred feet up, we looked down into the "Landscape of the Moon" which was in reality the bottom of the old Tengger Volcano. The narrow and shallow steps cut up to the crater's rim, an hour's ride further, were difficult to climb because they had been deeply covered with ashes from the constant eruptions. Steam explosions were occurring at the bottom with an awe-inspiring noise. At the edge of the crater shelters of huge timbers had been built, and when it was time for an eruption, the guide urged us into one of these. From there I saw the actual eruption, its showers of hot rocks and ashes spurting into the air and thundering down.

On the return journey the atmosphere was transparent and pellucid and the scenery majestic. Java was the most volcanic island for its size in the world, and periodic eruptions from one or more of the craters sent out great clouds of fine ashes which drifted and settled over the landscape. The soil thus fertilized was watered by

473

the daily rains, creating ideal conditions for plant life. Even the tops of the mountains were sown with crops of potatoes, carrots, lettuce, and corn.

All Java was like a garden; not an arable plot went untilled on this island of thirty million inhabitants. Lalang, the universal grass pest of the Eastern tropics, could not grow because of the intensive cultivation. I was always reminded of what would be possible in the Philippines, so impressed was I with the great wealth of Java's products—its sugar, kapok, pineapples, mangoes, cocoanuts, rubber, and spices. Irrigation ditches for the thick-standing rice radiated in all directions like the veins of a leaf. It was strange to see rice being planted and harvested in the same field.

Sugar cane, ten feet high, grew in vast fields. The land was prepared by heaping up, with hoe-like *choncling* tools, large masses of earth between which deep canals were left. Sugar harvesting seemed to be a tremendous operation in which enormous numbers were employed. The roads were literally congested with carts carrying cane to the mills. Throughout the island, traveling by train, motor, or horseback, it was impossible to get out of sight of a human being. Javanese, in their flat, neatly tied turbans, the subdued colors of their raiment producing a terra cotta effect, trooped up and down about their business of gaining a livelihood.

I could not help being impressed by the fact that the white man made beasts of burden out of these people. But it was probably the dense population rather than the Dutch dominance which made them so eager to work. In some places Malays are indifferent and indolent, but in Java, where the struggle for existence is more severe, they are wide awake and ambitious. I have never seen more willing labor anywhere. They seemed to toil from sunrise to sunset with a cheerfulness beyond belief.

When I first went to Java the peasantry were gentle people, cringing and never standing in the presence of Dutch officials, who ruled with a heavy hand, allowing the Javanese only inferior positions in the Civil Service, and maintaining domestic discipline literally by spanking. They had been for years imposing upon these Mohammedan Malays, differing from them in almost every respect, laws and regulations which suited their own ideas of hygiene. But by

1926 the Javanese were becoming more and more restive, and more and more aggressive in their resentment. They held parades protesting against Dutch domination, blew up bridges, and killed their masters, who for so many years had punished them as though they were children. The reign of terror was so strong at Weltevreden that every house had to be protected by a night watchman. Thousands of *insurrectos* were sent to exile in New Guinea, where they still remain.

After years of cautious preliminary skirmishing on our part to secure an invitation from Java, the Dutch suddenly capitulated and asked us to cooperate in health work. This surrender was due to an unpremeditated circumstance. I was in Geneva serving on a Commission to draft an International Sanitary Code, of which the retired Chief Health Officer of Java was also a member. Hardly had I finished my address to the Health Section of the League of Nations on the activities of the Rockefeller Foundation when he dashed up, shook my hand, and said, "Now for the first time I understand what the Rockefeller Foundation is trying to do. I'm going to see that you receive an invitation to go to Java at once."

True enough, the invitation shortly arrived.

In the ten years which had elapsed since I had begun my visits to Java, the situation had changed. A new Governor General had been appointed who had become familiar with modern publicity methods while Minister to Washington. He had substituted an official policy of persuasion for that of force in dealing with the Javanese.

The members of the Civil Service, however, trained in the old tradition, found the orders of the Governor General abhorrent, and gave lip service only. We had the feeling we were being allowed to make our demonstration only in order that they might demonstrate to us how wrong we were. We encountered both active and passive resistance on every hand from the rank and file of Dutch officialdom. The Chief Health Officer, Dr. van Lonkhuyzen, said in so many words to our representative, "I'm sorry you've come, and the original invitation was only sent because it was forced upon us by higher Government officials."

We were assigned to Serang, an insurrectionary district about sixty miles from Batavia, which bore the reputation of being particularly cantankerous and difficult. Dr. van Lonkhuyzen freely admitted he did not believe in our campaign of education. It was the old story that it could not be done, at least not in Java, and this he knew because of his long experience.

The Dutch, who heretofore had been administering vermifuges to hookworm cases only when they came into the dispensaries, were now beginning to subject them to an intensive course of treatment. Villagers were brought in by the headman, much the same as cattle would be driven to market. Groups were herded together and then made to pass in single file to a table where the medicine was poured down their throats. The Dutch were greatly interested in their work and proud of it.

Dr. John Lee Hydrick set about proving to the Dutch that in spite of the virtues of their chenopodium, the important thing in Java was to prevent reinfection, and a soil pollution campaign, accompanied by the building of latrines, had to be carried on simultaneously with treatment. He had not been working long when the Dutch, with their old feeling of superiority, stated, "Your methods are too slow; we'll show you how to do it."

The great day came when the comparison of results between the two methods was to be made. The Governor of the district and other officials first examined everything that we had been able to persuade the people to do in the territory in which we were working. They were apparently much impressed until Dr. van Lonkhuyzen said, "The people here have built ten thousand latrines, but we've built one hundred thousand at less expense. I want you to see our installations."

I too was eager. Dr. van Lonkhuyzen, Dr. Hydrick, his secretary, and I set out for Kroja, the village in Central Java where the Dutch had concentrated their work.

At Kroja we dismounted from the automobile and marched in procession to the first latrine, standing new and trim. I lit a piece of paper and threw it down the hole; the latrine had not been used. We marched to the second; it too was as it had been built—and so on down the line, every single one was immaculately clean.

Dr. van Lonkhuyzen, somewhat discomfited, asked the local

Health Officer for an explanation. "It's not customary for the people to begin using the latrines until after they've taken the treatment," was his excuse.

"Your campaign has been going on for some time. Isn't there a town where the people have already been treated?" I inquired interestedly.

"Oh, yes, we have some latrines which have been constructed for several months in another town."

"Let's go there," I suggested.

"Oh, it's much too far, and the heat is too great."

"Well, let's have something to eat first and then go."

After lunch the reluctant officials climbed back into the automobile and we motored forty miles to another village. More hot and more tired, they once again dismounted and once again the procession formed. It was the same story. The latrines which had been built for several months had still not been used.

"I surrender," said Dr. van Lonkhuyzen. "I thought we had something on you. But I'm convinced now. We must have public health education in Java."

Meanwhile Dr. Hydrick was perfecting his technique of instruction. He took advantage of the peculiarly Javanese institution of the *mantri*, a term used to designate a native technician in any field. It was astounding to see to what an extent the *mantri*, who usually possessed a good academic background, was being used in the different government departments. He might be a postal or telegraph helper, or an agriculturist, or a nurse or operating assistant. Since Dutch doctors did not understand what was meant by public health nursing, it too was regarded as a menial duty and delegated to the *mantri*.

Dr. Hydrick learned both Dutch and Malay, and then instructed a selected group of *mantris* in the story of hookworm. Each *mantri* would go into a Javanese home, sit on the floor with all the family collected about him, describe the hookworm, and demonstrate its presence in the soil with the Baermann apparatus. They usually seemed to understand it but, taking no chances, in a few weeks' time he would go back and repeat the story. Upon a third visit he would question them. They welcomed this opportunity to repeat the lessons

477

they had learned. He would ask, "Where does the hookworm live?" or "How do you get anemia?" If they could not answer, the *mantri* knew his instruction had been poor. On the fourth interview the school children were also present. An old grey-headed grandfather might be corrected by a little child. But invariably an animated discussion would begin, all appealing to the *mantri* as judge to decide which was right.

I spent a great deal of time myself going from village to village and from house to house. I saw children singing health songs with gusto, but experience in many countries led me to question whether the words of these songs had any effect or made any impression on the children's minds. This business of bringing the offerings of science to a rural population, and of making them a part of daily lives had many pitfalls and required the patience of Job. Trying to write my impressions amid fiercely biting mosquitoes and thousands of bugs, ants, and flying things that crawled down my neck as well as constantly obscured the page, heightened my admiration for the intrepid souls who stayed there from day to day and struggled with the health problem amid the filth, and, even worse, the skepticism which continued on the part of many of the Dutch officials.

Fortunately we had the full-hearted support of the new Governor General, who said to me, "You know the situation we're up against. We're ready to finance your work up to the hilt. We have one hundred thousand dollars available."

It was not all done at once but when the Dutch Civil Service was finally converted, it entered the field of education with every bit of its abundant energy. Moving pictures, charts, health-mobiles, pamphlets, printed matter—all were used for propaganda purposes. Ultimately a Museum of Health was installed in a large building specially remodeled for the purpose. Open-air movies and speeches were held on the immense Koningsplein in Weltevreden; sometimes as many as thirty thousand Javanese attended.

But these were merely outward manifestations of a complete change in point of view. Helping to bring about this reversal was our great contribution to Java. Every aspirant for the Netherlands Colonial Service had to go to school for several years at the Colonial

Institute in Amsterdam. He learned the Malay language, the folk-lore, religion, and customs. But the whole system of teaching has been changed at its roots. Where once the student was taught to command, now he is instructed in the principles of persuasion.

CHAPTER 27.   HUSTLING THE EAST

ONE hot June afternoon I set out along the Charun Krung, the New Road, for the palace of the King of Siam, in 1916 one of the few remaining absolute monarchs in the world. Formerly Bangkok, the Venice of the East, had had no streets, nothing but tree-shaded *klongs*, or canals. But King Maha Vajiravudh had tired of riding on the broad and placid Menam in his Golden Swan, propelled by its sixty paddlers clothed in Tyrian red, whose gold-leaved blades flashed rhythmically in the sun. He had seen the automobiles of the Western World and, desiring them for his own use, had in ten years bordered the *klongs* with over a hundred miles of roads, so that he could travel from one border of his city to the other in one of his forty-two cars. Beyond, there were and still are no highways —nothing but a vast paddy field stretching to the horizon as far as the eye can reach.

We passed by beautiful public buildings and the brick palaces of the multitudinous brothers, uncles, cousins, and nephews of the King. The countless wats were roofed in peacock-hued tiles and decorated with slim, sharp-pointed, gilt prachidees. These spires, shooting up suddenly and unexpectedly amid the greenery, were startling, no matter how often I saw them.

Though the thermometer was at ninety-five I had necessarily attired myself in heavy broadcloth morning coat; the hottest places in the tropics seem to have a predilection for formal dress on official occasions. But it was annoying, after all my sartorial preparations, to have the general effect spoiled. Just opposite the National Museum of Fine Arts a sprinkle of rain peppered my top hat so that it looked as though it had suffered a severe attack of smallpox.

Finally, we reached the bend of the Menam in the heart of the city where the great wall, with its crenelations shaped like the ace of spades, enclosed the King's compound. The sentries at the gate peered suspiciously into the car, ignoring the fact that it was one of the King's own, and that one of the King's own aides was sitting by my side. Once within, we went unchallenged between lines and lines of pickets, who came to attention as the car swept by. I later learned that a cow's crest on the car would admit anyone who had the forty-two ticals to pay for the privilege.

After twisting and turning and passing through three additional sets of gates, all of which had to be opened, we entered the inner enclosure, where Chululongkorn the Great, the King's father, had added the Chakkri Palace to the innumerable other buildings, which displayed all forms of Eastern architecture, simple and ornate. There was located the Dusit Mahaprasit Hall which "held in architectural form not some builder's plan, but an artist's dream of the fantastic." There also was the royal Wat Phra Keo. A myriad small bells under its eaves sweetly tinkled in every little breeze. Thousands of pieces of glass, incrusted in the walls, glinted in the sun; within its sacred interior, high on his altar, sat the Great Emerald Buddha.

After being introduced in one of the reception rooms to a number of military officers, who entertained me most politely in excellent English, I was conducted ceremoniously between rows of military officers of high rank to a one-room bungalow which, in contrast to the splendor of the main palace buildings, was small and unpretentious. I was shown at once into the presence of the King, who was dressed as a colonel of a British regiment. The room was almost filled with admirals, generals, ministers, and other officials, all adorned with gorgeous uniforms.

The short, stout, moon-faced monarch graciously motioned me to a chair and seated himself on a wicker settee. After the usual inanities about the weather had been exchanged, he suddenly asked, "What do you think of our medical school?"

"I'm not prepared to talk about it, Your Majesty."

"I want to know."

"Your Majesty, I hope you'll excuse me."

"But I want to know."

He must have observed that I had been glancing curiously at the semi-circle of faces surrounding us. Apparently believing I was embarrassed at the presence of these dignitaries, he turned to them and said, "You're dismissed."

Nobody moved.

"I say, you're dismissed!" the King reiterated in an unmistakable tone of command.

Expressions of astonishment spread over their faces. Reluctantly, with sabres clanking, they filed out, and the other door closed behind them.

"Now we're alone, tell me about my medical school," the King persisted.

"Your Majesty, really I can't."

"No one ever tells me the truth. I hear only what everybody thinks I'd like to hear. Please give me your frank opinion."

I was conscious of dozens of beady eyes peering between the slats of the Venetian blinds. The obvious assumption was that the King's entourage, who had been barred from the room, were going to make certain their King should not be assassinated.

"Does Your Majesty really want to know?"

"Yes, I do."

"Then, I'll tell Your Majesty. I have visited medical schools all over the world, West as well as East."

"Yes, yes."

"I regret very much to say that Your Majesty's Royal Medical School is the poorest I have ever seen."

As though he were on springs the King leaped up and ejaculated, "This cannot be!" He paced up and down angrily. "This is simply outrageous! This cannot be! Nobody ever told me that."

"Your Majesty asked me for my frank opinion. I've given it."

"But every year I've sent a group of our best young men to Europe and America. Some of them are teaching in the school now."

"I've seen your young men. Many of them have picked up our bad habits, and few of our good ones."

"Don't they use their time properly in America?"

"I'm just making an observation, which is beside the point. The fundamental difficulty is that Your Majesty hasn't a good school."

"My government has no more funds that could be used for that purpose."

"Siam has beautiful colleges of fine arts. What good do they do if the people are sickly and die before their time? It is reasonably assumed that Siam has a death rate of thirty to forty per thousand. Dead people don't enjoy fine arts. The first thing Siam ought to do is get good health."

I went on to explain to him that curing his subjects of hookworm would make them happier and improve their economic efficiency, thereby making little Siam more powerful; further that our sole desire was to cooperate with the medical officers of his own government, but first he would have to produce good ones, and this could only be brought about in a better training school.

"Where do they have a better school?" demanded the King.

"In the Philippines."

"Oh, the United States is disgustingly rich. You Americans pour millions into that country. It's quite understandable, of course, why a school there should have high standards."

"I beg Your Majesty's pardon, but the United States has never contributed anything to the Philippines."

"Then you must grind the Filipinos down with taxes so that they cannot get their heads above water."

"No, Your Majesty, they're the lightest taxed people on earth. Three dollars per capita covers everything. The Siamese tax rate is far higher than that."

"Well, what can I do? I can't afford any more money."

"Your Majesty would not need to. Competent instructors cost little more than incompetent. The Rockefeller Foundation would be glad to supply the nucleus of a foreign staff and provide fellowships so that the Siamese would eventually be able to take over the instruction."

The King thought for a few moments, and then said, "This is my golden opportunity. I'm usually so burdened with foreign advice that I can't take any action that does not trample on the rights of somebody. But now the War has freed me to some extent of advisers. I'd like to pay for my own teachers. Could you recommend suitable ones?"

483

"I'd be very glad to."

The King then apologized for having lost his temper, and went on to say, "I'm not in a position to suggest these changes myself. But if it could be arranged for one of my family to see the school in the Philippines, and the suggestion came from him, perhaps my foreign advisers would not object. Could you manage to have him received incognito so that he could see the situation as it really is?"

"I'm sure there'll be no question about it. I'm going to the Philippines myself from here."

"He'll be there almost as soon as you are."

This appeared to terminate the interview. The King rose and I also. "Wait a moment," he said, and called a servant to whom he spoke in Siamese. I was conscious that the interview had been prolonged beyond the usual time, but shortly the servant returned with a small plush box in his hand. The King tendered it to me with the words, "I give you this in confirmation of my promise to support the work of the Rockefeller Foundation in Siam."

I bowed myself out. On my return to the hotel, I opened the case and found I had been decorated with the Fourth Class of the Order of the White Elephant, Busanabaran. Its value to me lay in the fact it betokened a pledge from the King to support a movement for bettering health conditions and improving medical education. The receipt of this honor was contrary to custom. It is the usual practice that those upon whom honors are to be conferred are asked in advance to indicate their willingness to receive them. This rule has enabled me to follow out my determination never to accept honors.

Prior to the War, perhaps five hundred Europeans were "employed" by the Siamese government, chiefly on the insistence of Great Britain, France, Belgium, and Germany. Many of these seemed content to draw their salaries and follow any other path than that demanded by the situation.

With advisers of many nationalities often giving conflicting counsel, it was plain how the Siamese had been pulled first in one direction and then in another, all efforts lacking coordination. They had developed into a set of apologists, and were constantly confronted with the necessity of giving the least offense to those whose advice they did not accept. The game of the different legations was to have their nationals appointed to office. The amount of intrigue and countermoves that went on backstage was unbelievable. The community presented the picture of a few whites quarreling among themselves, and a huge native mass that did not know what it wanted.

Because Maha Vajiravudh firmly believed that his numerous white advisers should be replaced with Siamese, he fell in readily with the Rockefeller Foundation policy of extending aid by training and guiding the Siamese and then allowing them to continue the work themselves. The difficulty was to direct the royal attention to health and away from his hobbies of building palaces, repairing wats, and increasing the army and navy.

The King was also said to be busied trying to find surnames for his eight million subjects, none of whom had any. Trying to keep names and titles straight in Siam drove me nearly to distraction. Almost all the officials, and especially the Princes, had more than one, and even these were changed every few months by the King. I sometimes searched for days and even then was unable to find the later names of men I had known well on previous trips. To make matters more difficult for the visitor, the spelling differed in the various provinces.

This son of Chululongkorn, educated at Oxford, had one Occidental idea which conflicted with the Oriental traditions of his country. He had steadfastly refused the request of his subjects that he wed, according to ancient Siamese custom, one of his own half sisters, although he himself was a product of half sister marriages for four generations. The story went that Queen Victoria, whose great pet he had been, had told him polygamy was wicked, and he had promised her not to marry into his own family. He remained in a quandary for years, but finally lifted a commoner to royal rank.

The King's avocation was supposed to be writing plays, but he had also composed a primer on hygiene and education, good in every way except that it recommended a local quack's medicine for stomach trouble. He was supposed to have a deep sentimental interest in insanity, and it was also reported he had paid out of the privy purse the expenses of one year's vaccination campaign.

But the King's medical enthusiasms had been badly directed. The Medical School fully deserved the reputation I had ascribed to it in my interview with him. The entrance requirements were those of the eighth grade. Almost any male was admitted who could read and write and was of average intelligence. The school was deplorably lacking in equipment. No laboratory facilities were provided, and not one microscope was available for student use; in fact, there were only a half dozen serviceable microscopes in all Siam.

In addition to the regular curriculum a course in Siamese therapeutics taught the application of local herbs, barks, flowers, and ground sharks' teeth. The old Chinese materia medica was also included, and drugs were prescribed for dosage without any scientific testing of their medicinal value. The study of physics had to be attempted because the subject had not been taught in pre-medical school. Sometimes the study of anatomy was omitted entirely, because no teacher was available or because the students objected to the odor of the dissecting room. The instructor in bacteriology quite obviously ought to have been working in medicine.

Textbooks in Siamese could not be kept up-to-date because the language lacked means for expressing the recent medical terminology, and consequently neither teacher nor student was able to avail himself of scientific discoveries as they occurred. The only solution appeared to be that classes should be conducted in English, but this, I was assured, was impracticable unless the Siamese could be persuaded of the inadequacy of their own language.

Moreover, the attitude of the students would have to be changed. As one of the professors told me, "Siamese will learn accurately from a book all the steps of an operation, but they have no desire to perform it." They also objected to having examinations held, and the authorities, in the desire to have everything as pleasant as possible, would often omit these annoyances; a favored pupil was sometimes allowed to complete the four-year course in eighteen months. The majority of the students sat in the shade and smoked pink lotus leaf cigars.

Siam's greatest need from a health point of view was undoubtedly the improvement of its medical education. Only thirty students graduated per year, which meant that one new doctor was turned out annually to tend each 266,666 Siamese. The few students educated abroad found when they returned that their profession was so unprofitable and held in such low public regard that they usually went into the army.

In the midst of this inefficiency and lack of proper facilities sat Prince Rangsit, who was credited with being one of the genuinely public-spirited men of Siam. Although not himself a doctor of medicine, he had been educated in Germany in pedagogy, and was struggling valiantly to make progress and improve the condition of the school. But he had been able to accomplish little beyond repairing some of the more decrepit old buildings and fitting up additional lecture rooms.

Shortly after I reached the Philippines, Prince Rangsit, using the name of Krom Mom Jainad, arrived. During his stay of almost a month Governor General Harrison arranged for him to see everything that might be of value or interest to him, and I conducted him personally from hospital, to school, to Bureau of Science, and even to the Fire Department, so that he might see how America ran her affairs in the Orient. Whatever lurking suspicions might have remained in his mind as to the altruism of American motives apparently were thoroughly allayed.

In the course of our conversations, Prince Rangsit became more and more confidential, and gave me details of the difficult situation in which Maha Vajiravudh found himself. The King had a good heart and did not desire to believe anything unpleasant about anybody; consequently he was frequently deceived. Prince Rangsit's firm belief was that if the clique which controlled the King's public attitude did not take kindly to the new medical program, its future was hopeless. Too overwhelming a victory for the Allies would also make the situation more precarious for Siam because the balance of power, which made for their sole safety, would be upset.

The beginnings of our long labors in Siam were complicated by the tangled skein of politics. To win the confidence of the Siamese generally was a difficult task. They were suspicious of almost every proposition put before them, although they were somewhat less wary of Americans, than of Europeans or Japanese, who were not demanding their share of appointments. Almost every time they had come in contact with the white race they had lost something. Both French and British, on trumped up excuses, had, in the most approved empire-building fashion, appropriated choice sections of their territory.

More bitter to endure were the extra-territorial rights which had been fastened upon the Siamese by the leading European nations, Japan, and ourselves. The subjects of all countries having consuls in Siam—Great Britain, France, Netherlands, Denmark, Norway, Sweden, Spain, Portugal, Italy, et al.—were exempted from Siamese laws, which were made by royal decree and were not often likely to be in accordance with Western legal procedure. Moreover, every regulation affecting foreigners had to be approved by their home governments, and when no statutes of their own covered the situations, the English common law was used.

The Siamese were allowed to charge only a three percent customs duty, and this did not provide sufficient income. To make up the deficit they were compelled to adopt an onerous and difficult system of taxation such, for example, as taxing each fruit tree. Most important from our point of view, before any sanitary regulation could be put into effect, the consent of the foreign powers had to be secured.

Siam was constantly trying to rid herself of extra-territoriality. Long years ago she had attempted to negotiate a treaty with Great Britain by which this onerous obligation would be abolished in return for the cession of Trengganu, Kedah, and other possessions on the Malay Peninsula. But Great Britain stipulated that the agreement would only be effective when she judged the Siamese courts were functioning to her satisfaction, and that, in any case, a British judge should sit with the court when a British subject was concerned. Siam did not agree, but lost the provinces just the same, and with them some of the richest tin mines in the world.

A health organization in the modern sense was non-existent in Siam. The few health activities carried on were in the hands of foreigners. Our Minister was asked to assist in obtaining two Americans for the so-called Bangkok City Health Service. He submitted two names, but as soon as this news was spread abroad, the British protested and demanded these appointees should hold office only until the end of the War when British successors must be assured. The Siamese government resisted feebly but finally had to agree.

Siam's experience with France, which was nibbling off bits with every treaty, was equally unfortunate. To obtain French approval for the abolition of extra-territoriality, the Siamese had agreed, among other things, to keep a Frenchman, practically in perpetuity, at the head of the Pasteur Institute. It was directed by the French, although built and subsidized at Siamese expense. When I first went to Siam, the War was going badly for the Allies, and France had her back against the wall. The French incumbent had gone to the front, leaving control to Siamese. Mismanagement was evident, the place was dirty, rabbits were dying in their cages. Out of the dozens of biologicals usually manufactured in such an institution, only rabies and smallpox vaccine were being made. I shuddered to think of such tremendous forces being placed in the hands of half-educated and wholly untrained Siamese.

At Prince Rangsit's request I suggested a new head for the Institute. But the French no sooner heard that the Siamese had chosen an American, than the Frenchman was released from service and scurried back to resume his position. Two days later the American, Dr. Ira Ayer, appeared. The bewildered Siamese had to do something about this contretemps and hastily created for him the post of Sanitary Adviser to the Minister of the Interior at a higher salary.

Some years afterwards I was in Siam while a frightful cholera epidemic was raging. I was then on such intimate terms with the leading Siamese that I could talk with the utmost frankness to them in private, because they knew I would not humiliate them in public.

"This epidemic is disgraceful. Why don't you stop it?"

"We would if we could get the cholera vaccine. But M. —— is so busy with his private practice that he has no time to spend at the Institute, and we are forbidden to make the vaccine ourselves."

Eventually the French were shamed out of their attitude, and ceased insisting on the letter of their rights.

Siam had had a long series of American advisers, beginning with Edward H. Strobel from Harvard, who had pleased Chululongkorn so much he had thereafter had a predilection for advisers from that institution. Francis Sayre, a graduate of Harvard Law School, negotiated many of the arrangements for relinquishing extra-territoriality. Upon his successful conclusion of treaties with foreign powers in 1927, Siam was immediately enabled to increase its revenues by advancing the customs duty, thus relieving to a great extent the internal tax burden.

My first impressions of Siam and the Siamese had made me wonder whether we could overcome the mental torpor and lethargy of this race, which appeared to be a hybrid between Chinese and Malay. The more I inquired, however, the more hopeful I became. The barrier to introducing sanitary measures was not insuperable. Although the Siamese had no reverence for the medical profession, or any science, as such, they had no religious objections to killing rats or, from the medical point of view, no taboo as regards human excreta. The population was apparently not increasing, and the million and a half Chinese did most of the productive labor. The Buddhist Siamese, like the Christian Filipinos, controlled only a small part of the commerce of their own country. The earning power of the Siamese laborer was from fifty to one hundred percent greater than that of the majority of other Orientals, so that prospects of the country's being able to support a higher standard of living were excellent.

In Siam there was the greatest divergence between upper and lower classes. The latter were completely illiterate. Culture was confined to a small minority, most of whom had been educated in Europe. They impressed the traveler as being among the world's most pleasant peoples, conversant with art, literature, politics, and the humanities, and were socially gracious.

As I saw our program in Siam, the first step was to start a hookworm campaign; second, to stimulate the government to set up higher medical standards; and, third, to create scholarships for medical students. It was obvious that in Bangkok politics would hamper us to such an extent that I soon discarded the idea of beginning work in the capital. The proper procedure seemed to be to make a rapid survey and to initiate operations in a rural area which was heavily infested, and quickly prove the value of demonstrations.

All sorts of complications had to be smoothed out before hookworm work could be inaugurated. In spite of the King's agreement, his ministers had to be dealt with, one by one, and persuaded to cooperate. Many Siamese officials were frank enough to state they could not understand how such help as the Rockefeller Foundation offered could be entirely disinterested.

The suspicions of the interested foreign powers had also to be quieted. The British Minister and Consul had to be convinced we had no intention of replacing British with American doctors. By diplomatic maneuvering, and our common interest in leprosy, I made friends with Dr. Morden Carthew, the British medical adviser. Though not antipathetic, when I told him of our intention to start in the interior, he denigrated the idea and said we could make no headway with the preponderant lower classes. But if we were determined to continue our foolhardy venture, we should at least confine our activities to the upper classes, who might understand our objectives. And if any progress at all were to be made we must first get on our side the royal princes who, like Rangsit, had been educated abroad. Once the medical profession could be given greater prestige, it might be possible to disregard class distinctions and have men from below in key positions. Social rank was no bar to political advancement in Siam.

But even the upper-class Siamese, in Dr. Carthew's opinion, wanted to be left alone, and resented the disturbance to their tranquillity when it was pointed out to them how much plague or cholera or other disease existed in their midst. "They want to be considered civilized only in order to make favorable impressions on foreigners so that they can negotiate loans. The Siamese are interesting and plausible conversationalists, but when steadfastness is needed, they'll probably fail." On the whole he looked upon what we were trying to do as hopeless.

In spite of Dr. Carthew's warnings, we continued on our chosen path. The preliminary survey indicated as a strategic point of attack the ancient northern city of Chiengmai near the Burmese border, once capital of the Lao kingdom, now a provincial unit of Siam. It had long been an important trade center for Chinese, Burmese, and Siamese, and the teak trade was mainly conducted from there.

On my first visit of inspection to Chiengmai with Dr. Sawyer, my companion on that trip, we traversed a series of plains, dry and warm even in March, and intersected everywhere with *klongs*, that were the real lines of communication. Each of the three days' journeys ended at a town equipped with comfortable rest houses. "With" provided bed and meals; "without" furnished a cot and allowed the traveler to supply his own bedding and food. The third day we rode on a construction train, sitting in comfortable wicker chairs at the front of a flat car. It was an unexpectedly pleasant method of travel. A canopy protected us from the sun, and, since the car was pushed ahead, the smoke and embers from the wood-burning engine drifted behind us.

As we climbed through cooler mountain passes, dense with bamboo thickets and forests, we could see "elephints a pilin' teak, in the slushy, squdgy creek."

Siam was almost entirely dependent for livelihood and prosperity on rice and teak. The trees were felled, trimmed, and rolled into a stream, where they floated along lazily until the coming of the dry season. On the mud-caked bottom they would lie until the next year's rains once more lifted them forward. Three years of alternate motion and rest sometimes elapsed before the logs finally drifted down the Menam highway to Bangkok.

Almost immediately upon my arrival in Chiengmai I met the British Consul, who invited me to dine with him. "I'd be delighted," I replied. "Where shall I come?"

"I'll send for you."

Twenty minutes before the dinner hour a tiny turbaned mahout, gaily dressed in crimson and white and gold, appeared before me. "The elephant waits," he announced.

"What's that?" I interjected. "I don't want any elephant." But the boy did not know enough English for any extended expostulation, and willy nilly I had to comply with what was apparently the customary method of attending dinner parties in Chiengmai. The little fellow conducted me to the door and with his hook prodded the elephant, which sank ponderously to its knees. I climbed the short ladder into the howdah and seated myself on a cushion. The mahout leaped nimbly to the elephant's head and we were ready. The great beast lumbered to its feet, the howdah lurching precariously. I was not at all prepared for what followed. As we set off I was shot forward and then suddenly back, until I thought my head would be jerked off. It did not seem possible that I could stay aloft.

I was entertained at Chiengmai most cordially. One pleasant afternoon I was received by the Chao Dara, widow of the late Chululongkorn, and daughter of the last Lao King. She lived in royal dignity, and her train of servants were required to enter and leave her presence on their hands and knees. She took me to a spacious open hall where the expert silk weavers of Chiengmai had been gathered together. The fiancée of the King had decided to wear the Lao skirt as court dress instead of the breeches-like penung of the South, and, because the Chao Dara possessed to an unusual degree the gift of artistic expression common to Siamese, the designing of these garments had been entrusted to her. Materials, beautifully patterned in blues, pinks, greens, and reds, shot with gold and silver, were rippling from the busy looms.

Chiengmai was noted for its lacquer craftsmen. One quaint little shop was filled with round lacquer boxes in every stage of manufacture. I gazed in fascination at the dexterity of the workmen as they filled in the interstices of the woven bamboo frames with thick waxy material, then applied a beautiful smooth surface of red, black, or gold lacquer concealing the framework, and, lastly, scratched fine patterns on the surface and filled them in with pigment. The shop was overhung by palms and stately oil trees, and looked at the ruined brick wall of the ancient town across the moat. In this a Lao, armed with a basket-like net hanging from the end of a long bamboo pole, was patiently fishing for the tiny fish that flickered under the lily pads.

Most common of all sights in Siam was the endless procession of priests, bright in their yellow robes, who everywhere, with their begging bowls in their hands, were asking for rice. The greatest charm to the traveler in Chiengmai, as in all Siam, lay in the wats. Almost everywhere I turned rose a temple, glowing in blue and gold and red, or stately in its dim and quiet ruins. The gateways were guarded by grotesque dog-like images that would frighten away a host of evil spirits, unless perchance they were protected by a sense of humor. On the eaves the little bells, designed for the same purpose but in a pleasanter humor, jingled tunefully. At either end a series of overlapping gables, each surmounted by a strange, snake-like projection, suggested to the International Health Board mind a hookworm rampant.

We had sent Dr. M. E. Barnes, an excellent choice, to Chiengmai. His early upbringing had made him at home with the Oriental mind. Born in India, he knew Hindustani, and had a sound linguistic basis on which to build. He learned not only the Lao tongue but also the Siamese, not an easy task because the differentiations between the two are so subtle. The Siamese language is supposed to be among the most difficult in the world—with its seven tones commensurately more difficult than the four-toned Japanese or Chinese. Seldom could a foreigner master all seven, but Dr. Barnes knew enough of them to be able to give public addresses.

The Siamese were always affable and pleasant, ever ready with the making of fine promises, but taking an eternity to carry them out. Dr. Barnes would ask villagers to come to a certain place at a certain time; they would not be there. He would request local officials to make announcements; they would not be made. To cope with this amiable lethargy, Dr. Barnes devised an extraordinarily effective system of using the Buddhist priests. Although most of them were illiterate, they liked to be considered progressive, and Dr. Barnes diplomatically turned this vanity to his own ends. He proved to these bonzes how, when the Rockefeller Foundation cured their people, they would be the ones to reap the rewards of gratitude.

I was fortunate enough to be able to attend the opening meeting of Dr. Barnes' hookworm campaign in the Wat of Amphur Sansai near Chiengmai. It was filled to the walls with men, and even a few women had timidly crept inside the temple door. From the dusky recesses before them a great gilded Buddha, smiling and complacent, gazed out at the sea of dark faces. The dimly-lighted temple, the image, the tall pillars, the chief priest draped in yellow, the reverent audience in their penungs, presented a picture impressively Oriental, and one pervaded with a spirit of satisfaction with things as they are. Seated on their heels on the floor, these men and women waited patiently to receive the message for which they had been summoned. The only foreign intrusive notes were struck by the hookworm chart which hung on the front of the altar, and by the models of latrines displayed on teak tables, carved and inlaid with mother of pearl.

In sing-song Lao Dr. Barnes described the busy little hookworm in their midst; there were signs and sounds of approval. Then Major Boriracksh, Medical Officer of the Siamese Army, added what was obviously enthusiastic corroboration. Although I could understand no word of what was being said, the Siamese seemed like children listening to a story hour.

Dr. Barnes scored a signal success in Chiengmai, and grew to be admired and trusted by the Siamese as few foreigners had ever been.

Because of his achievements there we were able to storm the citadel of Bangkok, and take up the vital questions of a first-class medical school and an efficient health service.

In Bangkok we had more or less the same problems which had confronted us in the Philippines, but nothing like the authority to carry through reforms. The Siamese were so receptive to ideas, and so many people were offering advice gratis, that the result was often a jumble. They had violated all the principles we held dear in the establishment of a medical center by building the main school across the river, and the pathological laboratory on the city side.

Insanity was prevalent, much of it due to overindulgence in the dangerous drug bhang, or hashish, a derivative of Cannabis Indica, the Indian hemp plant. Smoking, chewing, or drinking hashish was an extremely common habit which the government was loth to stop because the foreign advisers made no objection to this source of revenue. The Siamese had abandoned the practice of chaining their insane to posts, and had built an asylum across the Menam from the city proper. But in the year which had elapsed since its building, not a single Siamese official of any rank had paid it a visit. The approach to this series of small buildings, each of which looked unhappily like a cage, was along a beautiful *klong*, shaded with blooming trees, but the pools in the grounds themselves were stagnant and covered with poisonous green slime. A separate enclosure was set aside for mad priests, which made me wonder how many people were driven crazy by religion. Formerly beriberi had kept down the number of patients until the Health Department, under my inspiration, fed them unpolished rice; thereafter so few died that overcrowding became serious and only the city insane could be accommodated.

The public market, which belonged to the privy purse, was highly insanitary. It was completely closed in by a set of crowded and dirty shacks in which lived the people who prepared food and ices for the vendors. In a filthy well were kept fish destined for public consumption. After trying for years to have this market renovated, the Health Department finally took a series of photographs and sent them to the King. He was shocked and at once ordered repairs made. But then the government officials also went to the King, and said, since it was understood the building was to be torn down soon, repairs

495

were useless. This same excuse served to hold up improvements for years.

The serious health problems of Bangkok did not obtrude on the public notice, but the Siamese were extremely sensitive about their mosquitoes, which were criticized by every foreigner. Although not malaria carriers, they were the worst pest I had ever seen anywhere in the world. When I first went to Siam in 1915, at every dinner party my hostess, upon receiving me, would, as a matter of course, hand me a small bottle filled with oil of eucalyptus which I was supposed to pour over myself in liberal quantities in the hope of discouraging insects. But mosquitoes swarmed in such numbers that the preventive was of no avail, and I usually returned to the hotel with my feet, ankles, and hands swollen beyond recognition. Guests used to cover their legs at table with bags. The last time I was there Flit had become popular, and every half hour a servant would pump a liberal supply under the table, while the guests sprinkled neck and arms with Sketalene.

I was often asked by the Siamese what they could do about mosquitoes, and I advised a survey to determine the cost of control. But they never seriously put themselves to the task of eradication.

The man who might have done something about this and other far more important matters was Prince Dhamrong, the leading elder statesman of the royal family. It seemed to me that he represented the highest point Siamese civilization attained under the old régime. He was charming and gracious in his manner, philosophic in his comments, and it was always a pleasure to converse with him. Had there been many others like him our road in Siam would have been far smoother. He had a magnificent estate, a most tastefully furnished house, and a garden beautifully planted with flowers, among which there were many evidences of Buddhist ornamentation. He said he was not only a professed Buddhist, but also one in actual practice. The moral code of Buddhism, in his opinion, was much like that of Christianity.

"I assume you are a Christian as I am a Buddhist," he said. "It has always interested me why religions are so at odds. What they really disagree about is the hereafter. But I as a Buddhist know nothing of it, and you as a Christian know no more. Why should there be all this acrimony about something we neither of us know anything about? The guess of a Buddhist may as well be right as the guess of a Christian."

The official with whom I had most to do was Prince Sakol, pronounced Sakon, one of the King's first cousins who had recently graduated from Oxford and gave promise of becoming very efficient. In 1915 he had been considering going into the Treasury Department, but I had persuaded him to cast his lot in the public health field by showing him the far greater opportunities there. According to a peculiar custom in Siam, each generation of titled persons lost or stepped down one grade of nobility, eventually becoming plain *nais* or misters unless, by the performance of some meritorious deed, new titles were conferred upon them by the King. Prince Sakol was anxious to prove himself, but he labored under the great handicap of having married a German girl when he had been in Europe, and Siam and its rigid social system had seemed very far away. Upon his return he found his wife ostracized and himself looked upon as having lost caste. Nevertheless, by merit and determination, and in spite of the unhappiness of his social lot, he rose steadily and in 1926 succeeded Jainad, the former Rangsit, as Director of Health.

Even Prince Sakol, honest as he was, would exaggerate our alleged shortcomings in fulfilling our part of the contract, and minimize those of the Siamese. His burden of complaint was that our agreement called for two foreign doctors, and he submitted records showing that, owing to vacations, lapses of a few months had occurred during the past two years of the five-year contract. But he ignored the fact that the Siamese had transferred men out of our units or failed to furnish them altogether. Their capacity, like that of trained lawyers, to split into infinite details some inconsequential matter and obscure the important point when it suited their purpose was at times most trying to the patience.

Each year, as their proportionate share of the budget increased, the Siamese seemed to believe that we were taking something out of their pockets. We knew, of course, that this sentiment was a defensive reaction because of their own realized yet unacknowledged shortcomings in complying with their agreement with us.

The Prince who should have been King after the death in 192

497

of Maha Vajiravudh (Rama VI) was Songkla, the only available son of the first queen, but practising medicine appealed to him more than a throne. He had received an M.D. from Harvard Medical School, but unfortunately had been recalled for a funeral before he had an opportunity to serve an internship in the United States. The King had frowned upon the idea of any member of the royal family being in a subordinate capacity in the hospital at Bangkok. Prince Songkla, therefore, had gone to the Missionary Hospital at Chiengmai. Because of his talents and influence, he was, above all others, most useful to us in removing friction and adjusting differences. His early death was a great loss to Siam.

On Prince Songkla's refusal to be king, his half brother Prajadhipok was chosen. King Prajadhipok was always quiet, efficient, sincere, and a conscientious worker. But he was not the best of the princes. The power behind the throne was Prince Nagor Svarga, pronounced Lakan Siwan, head of the Supreme Council of Five and an able administrator. He had much initiative, hard common sense, and a desire to have the government administration in Siam reach a high degree of efficiency. He made quick decisions and pushed his projects through to successful conclusions. Although an opponent of Prince Sakol, he was a great friend of Dr. Barnes who, believing he was the man best fitted for the position and anxious to see the Health Department under his direction, persuaded him to become Minister of the Interior.

Hope was expressed on all sides that the new King would inaugurate a more progressive régime. But the putting of princes and other titled persons into high places still continued, regardless of their training for the jobs. The cringing attitude and the deferring, even in scientific matters, to those of higher rank, was common. It was especially amusing to observe the attitude of Prince Sakol's subordinates, who would deliver no opinions until he had given his. Since our views often reached the Prince only through these same subordinates, delays and misunderstandings were inevitable. Many ministers required their heads of departments to sit on the floor in their presence, and during the later years of Prajadhipok the former custom of requiring servitors to approach him on all fours was resumed.

HUSTLING THE EAST

Until a few years ago Siam was perhaps the most peaceful country in the world. The people had no democratic rights and did not possess the vote; all orders were issued from the capital at Bangkok. But apparently they were perfectly satisfied and contented to have an absolute monarchy. Almost out of a clear sky came the Revolution, aimed at the princes who, without regard to merit, had so long held all the important offices. Its causes were so ill-defined that nobody could quite put his finger upon them. Among the reasons offered was that America, by its example in granting so many powers to the Filipinos and providing them with an Occidental standard of living, had stirred up the fires of independence smoldering here as elsewhere in the East.

When King Prajadhipok had returned from his cataract operation in New York in 1931, Prince Nagor Svarga had told him a revolution was brewing, but the King would not believe it. "You're the King," said Nagor, "and I can do nothing, but you could stop it if you would do such and such things," and he outlined a course of action. But the King merely intimated he would institute reforms in the near future. Long before he was prepared to move, the revolutionists won over the Army, and then it was too late.

The Revolution of 1932 altered the monarchy from absolute to constitutional, with an elective assembly and an executive council. Most of those who had formerly been assistants now became ministers. On the whole, the best men were chosen, and few reprisals were attempted; the royal family retained most of its property, although all were banished except the King.

I later met Prince Nagor Svarga, now called Parabitra, exiled in Bandoeng, Java. It seemed odd to see this Prince who, at Bangkok had lived in such regal splendor, now occupying a simple bungalow. I called to mind how only a few years before, when the Far Eastern Association of Tropical Medicine had held its 1930 meeting at Bangkok, Prince Nagor Svarga had outdone himself in providing welcome. The atmosphere had been one of hospitality, that in Siam was so peculiarly inspiring with its sincerity. To terminate the festivities, he had given a reception and dinner to one hundred and thirty guests, served luxuriously in his immense grounds. Afterwards he had offered for our entertainment a gorgeous spectacle in

499

which several hundred Siamese portrayed a Buddhist play in dance.

In 1935 King Prajadhipok refused all requests to return from London, whither he had gone for a second operation, because the Revolution had deprived him of so many powers, chiefly that of pardon. He abdicated his throne and remained in England. The present heir apparent is the son of Prince Songkla. His mother is struggling to keep him at school in Switzerland and out of the confusion of Siamese politics.

Many of the trying customs of the old governments are being continued in the new régime. The higher-ups make plans in secret without consulting the bureau chiefs, who never know the objects of the policies they are directed to pursue. The office force finds it difficult to realize the old days are gone, and that they may express opinions without knowing what their superiors think. They still speak in whispers, and wait for all plans to be handed down to them from above.

The great problem in medical education in these later years was whether to have a large number of poor doctors or a small number of very good ones in Siam. The poor ones could undoubtedly give relief to many people, and the few good ones could only reach a limited number. I had been concerned with this question for thirty years and found it exceedingly difficult to decide which was the better course. But I knew that dealing with environmental sanitation such as water and sewage would produce much greater results in the form of a reduced death rate and morbidity than all the junior doctors could ever accomplish. The Siamese ultimately saw the matter from the Rockefeller Foundation point of view.

To Dr. A. G. Ellis belongs the major credit for building up the Medical School in Siam. He had been selected by the Foundation as Director and later employed by the Siamese themselves. It was amazing to me that any human being could have lived through the daily round of disappointment and discouragement. He was able to see the hands of progress move around the clock, although they were turning so slowly no one else could detect their motion. It was due to his sacrificial efforts that the Medical School, with a completely Siamese faculty, became a modern institution.

As far back as 1926 it had seemed advisable for the International

Health Division to withdraw from Siam, for a time at least, until the government, of its own initiative, should present a sound plan for continued cooperation. The attitude was all too prevalent that we were forcing the Siamese to do something they were not convinced they wanted to do, and that we only offered them fellowships, which they keenly desired, in order to bribe them into doing something the value of which they considered debatable. They apparently failed to understand that we were there to help them in their struggle for something better. On the other hand, they were so innocently nice that we had a feeling we ought to help them, and that any failure on their part must be due to their not having understood. My conclusion was that if the Rockefeller Foundation's investment were to yield worth while results, a well-qualified adviser would be needed on the scene for many years.

In 1929 the Foundation finally withdrew completely from Siam except for such an adviser. Dr. Louis Schapiro, who had done brilliant work in Panama, volunteered for this thankless task. He had refused our offer of retirement, although he knew his term of life would be shortened by any strenuous labor, saying he would rather die in harness. He became a tremendous favorite in Siam. It was during his service that a sanitary engineer was brought from the United States to develop the installation of reservoir and pipe line distribution systems in the cities and towns of Siam. By efficient prodding, and helped in every imaginable way by Prince Nagor Svarga, he even succeeded in starting health centers. When Dr. Schapiro died we did not replace him.

In many ways over the years we had saved the Siamese from doing unprofitable and unwise things and often from spending money foolishly. But we had ourselves often forgotten the Siamese were the product of a civilization that did not want to hurry, and that, even when they tried, they were pulled back by the accumulated habits of centuries. The few progressive Siamese were still as scattered corks, bobbing upon a vast ocean, struggling against winds and currents that often carried them far from their goal. Only when I looked back over fifteen years of work could progress be noted. Many men whom I used to see in bygone years had passed on, yet things continued to move, and even made slow advance from an Occidental viewpoint. Graft and corruption, which had been so prevalent, were steadily lessening; efficiency slowly increasing, and finally the Siamese had come to accept, although probably they never completely understood, the Rockefeller Foundation form of altruism.

CHAPTER 28.   PEARL OF
GREAT PRICE

O NE by one the fertile regions of the earth have been swallowed
up by the land-hungry nations. Abyssinia alone remains as the
largest undeveloped area of productive terrain in the world. Even
now most Americans and many Europeans have little idea of its
desirability. This temperate zone paradise in the heart of equatorial
Africa is securely hemmed in by the barren wastes of the Sudan,
the inhospitable shores of West Africa, and the sweltering deserts
bordering the Red Sea. Comparatively few foreigners are familiar
with its clear sparkling days and bright blue skies, or have viewed
its forested mountains and translucent streams. Nevertheless, its European neighbors, Italy, France, and Great Britain, who hold the sterile
Red Sea coast once controlled by Abyssinia, are keenly aware that the
Abyssinian government, in spite of its boasted five thousand years
of continuous existence, has not kept step with the civilized world.
Their urgent craving to unbar the gates to these greener pastures is,
if not excusable, at least quite understandable.

Although my work for the Rockefeller Foundation had, in the
course of twenty years, taken me into practically every portion of
the two hemispheres, it was not until 1933 that I visited Abyssinia,
or Ethiopia, as the inhabitants prefer to have their country called.
The Foundation, which was then engaged in an attempt to eradicate
yellow fever from the world, had cabled me a request to collect for
them some blood samples in that remote mountain land.

One morning in early May, with the thermometer at 115 degrees, the Messageries liner *Leconte de Lisle* anchored off Jibuti, the gateway of Abyssinia. I had expected to make immediate connections for the Abyssinian capital, Addis Ababa. This did not seem unreasonable, since both railway and steamship line were French-owned. But the train, which ran only twice a week, had left ten minutes before our arrival. I had four days to wait for the next one.

Somewhat impatiently I inquired my way to the hotel. It turned out to be much like that one finds in a village in France, even to the little sidewalk café. There French officials and Levantines were trying to shelter their drinks from the dust which rose in clouds as the motor cars chugged laboriously through the hot sandy streets.

The days wore on but the thermometer remained static. Although many years in the tropics had made me pride myself somewhat on my indifference to heat, Jibuti was an oven in which I was slowly being baked. The only way I could get a night's sleep was to throw off blanket, sheet, and pajamas, and turn two large electric fans upon myself. At table an open shirt, no coat, and shorts was the accepted dress.

The United States was at this moment fervently engaged in going off the gold standard. As the dollar tobogganed down, those travelers in foreign parts, including myself, looked on bewildered and helpless. American money, before the War practically unknown, had in succeeding years become standard. American tourists, eager to spend their dollars, had literally made them all mighty throughout the world. The urchin who dived for coins in Jibuti harbor knew their value. Now, almost overnight, this confidence was destroyed.

I trustfully took my American Express checks to the Bank of Indo-China, the only one in town. The cashier shrugged his shoulders; he could quote no rate of exchange. He would, as a special favor to me, cash one check for twenty dollars, but no more. Since the fare to Addis Ababa was almost three times this figure, it appeared that, for lack of a few francs, I might be prevented from carrying out my commission.

In the white hot sunlight I went tramping from place to place, hoping to find some merchant who would take my money. My hopes were not unduly high; I knew the normal reluctance of the French to extend credit would be enhanced considerably by the current financial crisis. It was by the sheerest good luck that I finally encountered a shopkeeper who owed bills in the United States which we could pay with my express checks; from him I obtained seventy dollars.

The first of the long three days required for the railroad journey —the train did not run at night—lay through sand barrens, stippled thickly with black rocks, called, from their obvious resemblance, nigger heads. I could see occasional dust devils whirling in the distance; about noon one of these engulfed the train. I hastily banged the windows shut, but the fine choking dust penetrated everywhere. Without any ventilation, the heat was so intense that sand and sweat caked on my face. My teeth grated on the fine particles and my eyes soon became as bloodshot as those of the desert inhabitants themselves. The one electric light which, with true French economy, was the size of a glass bead, gave little illumination inside the compartment, and had not the slightest effect upon the outer darkness. Water of any sort is rare; the rivers which come rushing from the mountains of Ethiopia are sucked into the desert long before they reach the sea. Moreover, malaria and dysentery, the age-old enemies of man in the tropics which have so often defeated his plans, are ever lying in wait.

After climbing steadily all day long, at nightfall the train pulled into Dire Dawa, at an altitude of nearly a mile, and, in contrast to the coast, delightfully cool and refreshing. This was the border of Ethiopia, the legendary country where Prester John and the Queen of Sheba once had ruled. Pandemonium was raging. At least five hundred of the coffee-colored, hooked-nosed townspeople, gesticulating and shouting wildly, were gathered around the station. I innocently assumed they were celebrating the arrival of the train, but I soon discovered my error. We were to be the victims of their barbaric holiday. In apparent delight at the opportunity of humiliating white people, the black soldiery rudely pushed us into the Customs House with their guns. One after another, the passengers' bags were seized, roughly opened, and each article held up for the edification of the crowd. Whenever a bit of feminine lingerie was flourished triumphantly in the air, the howling mob greeted the display with appreciative shouts of joy. I could sense the resentment of the inspectors, who seemed to regard us with that intuitive aversion which so many Americans feel toward members of the black and yellow races.

When my turn came, I exhibited to the Customs Official a permit from the Ethiopian Minister of Foreign Affairs, which I confidently expected would exempt my personal belongings from being passed in review before the population of Dire Dawa. Without even pretending to examine it, he waved it aside. I asked him, by signs, to take me to his chief. But the latter, glancing at it briefly, merely replied, "We don't know what that is."

Still unwilling to lose faith in the efficiency of this document, I sought the Customs Office up the street. The only comment of the department head was, "We never honor these things"; for the third time I was ordered to open my bag.

Obediently I returned to the station, only to find that the short-lived interest had subsided, and the crowd was melting away. One by one the guards, with the inspection only half over, were also departing, and in a few moments I was left alone with my still unopened bag. It was simplicity itself; I merely summoned a porter to carry it to the hotel.

The second day's ride was somewhat less monotonous than the first. There were occasional scrubby trees and even small patches of cultivated land. The third day we slid through lush valleys, skirted steep river cañons, and chugged up wooded highlands. It was difficult to believe that these Delectable Mountains could be only twenty-four hours away from the arid inferno of the coastal regions. I could well understand why Italian eyes should strain toward them so covetously.

In the last few hours of the third day we mounted abruptly from three to eight thousand feet. From the mountain rim, looking far down over the terraced orchards of apple and pear and peach, and the fields of waving grain, I could see the tiled roofs of Addis Ababa, lying prettily in its grove of eucalyptus trees.

As soon as I had deposited my bag in the hotel, I started out for a brisk walk to stretch my legs and sniff the spring fragrance. I had gone no more than half a mile when I was stopped by sentries, and taken to a guard house. I had not the faintest idea of my offense, but I have always deemed it unwise to display anger under such circumstances. I smiled my pleasantest, and began to pass cigarettes among my captors. They received these overtures amiably, but, whenever I attempted to go on my way, their bayonets promptly barred my passage. I knew not a word of Amharic, the language of the country; but I tried in turn my English, French, German, and Italian—all to no avail. For some thirty minutes we smiled at one another with continued amiability.

Then it occurred to me that perhaps in that direction might lie some military arsenal or government preserve which I was not supposed to see. "Possibly," I thought, "if I am able to show my willingness to return upon my tracks, I may be allowed to leave." I indicated this in pantomime, and, behind the smoke screen of a final round of cigarettes, departed in peace.

The next morning I described my adventure to the American Minister and asked whether he could furnish any explanation.

"Very easily," he assured me. "Nobody is supposed to go unescorted in the streets of Addis Ababa. Any man of social standing must have at least three or four retainers tagging after him. If he's really important, three hundred may follow him to the market place to buy a chicken."

"But I have visits to make and work to do," I protested. "I must be back and forth all the time."

"Don't worry," he replied. "We have a standing arrangement with the government that one uniformed legation guard ranks as high as a retinue of fifty. The two I'm going to lend you will put you well up in the social scale."

Thereafter, where I went, they went. If I walked, they walked. If I rode, they rode; one in front and one behind. If I played tennis, they had to accompany me, as guarantors of my social standing.

My first duty was to pay my respects to Belaten Gheta Herouy Woulde Selassie, Minister of Foreign Affairs. Although Abyssinia had a Parliament of two houses, and a full-fledged cabinet of ten high-sounding ministries, these were generally regarded as the Emperor's window dressing. The exception was Herouy who, for services rendered, had been rewarded with a sort of grand viziership.

I explained to Herouy that I had come to Ethiopia to secure yellow fever blood specimens. There would be no objection, he assured me, provided there were no cost to his government. To my astonishment I learned that the army of Ethiopia was without medi-

507

cal protection—no doctor, no nurses, no splints, not even a box of pills. I discovered later that there was but one native doctor in the whole country, and that even the Emperor's Greek physician was said to have been merely a sergeant in the medical corps of some army. Herouy made it apparent that Ethiopia, beyond controlling the sale of narcotic drugs, had no desire to establish a health service. He regarded leprosy as the country's most important health problem and stated incidentally that he was certain this disease was hereditary in Ethiopia. By presenting him evidence from my own experience, I tried to persuade him to the contrary, but he remained unconvinced.

In contrast to the average Abyssinian, Herouy was coal black and, instead of the usual wavy or even straight hair, he was crowned with kinky white wool. He appeared to have negroid characteristics, but this could hardly have been possible, since the Ethiopians, proud of their Semitic heritage, regard the Negro as fit only for slavery. No one even suspected of Negro blood can attain to any position of importance.

It is unfortunate as well as unintelligent that the people in the United States, without investigation, and with characteristic impulsiveness, have actually encouraged American Negroes to go to Abyssinia to establish friendly relations. Nothing could have caused more irritation. Such typically American attempts at missionary work have ended in complete futility.

In a way it was refreshing to find myself in a country where statistics did not exist. Anybody could prove anything, and opinions assumed the force of facts. Nobody knew whether there were three or fifteen million Abyssinians. They were born and they died without record. But apparently the high birth rate was balanced by the high infant mortality.

The Coptic Church of Abyssinia, an ancient form of Greek Catholicism, was all powerful in the country. Originally it had followed the Nile up from Egypt, and for many centuries had maintained its identity, although cut off from the rest of the Christian world by the Mohammedan encirclement. It was intensely jealous of encroachments on the part of other Christian religions. The priests always considered it a favor when they permitted the missionaries to build hospitals and schools, and made it clear that there must be no proselyting. The latter did their best to fulfill these requirements, but they often forgot, and one of the principal duties of the foreign legations was to straighten out the resultant difficulties.

Four mission hospitals had been built at Addis Ababa, and a few dispensaries were scattered throughout the provinces. These took care of a small portion of the sick; what became of the rest was a mystery. The Swedish Hospital was said to have received substantial grants from the Emperor. The French Menelik Hospital, on the other hand, was treated like a stepchild, and looked it.

Some years ago the Emperor had had a modern hospital constructed and completely equipped. Just before the opening ceremonies, he asked to see the budget. He examined the figures. "We won't open the hospital," was his sole comment.

For several years the building stood idle. Then some American Seventh Day Adventists discovered it. "Here is a beautiful hospital," they said to each other. "Instead of constructing one for ourselves, we shall ask the Emperor for this."

"Oh, yes," Haile Selassie told them. "You may have it as long as it does not cost me anything, and is used for the benefit of my people."

The exultant missionaries went to install themselves, but found to their dismay that much of the equipment had mysteriously disappeared. However, the once poverty-stricken Menelik Hospital, not far off, had somehow or other come into possession of suspiciously similar instruments. The Adventists wrote a letter, informing the Menelikers that they would appreciate the return of the equipment which now belonged rightfully to them. There was no reply. A second note received the same inattention. The Adventists then returned to the Emperor with their complaint.

"I'll see that you get the instruments," he encouraged them, and promptly took the matter up with the French Legation.

The affair had now become a matter of state. After the usual diplomatic delays, a reply was eventually elicited from the Menelik Hospital authorities. They would not admit that they had these instruments, but, even if they did have them, they could not very well return them. Such an action would be an admission that they had taken them, and consequently a reflection upon their honor.

At last accounts the Adventists were still waiting for their equipment.

As I crossed the veranda of the American Mission Hospital on my first visit there, I observed several advanced cases of confluent smallpox, relapsing fever, and typhus; no isolation ward for such infectious diseases had been provided. But the relatives or friends of stricken ones, hearing of the miracles performed at the Hospital, would leave them in the grounds under cover of darkness, and the doctors made shift to care for them.

Because of these limited facilities, the doctors and nurses themselves suffered terribly from infectious diseases. The quality of their bravery was greater, perhaps, because, in the last analysis, their primary interest lay in religion and not in medicine. Caring for the body was merely a means by which the soul might be saved.

Probably few diseases are more deadly than yellow fever, and nobody as yet has been able to discover an organism. In the course of laboratory research many deaths have occurred among the workers from merely handling the virus. A section of a blood vessel in the leg of a mosquito contains enough poison to kill an adult human being, and one infected mosquito can start an epidemic.

For thirty years the scientists of the world had tried to convey yellow fever to every variety of animal from snake to monkey. Finally Dr. Adrian Stokes, a British specialist, made the important discovery that it could be transmitted to a certain type of Indian monkey, but just at the moment of triumph he contracted the disease and died. His contribution made it possible to proceed with experimental work, and, in time, a practical blood test was developed which could determine whether any people in a given area had ever had yellow fever.

The history of the virtual conquest of yellow fever exemplifies the value and necessity of collaboration in science. Economically a country may be self-sustaining, but in the medical world international cooperation is essential. Any great advance today seldom results from the efforts of one person or one race. British, Americans, French, and Dutch, often working along unrelated lines, all added their little pieces of information which made it possible to put the yellow fever puzzle together.

PEARL OF GREAT PRICE

Dr. Henry R. Carter, inveterate reader and student, supplied one of the missing pieces. He searched through the diaries of the early explorers of America to find some evidence of the existence of yellow fever on this continent before Columbus. He found none. The inevitable conclusion from his work, coupled with other evidence, was that yellow fever had come to America with the slave trade. West Africa was thus established as the seed bed of the disease.

I knew that residents of Addis Ababa would be free from yellow fever, because the stegomyia does not fly above the five thousand foot level. However, the American Mission Hospital contained enough lowland patients for my purposes.

The first time I tried to make tests, the sterilizer refused to work. Then, the doctor upon whom I depended for assistance developed sinus trouble and amoebic dysentery. The ordinary procedure was to collect each specimen in a glass tube and then fuse the end in a Bunsen burner. But there was no gas in Addis Ababa. I tried an alcohol lamp; it was not hot enough. Nor did a blow pipe prove more adequate. Finally, by pumping vigorously on a Primus stove, I managed to seal the glass tubes hermetically. In spite of these difficulties, I had secured thirty blood specimens at the end of three days, although I was somewhat dubious as to their sterility.

The next problem was to contrive some method of keeping the blood specimens on ice during the three days' run to Jibuti. I had to construct an emergency refrigerator, much like those I had formerly used for carrying smallpox vaccine into the Mountain Province of the Philippines. I received sufficient ice from the Addis Ababa brewery to keep the tubes chilled until they could be shifted to the steamer's refrigerator at Jibuti.

I was naturally interested in observing the incidence of diseases other than yellow fever in Addis Ababa. The enormous bazaar was the logical place to seek them. The boisterous, good-natured crowds were milling around the little baskets of native commodities and cheap foreign hardware spread on the ground. Unmistakable cases of leprosy and smallpox were circulating freely among the people.

Nobody apparently minded the jostling and pushing. But the traffic problem had become exceedingly serious with the advent of motor cars, which dashed recklessly over the few asphalt-paved streets, and sent the innumerable curs yelping. Abyssinia, with the aid of Belgian policemen, was trying to install traffic rules. Great difficulty was being encountered with the more primitive forms of transport. The puzzled drivers of donkeys and camels failed utterly to comprehend what was expected. They calmly plodded and padded along, regardless of upraised hand and verbal admonishment. When the vociferous Belgians would come tearing after them, accompanied by interpreters to explain the infractions of the rules, they would merely look puzzled and scratch their pates.

On one of my walks around the town I noted a number of small shelters scattered over the hillside on which stood the rambling congeries of buildings which comprised the royal palace. Squatting under each thatched roof was a forlorn-looking individual, munching his lunch. All were there in accordance with the Emperor's unique method of disciplining government officials with whom he was not pleased. The imperial income was mainly derived from coffee and goatskins, the tribute of the kings or other governments. The only traceable revenue in coin was the customs duty, usually paid in the old Maria Theresa dollar, minted in Austria and imported as a commodity. This money, however, was apparently not sufficient for the Emperor's needs, because it was said the servants' wages at the palace were a year in arrears.

The great depression had affected Abyssinia very little. The landowners had merely required extra duty from their slaves, and the government twice as many goatskins and double the quantity of coffee. Each of the Emperor's unsalaried governors had to collect the additional tribute and also support himself. What was more difficult, he had to keep everybody satisfied. Retaining or losing his province depended upon the number of complaints against him. No questions were asked as to how much of the revenue he diverted to his own uses, but the balance was obviously delicate.

The system worked as follows. A countryman would start to drive a herd of several hundred goats from a distant province to the market place of the capital. Two or three would be appropriated by the first government official he encountered. As he proceeded, his animals would diminish, until he might reach Addis Ababa with only a few stragglers. If this process of depletion could not be accomplished without hard feelings, he would set up a loud outcry.

The unlucky official would be promptly ordered to appear at the palace for an interview at six in the morning. He would take his place under one of the shelters and wait there. The Emperor might not see him for one month, or two months, or even six months. But he had to appear each morning at that same early hour. This chastening process was guaranteed to tame even the most recalcitrant.

Haile Selassie regarded himself as the ranking Emperor of the world. Only the Mikado could approach him in dignity. As for the King of England, he was a mere absentee Emperor, and not to be included among the proper emperors. Haile was now on a tour of his provinces, and was due to stop for the day in Addis Ababa on his way South. He usually saw nobody on such occasions, but through the personal friendship of the American Minister who had known him well in the days when he had been simply Ras Tafari, a Prince of the royal house, I was granted an audience.

I presented myself at the palace and was conducted to an anteroom. The Emperor was always prompt for Europeans and Americans, though his dignity demanded that he keep his own subjects waiting. Almost immediately upon my arrival, the doors were thrown open, and with the prescribed three bows and three steps between, I approached the throne on which was sitting his Imperial Majesty Haile Selassie I, King of Kings of Ethiopia, Conquering Lion of Judah, Elect of God as proclaimed in the seventy languages of Ethiopia, and heir presumptive to Palestine through descent from King Solomon and the Queen of Sheba.

The Emperor was resplendent in a royal scarlet coat, gorgeously decorated with broad bands of gold, and his feet were ornamented with shoes, brocaded in the Chinese manner. He was short of stature, perhaps five and a half feet tall, brown in complexion, with full black beard and a Hebraic cast to his nose.

Haile Selassie was educated in French and speaks it fluently, but he prefers to use his native Amharic, which sounded to me much like Arabic. The interview had to be conducted through an interpreter. I have often found the interpreter system a help rather than a hindrance. If such an intermediary can convey the spirit of what is said as well as the bare words, the pauses, particularly where an ill-chosen word might have a bad effect, permit a more careful phrasing than would otherwise be possible.

I told my royal host how the course of yellow fever was being traced in Africa, and recounted the story of the Panama Canal as an illustration of what sanitation had been able to accomplish. I described the early failure there, and told how the difficulties had been overcome. Although my audience was to have lasted only ten minutes, he became so interested in my social sales talk that he asked me to remain for tea. During the rest of the afternoon I tried to show him how his own country would benefit by the establishment of a sanitary organization.

The Emperor was as thoroughly convinced of the importance of leprosy in Ethiopia as Herouy had been. He showed great interest in the work of the American Mission to Lepers, for which funds were even then being raised. Later he himself opened the Ethiopian Leprosarium with elaborate ceremonies. Nobody knows, of course, the number of lepers at large in Ethiopia, but it is probable that the disease is relatively unimportant there as compared, for example, with the Philippine Islands or India. If similar sums were spent on vaccination, thousands of lives would be saved and innumerable cases of blindness prevented. Or by a cleanliness campaign, at a cost well within his resources, Haile Selassie could free his people from typhus and relapsing fever—both lice-borne diseases.

In my enthusiasm I was led to remark somewhat jocularly on the backward condition of Ethopia. He bore with me in gentlemanly fortitude, then inquired politely, "You are an American, are you not?"

"Yes," I admitted, somewhat puzzled as to the object of his query.

"How many unemployed have you in the United States?"

"About twelve million, I should imagine."

"Well," he continued blandly, "my government has been in continuous existence for over five thousand years. We have no unemployment; we have never had any. We have no starving. All my people have homes to live in. They have clothes to wear. They are happy."

I could think of no answer. I have not yet been able to think of one.

In this interview politics were not mentioned. Elsewhere I inquired assiduously of British, French, and Italians, and, from a composite of their views, tried to ascertain the truth. It appeared that, as late as December, 1925, Great Britain and Italy had made a secret treaty about spheres of influence in Abyssinia. Italy was anxious to run a railway through the highlands to connect her two separated provinces of Somaliland and Eritrea. In return Great Britain was to be allowed to construct a dam at Lake Tsana by which the flood waters of the Nile could be controlled.

Since Americans are generally credited with having no territorial ambitions, the J. G. White Engineering Corporation of New York was employed to make the preliminary surveys for this project. The press of England immediately cried out against it, intimating that this was a clever Yankee trick to regulate the water of the Nile so that Americans would have a stranglehold on the British-owned cotton industry of the Sudan. Not merely was this ironical in view of the secret treaty, but the British editors failed to realize that Americans, even to protect their own markets, seldom have exhibited such foresight.

Finally, with funds furnished by the Sudan, and with the full consent of Great Britain, the survey was made.

Then it developed that the plans, if carried out, would cause the flooding of many Coptic churches in that section of the country. Abyssinia, therefore, rejected the proposals.

However, the English government and the Sudan were so anxious to have the water impounded that still further pressure was exerted on Abyssinia. She finally consented to a second survey, to be paid for by Egypt, an equal sharer in the potential profits of the scheme. Churches subject to flooding were to be protected by coffer dams. The Abyssinians were to take what water they needed for their own crops and to be paid a royalty on all water flowing from the dam.

There remained the question of building a road to the dam site. Great Britain naturally desired to have it constructed from the Sudan. But the Abyssinians vetoed this idea categorically. According to their fundamental policy, all roads in the country should radiate from Addis Ababa. France, Great Britain, and Italy, with amazing celerity, shift sides according to the economic or political interest of the moment. In this case French Somaliland battened parasitically upon traffic to and from Abyssinia, and she trembled for her railroad receipts should a motor road approach Addis Adaba from the South. Consequently France nobly helped the Abyssinians carry their point. It was agreed that the road should be built from the capital to Tsana, a distance of several hundred miles.

In order to finance this undertaking a bond issue was proposed. But the preferred place to float such a loan was the United States, in which foreign bond issues had attained an unenviable notoriety. Consequently, after the medley of promises, threats, and reprisals, nothing has been done.

The Abyssinians had enough political acumen to perceive that their best hope of survival lay in the mutual jealousy of the three big dogs barking outside the Abyssinian manger. Hence they had joined the League of Nations promptly, and whenever any country had encroached, they had clamored so loudly that the aggressor, alarmed at the light of publicity, had withdrawn as gracefully as possible.

When Abyssinia has been arraigned for culpable backwardness, her holding of slaves has usually been made the chief charge against her. It is true that when the Abyssinians wanted more slaves they went out and captured them. A prerequisite to the League was the promulgation of a decree abolishing slave trading. The Emperor, who had been to Europe and had progressive ideas, was full of fine intentions, and wrote stringent regulations punishing it by death— but nobody would enforce them.

I suspect that political agents have used the subject of slavery in Ethiopia for their own propaganda purposes. Earnest people who write articles are legitimately outraged by the situation: no one would wish to condone this state of affairs. I must admit, however, that the slaves, of whom it is estimated there are about three million, seem cheerful and well treated. In almost every way they form part of the household.

After joining the League, the Abyssinians were told they must abandon slavery altogether. When ordered by the Emperor, they obediently released ten thousand. But the slaves owned no land and consequently had no means of earning a living. They did not know where to go or what to do, and promptly ran back to their old masters. A short while ago I was told that the Abyssinians were willing to free all their slaves, but when I was there they were still waiting for the League to explain what to do with them when they were freed.

Raids have been made into British and French territory and the Abyssinians have undoubtedly created disturbances along the border of what the Italians have regarded as theirs. But the Abyssinians may argue with truth that they cannot tell when they have left their own territory, because their hundreds of miles of border are unmarked.

The regular Abyssinian Army, although comparatively small in numbers, is exceptionally brave, and has been well drilled by European officers. The soldiers have always claimed no conscription would be necessary; they liked to fight. Nor had the Emperor, frugal in other things, been niggardly in the matter of military equipment.

I heard several times the story of the American Army Colonel who was one of the three representatives of the United States at the coronation. At his interview with Haile Selassie, this officer had presented a machine gun of the latest pattern. He and his gift were received most graciously and, as a return courtesy, the Colonel was invited to attend a review the next morning. The infantry and the cavalry passed, and then came a number of machine gun companies. Each had a gun the exact counterpart of that which the Colonel had just donated to this backward country.

With his unfailing courtesy the Emperor did not, then or later, mention the matter.

Whatever the outcome of the present movement, it is obvious that Abyssinia cannot remain indefinitely in her present stage of development. If Italy does not find her way in, it is only a question of time before some other country will do so. It may not be with the fanfare of trumpet and beat of drum, but the march of civilization cannot indefinitely be postponed. It is an all-penetrant force, ineluctable and ineludible, before which the Conquering Lion of Judah must ultimately bow.

CHAPTER 29.   PILGRIM'S PROGRESS

CHOLERA has always followed the trail of the pilgrims. Every year the ghats of Benares are dotted with the brown bodies of Hindus who have come from all over India to the Holy Ganges to bathe and drink. Instead of healing all their infirmities and purifying their souls, as they trustfully believe, the filthy water contaminates their bodies.

But in India the danger is centered within the one country. The route of the faithful to Mecca endangers the whole world. From India, Egypt, Persia, Iraq, Turkey, the Malay Peninsula, Borneo, Java, and Mindanao the hordes converge on the Holy City of Mahomet. Seventeen thousand passed through the Quarantine Station at Tor on the Red Sea in one year. With the exception of Egyptians, who are given cholera and smallpox vaccinations on leaving for Mecca, practically none of the pilgrims was protected. Sooner or later cholera appears among them; whole shiploads of these people have tragically perished, although through international action in establishing a quarantine station, and the general use of cholera vaccine, such outbreaks are becoming less frequent.

Each country through which the pilgrims passed wanted to secure a share of this tourist trade, and constantly squabbled as to how the routes should be mapped. In 1927 an International Sanitary Convention at Paris agreed that pilgrims must use certain prescribed sea routes.

We were most anxious to help the nations control disease along these new pilgrim paths, which not only affected the route to Mecca,

519

but also threatened Europe with invasions from the Orient. Through international action, the Conseil Sanitaire Maritime et Quarantenaire d'Egypte was established many years ago, which through its control of quarantine at the Suez Canal has served as a filter to protect Europe against the invasion of dangerous communicable disease. A laboratory at Bagdad, where careful diagnoses could be made, would do much to bring this about. I made several trips there and was well on the way to success when the British decided to give up their mandate.

King Feisal also was in agreement with our ideas, and we discussed it at dinner in his palace, a single-story Moslem building containing many rooms. The gorgeous uniforms of the servants gave the effect of departed glory. King Feisal had been French-educated, but his hatred of the Gaul was so great that he made desperate attempts to speak English, although with poor success. Unfortunately for our plans King Feisal died before anything could be accomplished.

Iraq, because it has proved to be the center of one of the world's great oil districts, has become a rich country. A pipe line runs all the way from Mosul to the Mediterranean at Haifa in Palestine, with a branch to the French in Syria.

As usual the Medical Department lacked funds; the few medical men there had a problem facing them so huge that they resembled pygmies trying to move a mountain with a toothpick. Half the public income went for defense and police; health received but a twentieth.

Of the rural population an indefinite number of thousands were wandering Bedouins who cultivated the soil and drove their cattle to spots favored by weather conditions at particular times of the year. They were an important factor in the spread of disease, and most difficult to control, especially in such matters as smallpox vaccination.

Owing to the rapid increase of power pumping along the Tigris, the area of nearly five hundred miles along its banks between Bagdad and Basra was rapidly coming under cultivation, bringing with it the malaria menace. Another source of danger was the extensive maze of bazaars in Bagdad. The dark cellars, the innumerable underground passages, and the multitude of grain deposits, made rat-proofing almost impossible. Moreover, in some districts fifty percent of the population was estimated to be infected with the bladder variety of bilharzia, although it was not known what variety of snail was responsible. Research work was badly needed.

Scarcely any missionary or other philanthropic aid was rendered to hospitals. The demand for bed space in the Bagdad Hospital far exceeded the supply. Each morning even the desperately sick were carried in litters to the hospital grounds in the hope of being able to pounce upon a bed made vacant through death or discharge. At evening the unsuccessful ones were dolefully returned whence they had come.

In spite of these health handicaps, Bagdad radiated an air of optimism about the bright future of Iraq. None of the thousand British considered it a handicap to live there. In summer the temperature reached as high as 118, but the nights were cool. During the British occupation Government House was a fine building with spacious grounds located beside the Tigris, and with all the swank and military incidental to Government Houses in other British countries. After giving up the mandate, Great Britain still kept the right to have a certain number of judges and to station forces in Iraq west of the Euphrates, to control foreign relations.

Over the border in French-mandated Syria, traveling conditions were far less pleasant than in Iraq. The usual French officiousness cropped up at the border. Although a half-million-dollar bridge over the Euphrates had just been completed to encourage international travel, I had to undergo four customs and two passport examinations at Deir es Zor. The officials refused to return the latter without so-called overtime, rated at a pound and a half per passport, and infinite annoyance was caused by having to tramp from office to office.

Syria was a land of milk and honey compared with the terrible dryness of Palestine. The French were pouring money into it to make it go. After years of disturbances, peace had only been achieved at the point of the sword. The marvelous ancient buildings of Damascus, one of the world's oldest cities, had been half destroyed by French airplanes to give a lesson to the "rebels." The French claimed revolution was in progress, a queer name for non-cooperation. On my last trip I had worked for two days after one of the bombardments helping with the wounded women and children who had been wantonly injured.

Things had quieted down in the Lebanon since the Druses had been given republic status, and Arab schools were made possible under partial self-government. The Health Service was entirely military, and, on the whole, very little had been done for the people of the country. I came away feeling that if we could make a malaria survey it might lead the way to a complete reorganization of health and medical service, and thereby give the Syrians the help in the control of disease they so sorely needed.

When I reached Beirut May 15, 1921, I could find no scheduled sailing for London, where it was imperative that I meet Dr. Vincent on June 1, for discussion of plans for an Institute of Hygiene. No steamship agent could suggest a possible route that would get me there in time. I myself was at my wit's end. In desperation I made the rounds of the harbor, asking everywhere. Finally I located the *Montazah,* an old freighter which carried no cabin passengers; her master said he was bound for Constantinople. On the assumption that I was to be the only passenger I bought a deck passage and purchased a box of oranges, little knowing how invaluable they were to prove, carted them and my bags on board and, feeling terribly sorry for myself, deposited them on the hot, sizzling, iron deck, and sank heavily on to the hatch.

It was rather lonely and I spent an uncomfortable night on the hard planks. The next morning we were in Tripoli, where we were to stay four to five hours. Taking advantage of the stop, I decided to go ashore. In this small town, contrary to my usual luck, I found nobody who could speak any language I knew. Finally I corralled a small boy who watched politely while I made signs to him, intended to convey that I was in a mood to see church architecture. He nodded in apparent comprehension and set off at a brisk pace, I at his heels. Twisting and turning through alleys and byways, we eventually reached a gate in a narrow street on which the boy pounded vigorously. To my astonishment, the doorway framed a lady who greeted me in an American accent. I explained that I also was an American on my way through; my small guide had apparently drawn his own conclusions.

The lady laughed and said the boy had done very well because she and her husband were the only English-speaking persons in town and had been able to use their native tongue only in speaking to each other. She was sure that her husband, Dr. Henry R. Boyes, in charge of the local missionary hospital, would be delighted to talk with me; would I not come in until he returned? She prepared tea, a pleasant change from the poor food of the galley. After tea Dr. and Mrs. Boyes showed me what there was to see in Tripoli, and waved farewell to me from the wharf.

I was appalled to find that I was no longer the only passenger on the *Montazah*. At least one hundred Levantines had now come on board to join me, bringing all their vermin with them. An hour later I had a complete set of my own. Up to that moment I had not known how to kill time; thereafter I had my hands full. A louse bite lasts three to four hours, and I was given no respite. No space on my body larger than a five cent piece was left unbitten. I scratched and scratched and scratched, convinced that my cup of gall was overflowing. But more grief was in store. That night we anchored and clouds of voraciously biting mosquitoes attacked us. At Latakiya we took one hundred cattle on board. Because the hold was full they were stored on the deck, where they bellowed and moaned. With this addition to our company we were decidedly overcrowded, and I had to fight to retain my place on the hatch. I was sure the worst had now happened.

But at Alexandretta several hundred sheep were waiting to be loaded. Though I could not see any possible place for them to be put, it turned out to be simple. They were stowed away under the cattle, and plaintive baas blended with mournful moos. As though bleating and lowing were not enough, the ships' officers—Scotch, Irish, English, Syrian, Greek, and Egyptian—added to the din by arguing and shouting incessantly in all languages.

I could no longer move, but at Mersina, the last Syrian port, more Levantines somehow shoved themselves into the cracks. There was now no space in which to lie down. Food in the galley was running low, but I did not dare make a dash for my share, because I would not only lose my place on the hatch, but also my bags and my oranges. I was reduced exclusively to a citrus fruit diet. I literally had to sit on the crate to keep out the grasping claws of the other passengers.

Adalia was the first Turkish port, but we were not allowed ashore under pain of arrest. Since the Allied occupation was in progress, both Italian and Turkish flags were flying over the public buildings.

The call at Rhodes was ever memorable. Cargo and ever more cargo arrived. Additional cattle were lifted on board by the horns in lots of six. It was a gruesome sight. Without the slightest provocation the crew would hit them with sharp cargo hooks when they were dumped on deck and, with a clatter of hoofs, were regaining their feet. Grass and hay were stuck on a trellis built over their heads. The deck looked and smelled like a barnyard. When the first officer would work his way along on his rounds, with wisps hanging from his clothing and in his hair, he would look exactly as though he had emerged from a haymow.

We anchored almost on the main street of Grecian Khios. Again I could not go ashore, and passed the time totting up our passenger list. I tabulated one hundred and forty cattle, two hundred and eighty-eight sheep, and three hundred and fifty human passengers, for whom one unspeakable toilet had to suffice. The fleas, lice, flies, and bedbugs were uncountable.

Many of my oranges had rotted, and the supply was running low. I had sucked them until my mouth was puckery, and I hoped I might never have to see another again.

After an endless day and night we arrived at Smyrna, from which we were not to sail until evening. Since a number of passengers had disembarked, I decided it would be safe for me to leave my particular niche I had guarded so long. I felt in desperate need of a bath, and it would be something to do to go ashore. I secured a rowboat, but at the pier the Greeks, who were in charge at the time, wanted to retain my passport. I had no intention of giving up anything so valuable. "Oh, no, you don't get that," I said, and returned to my rowboat.

A great wall stretched along the seafront, and I told the boatman to row a mile or so further. When we reached a point where no guards seemed to be in sight, I surreptitiously disembarked and spent a delightful day, chiefly taken up with an elaborate repast and a luxurious hot bath.

My man was waiting for me at the appointed time and place. As we crossed the Bay, I noted with sinking heart that lighters filled with baskets of fresh string beans were converging from all directions upon the *Montazah*. I hoisted myself on board and landed on beans. Not a spare inch was left on deck. Beans were piled over the top hamper, around the smokestack, and in the life boats. The only seat I could find was on a basket of the green legumes high up near the funnel. We were still two days away from Constantinople. I would pull out my watch and look at it. Then I would swear to myself that I would not touch it for a whole hour. I would sit and think over my sins for what seemed many hours and then take a peek. Ten minutes would have passed.

At nine in the morning we went by Chanak and were at last in the Dardanelles. At noon we were abreast of war-torn Gallipoli. The view up the Straits was magnificent; I was able to admire it in spite of the lice. Early the next morning we were in the vicinity of Constantinople. French, British, Italians, and Greeks were all there. The Turks were supposed to be the vanquished, and the Allies were running everything. But all were suspicious of one another; no uniform law, not even a uniform policy, was adopted. Constant bickering went on, and contrary orders were issued.

First Greek quarantine officers boarded us, and all were examined. No disease was found, and after an hour we were cleared. But hardly had the *Montazah* started again when we heard a shrill tooting, "Poopoo!" and a launch came alongside.

"We've been inspected," the Captain called.

"Who did it?"

"The Greeks."

"Well, we're the Italians."

Down went the anchor and another two hours were wasted.

"Poo-poo-poo!" This time it was the French, who inspected us all over again with much pother. It was now afternoon. Once more we started. "Poo-poo-poo-poo!" This time it was the British.

"We've already been inspected three times," yelled our Captain.

"Who did it last?"

"The French."

"We don't believe in the damned Frogs," and aboard they came.

Not until five were we off the waterfront. I had cabled ahead from Smyrna, and friends were there in a launch to meet me. But in other craft came hungry Turkish boatmen, and I was nearly pulled to pieces before I escaped their clutches. The moment I reached the home of my friends I requested an isolated woodshed. There I disrobed, bathed in an improvised tub, burned my clothes, and ended my intimate association with the vermin.

The eleven nightmare days were at last over.

I arrived in London in plenty of time for my appointment, but I was not to see New York that year. I started back around again under more pleasant circumstances and more civilized surroundings, to attend the meeting of the Far Eastern Association of Tropical Medicine, held that year in Java. By the time I reached Manila I had been away so long that I was eager for home.

Ordinarily, because sailings did not coincide, the trip from Manila to Peiping via Hongkong and Shanghai lasted two weeks. I believed it would be possible to cut the time in half if I could go straight to Shanghai and there make good connections for Tientsin, the port for Peiping. Opportunely I found a Captain of a Norwegian freighter who was going direct. I thought I was making wonderful sacrifices for the sake of the Foundation but, to my amazement, I was taken to beautiful quarters with sitting room, chairs, desk, rugs on the floor, bedroom, and bath. I was never more comfortable in my life. The Captain and I dined together in state. The first day out I remarked, "Is there much news on the air?"

"All you want," replied the Captain. "The wireless operator isn't doing anything. I'll see about it."

Hourly after that I was furnished reels of news about everything from everywhere. I did not know the world was so full of exciting happenings.

In due course early one morning we reached the mouth of the Whangpoo. The pilot boat brought a paper on board, and I read eagerly that four vessels were due to sail from Shanghai that day. The first of these was leaving from some fifteen miles below the city, just about opposite where we were to dock. When the tug which was to transfer me as soon as we had made fast did not appear, I summoned a Chinese sampan, dropped my bags into it, and started for the steamer. But just as we reached the middle of the river, I saw her cast loose and depart.

I had the coolie take me ashore, and carry my bags to the edge of the highway. While I was standing hesitantly, wondering how I could get conveyance up to the city from this forsaken spot, an impressive shiny black touring car came bowling toward me.

I held out both my arms like a semaphore. The Chinese chauffeur pulled to a stop, and a European lady, all alone in the tonneau, began to shriek at the top of her lungs. I had often been told that if a direct order were given to a woman, she would obey. "Shut up!" I commanded.

She stopped with startling suddenness. I explained to her that I had to catch a steamer; I asked if she would be kind enough to take me along with her since no taxi was to be had.

She explained that she was only going a short distance to pick up her husband and was returning home at once.

This would never do. "Put the baggage in the car," I decisively ordered the coolie who had brought me ashore, and who was looking blankly on.

The lady raised her eyebrows in surprise, but made no objection. I climbed into the car and sat down. "Tell your chauffeur to drive to the English Bund!" I said in loud tones.

She hesitated.

"Tell him to drive to the English Bund!" I shouted.

This time she obeyed, and we started off. Then I asked, "Why did you scream like that when I stopped you?"

"There have been terrible hold-ups near here," she explained. "I thought somebody might come to help me." Since she remained quiet, I trusted her fears had been allayed.

We were ambling along at about twenty miles an hour. "This is altogether too slow," I expostulated. "I'll never catch the boat at this rate."

"Oh, they're very strict in enforcing the speed laws around here."

"Tell him to drive faster," I insisted.

Our speed increased to forty miles an hour. We came shortly to the heart of the business section at the Astor House. The traffic light was just changing, and hundreds of rickshaws and other vehicles of all kinds were beginning to move across our path. I knew it would be minutes before we could get under way again. "Tell him to drive through the light."

We dashed across, narrowly missing half a dozen vehicles, and in Shanghai traffic a miss is something to remember. Behind us we heard a policeman's shrill whistle.

"Hurry up or he'll catch us!" I ordered.

Our speed increased to sixty miles an hour, and in a few moments we ground to a stop at the English Bund. My second ship was already in the middle of the Whangpoo.

"Madam, I'm terribly sorry, but I have to catch a boat. The next one leaves from the Chinese Bund."

"What will my husband say?"

"I have no idea, but I have to catch that boat. Tell your driver to hurry to the Chinese Bund."

Somewhat to my surprise she still obeyed. We reached the pier to find the gangplank already pulled in, the ship cast off, and swinging around to let the bow out. I hailed a coolie, and, as the stern almost grazed the pier, I told him to throw the baggage on board. As the stern was already swinging out I leaped after it into the atmosphere, hooked my right arm around the railing, pulled myself on deck, and turned to thank the lady. She had already fled, and I have always since been fearful of Shanghai lest I might meet her husband.

When I had recovered my balance, I looked about me. I was not at all sure of the steamer's destination. I was still standing in the midst of my belongings and wondering, when I heard the dinner gong. This was a welcome sound. I asked one of the sailors who had been eying my unceremonious boarding to direct me to the dining room. I followed his instructions. Only one place was set in the saloon. I sat there. In a few seconds the Captain, a bluff red-faced Britisher, came in. The moment he saw me in his chair, he started to bluster.

"What are you doing here?" he demanded.

"I'm one of your passengers."

"We don't carry passengers."

"Where are you going?" I countered.

"You'll have to get off!"

"I can't get off."

"This is a freight boat. We've no room for passengers."

"You haven't answered my question. Where are you going?"

"It's none of your business."

"There's no use getting excited," I said soothingly, and then addressed the steward, "Bring the Captain a plate, knife, and fork." "Captain, do sit down," I urged. "Let's discuss this amicably. I'm going to Peiping, where are you going?"

"We can't take anybody. The pilot's getting off at the bar, and you're getting off with him."

"Let's have a whiskey and soda," I proposed. He made no protest, and we sipped our drinks.

"Where are you going?" I asked again.

"Wei Hai Wei," in surly tones.

"Right on my way, and I've never seen it. Where do you go from there?"

"Chefoo."

"Couldn't be better. Right on my way too. Where do you go from there?"

"Tientsin."

"Fine, that's my port. I'm your passenger."

"Oh, no, you're not." He made as though to rise, but before he could carry out his intent, I suggested, "Let's have another whiskey and soda, Captain."

By the time it too had been partially consumed, the Captain had mellowed, and relations were much more friendly. "You must have a spare cabin somewhere," I insinuated.

A few more sips and the Captain finally melted, "Well, I guess I'll have to take you." He called a steward, ordered a cabin prepared, and I moved in. The Captain and I hobnobbed on the bridge and talked about the weather. A dust storm at sea fortunately provided a topic of conversation. It was red and thick and the ship was covered with it. He added to my meteorological knowledge with the information that it came from the Gobi Desert, and sometimes such storms traveled as far as seven hundred miles over the ocean.

I had a few uneasy moments as we approached Wei Hai Wei, fearing the Captain might carry out his early threat and leave me behind, but he did not. We took on cargo at Chefoo and left. By this time it appeared as though I might be able to get an afternoon train from Tientsin to Peiping. But just then a thick woolly fog enveloped us. The engine stopped; the boat slowed down.

"Captain," I said, "I've gone to extraordinary trouble to get as far as this. I'm still in a great hurry. Can't we get in?"

"Can't be done this afternoon, but I'll tell you what I'll do. I'll have steam up early and still get you to Tientsin in time for the morning train."

"All right," I said, "fine!"

I had a good sleep and awakened at daylight to hear the anchor chain coming through the hawse pipes. The engine started, and then stopped. I knew something was wrong. I pulled on some clothes and dashed to the bridge. "We're never going to get in this way," I said.

"Can't you see the fog?" the Captain retorted irritably. "I'm going to anchor again."

"Did you ever hear of Lindbergh?" I asked.

"That aviator fellow? Certainly!"

"Well, they say he has air sense; he knows where he is when he's flying. Now these Chinese fishermen—I know them. They have fog sense."

"Nonsense! We've every instrument right on the bridge, and we can't tell where to go."

"Let's call a fisherman over and see what he says."

The Captain demurred and made uncomplimentary remarks about land lubbers but in the end he blew his whistle, and soon a tiny Chinese sampan came alongside. Through an interpreter I asked, "How far are we from the mouth of the river?"

"Five miles."

"Could you steer us there?"

"Oh, yes."

I told the fisherman I'd make it worth his while if he could make good his word. The Captain was listening to these arrangements with considerable nervousness, but we were pretty good friends by this time, and he was used to my vagaries.

"Who's going to be responsible if the ship runs aground?" he queried rhetorically.

"We're not going to run aground. You're all deep sea men and don't know how to approach a coast. I'll tell you a trick I learned from a captain who knew his way around in shoal waters. Put out five fathom of chain at the bow anchor, and let it hang. You draw two and a half. Just go slowly and if there's shoal water ahead the anchor will catch."

"Damn it, I'll try," the Captain agreed with an impulsiveness not ordinarily associated with the British, and ordered the anchor chain let out.

Meanwhile, the Chinese made his sampan fast and climbed aboard. Standing at the bow, he gestured this way and that as we slowly plowed forward. Suddenly we emerged into the sunshine. Dead ahead were the two lighthouses which marked the mouth of the Pei-Ho.

I boarded the train and reached Peiping within a week after leaving Manila—a week earlier home for me.

CHAPTER 30.

GRANT BUT MEMORY

AND so I might have gone on mile after mile, year after year, crossing one ocean after another, from one land to the next, trudging through rains and snows, sometimes basking in the sunshine of delightful countrysides, sometimes sweltering in the intolerable heat of the jungle, encountering everywhere odd, interesting, and congenial personalities, many of them engaged in the same endeavor as myself. But everything must end, and I had seen enough of the world. On October 31, 1934, I wrote to the President of the Rockefeller Foundation, as follows:

Dear Mr. Mason:

Ever since I had the pleasure of talking with you at New Bedford last August, I have continued to give serious consideration to the question of being relieved of the burden of active responsibility in connection with the International Health Division. I trust it is unnecessary for me to assure you that I have made every effort to view the matter from all angles. It is with sincere regret that I cannot escape the reluctant conclusion that I should respectfully request you to be good enough to have the necessary steps taken to place my name on the retired list, at your convenience.

As I am sure you realize, I have found it very difficult to reach this decision, and to adhere to it. Nevertheless, the privilege of having had the opportunity in the beginning to assist in formulating and inaugurating the broad policies on which the Foundation's activities in the field of preventive medicine have been based will always be a source of great satisfaction to me. The same is true of each of my sixteen trips around the world which were made in an effort to promote field research and develop methods to bring about the more general use of scientific discoveries and knowledge of such enormous potential benefit to the advancement and well-being of the human race.

The only possible rewards for a life devoted to the public health branch of the medical profession are, of course, such professional standing and respect as one may earn, and the keen satisfaction of unselfish service to others. Perhaps, therefore, I may be pardoned for referring to the really extraordinary comparison of present day conditions, and the backward public health situation of 1914 when Dr. Rose came to the Philippines to interest me in the aims and work of the Foundation. This great progress, for which I rejoice to feel the Foundation is so largely responsible, fairly staggers the imagination. It would be quite impossible even to mention briefly the most outstanding of the accomplishments in each of the forty countries in which I had the privilege of making surveys and proposing programs in the early days of the Foundation. I shall never cease to be grateful to each of those who were charged with the duty of making the decisions which resulted in all of my recommendations being put into effect either directly by, or through the efforts of, the Foundation.

Although (and I believe wisely) the Foundation has not included leprosy among its direct benefactions, I have always been granted liberal facilities to do work myself in this field. Much of the progress that has been made in the control of leprosy throughout the world in recent years has been due to this friendly interest and this example to other organizations on the part of the Foundation. Similar generous treatment has also been accorded me in endeavoring to promote health work in a number of other fields. I deeply appreciate this consideration.

In conclusion, allow me to express to you personally, and through you to all those associated with this splendid organization, my sincere gratitude for the unfailing kindness and cooperation with which I have been surrounded throughout these past twenty years of fascinating service. During the years to come, I shall hope to serve the cause of humanity in ways which will not entail my spending so much time away from home. Regardless of the activities in which I may be engaged, however, I shall always look back upon my connection with the Rockefeller Foundation as my real life work, and shall always consider it both an honor and a privilege to do anything in my power at any time to further its aims.

Sincerely yours,
VICTOR G. HEISER.

AN AMERICAN DOCTOR'S ODYSSEY

Rockefeller Center
New York
January 14, 1935

Dear Dr. Heiser:

Thank you for giving me the opportunity of reading your letter of October 31st to Dr. Mason. What a record it makes! Think of sixteen trips around the world, a life devoted to the public health branch of the medical profession in almost every part of the world and work actually developed in more than forty countries! This is a record of which you may well be proud and which does you the greatest credit.

As Chairman of the Board of the Rockefeller Foundation and your warm friend of many years, I am happy to take this opportunity of expressing profound satisfaction in the work that you have done in your relation with the Foundation. And the best of it is that on the foundations which you have so well laid, there will continue to be built through the years superstructures that will render a continuing and increasing service to the health and the well-being of the peoples throughout the world.

In the hope that you may have in full measure the happy consciousness of work well done and a life well spent, I am,

Very sincerely,
JOHN D. ROCKEFELLER JR.

Dr. Victor G. Heiser
49 West 49th Street,
New York, New York

Perhaps I would never have fully realized how fortunate my lot has been had not the writing of this volume tempted me to peruse many pages of old diaries which might have remained indefinitely unopened in the trunks and boxes to which they had been consigned years ago. But obviously even the more striking experiences of two score years devoted to pursuing my profession in many corners of the world on highways and through trackless lands cannot all be set forth between the covers of one book.

Lack of space has prevented me from making any mention of the months I spent with the armies of Europe during the World War, and the references to China, India, Egypt, Central America and other countries are all too brief. Lack of space also prevents all mention of the years of effort to establish a museum of hygiene on the scale of the

Metropolitan Museum, the fascinating research for speedier relief of accidents occurring among the soldiers of industry, of my work with the Railway Sanitary Commission which happened to have such far-reaching influence, or of the extraordinary spread of child health education throughout the world which I had a part in developing with President Hoover, Dr. Emmett Holt, Dr. Frederick Peterson, and many others.

Such a career as mine has necessarily deprived me of close family ties, and many other experiences which enrich our lives. But the deprivations have been more than compensated by the opportunity to bring the discoveries of the laboratories to disease-bound millions who knew of no possibility of relief and scarcely hoped for any.

Mine has been an extraordinarily happy and satisfactory life. Among other compensations has been the host of friends who have made my path pleasant. In my mind's eye I can picture them in every quarter of the globe, and have a vivid and grateful consciousness that a welcome awaits me in the sixty-odd countries I have visited, should I resume my travel. Laying down active administrative responsibilities and breaking the habits and associations of a lifetime are tinged with unhappiness and a keen sense of personal loss. Yet the realization of an earnest effort to serve and the joy of past accomplishments soften the pangs of regret at this parting.

INDEX

Abyssinia, 503 ff.
Adventure with horse, 142
Aglipay, Monsignor, 45, 119, 161
Aguinaldo, Emilio, 45, 56 ff.
Albay, 181
Algue, José, S.J., 67
Al Mutanabbi, 439
American Mission Hospital, 510, 511
American Mission to Lepers, 255, 514
Amsterdam, 285
Ancylostoma, 268 ff.
Anemia, 269, 273
Antipolo, 114 f.
Antique, 181
Apayaos, 141
Aretaeus, 221
Army Board of Health, Philippines, 60 f.
Aron, Professor, 76
Artesian wells, 66, 124 ff.
Ashford, Dr. Bailey K., 268, 269 f.
Assatkine, Dr. Vera, 304
Australia, 344 ff.; labor conditions, 346 ff.; aborigines, 348; wild life, 348 ff.; social life, 350; internal difficulties, 351; health service, 353 ff.
Austria, tuberculosis in, 200 f.
Ayer, Dr. Ira, 489
Ayurvedic medicine, 337 f.

Baby leper story, 243 ff.
Bagac, 181 f.
Baguio, 72 ff., 200
Baker, Missionary, 384
Barber, Dr. Marshall, 164, 298 f., 453
Barnes, Dr. Milford E., 447, 493 ff., 498
Barnesby, Dr. Norman, 27
Basilan S.S., 67 f., 184, 205, 230, 233 ff., 243 f.
Batanes, 149

Batangas Province, 69
Belgian Consul, 286
Bellevue Hospital, 277
Benguet Road, 73 f.
Beriberi, 205 ff.; and rice, 206 ff.
van Berlo, 22
Bilharzia, 302 f.
Bilibid Prison, 52 f., 115 f., 205
Blue, Surgeon General Rupert, 255
Boccaccio, 80
Bombay Bacteriological Laboratory, 302
Bontoc, hospital, 135
Boriracksh, Major, 494
Borneo, 295 ff.
Borrow pits, 72 f.
Boston, 13 ff.
Bowditch, Major Edward, 418
Boyes, Dr. and Mrs. Henry R., 523
British Empire Leprosy Relief Ass'n, 217, 255
Brooke, Sir Charles Vyner, 297 f.
Brooke, Gilbert, 457
Brooklyn, 117
Brother Dutton, 239
Bruce, 444
Bryce, Viscount, 210
Buck, Mrs. Marie D., 463 f.
Burbank, Luther, 410
Burdette, Dr., 61
Burma, 252
Burnham, D. H., 72

Cacique, 46
Cairo Medical Congress, 82
Calderon, Dr. Francisco, 192 ff., 200
California, plague in, 97 f.
Caluya, 184 f.
Camorra, 24 ff.
Canada, 31 ff.

537

INDEX

Canadian Pacific R. R., 32, 265

Canazares, Don Francisco Lopez, 440

Cannon, Uncle Joe, 434

de Carera, Don Luis Geronimo Fernandez, 440

Carnegie, 370

Carpenter, Frank W., 149

Carranza, 322

Carrel, Dr. Alexis, 267

Carter, Major E. C., 218 f.

Carter, Dr. Henry R., 511

Carthew, Dr. Morden, 491

Carville leper colony, 257 ff.

Cebu Hospital, 262

Ceylon, 327 ff.; Kandy unrest, 334 f.; Health Units, 336 f.; malaria in, 458 f.; plague in, 93 f.; leprosy in, 218

Chalmers, Sir Thomas, 332

Chamberlain, Major Weston P., 208

Chao Dara, 492 f.

Chater, Sir Paul, 281

Chaulmoogra oil, 249 ff., 260

Childs, Eversley, 262

China, 293 ff.; beriberi in, 205; leprosy in, 212, 217

China Medical Board, 275, 293

China Sea, 230, 244

Chinese, and cholera, 120; in Manila, 166 ff.; smugglers, 168 ff.

Chinese evil, 226

Chiropractors, 190 f.

Choate, Joseph H., 30

Cholera, 100, 127; in Philippines, 100 ff.; and water, 102 f.; Koch's discovery of vibrio, 103; history of, 103 f.; quarantine and sanitation, in Philippines, 104 ff.; and flies, 115 f.; carriers, 116 f.; and hygiene education, 117 ff.; and Chinese, 120; and water, 121 ff.; in Java, 469 f.

Chopra, Colonel, 338

Chululongkorn, 489, 492

Churchill, Winston, 284 f.

Cigars, Philippines, 52

Clark, Dr. Philip, 363

Colonial Sugar Refining Co., 367, 368, 369

Conemaugh Valley, 3

Constantinople College for Women, 282, 315 f.

Cook Islanders, 357, 360, 390

Coolidge, President, 429

Coron, 228

Cortez, 218

Crane, Charles R., 323

Crewe, Lord, 329

Crown Prince of Siam, 317

Crown Princess of Italy, 23

Crozier, William, 93

Culion leper colony, 227 ff.; and beriberi, 207; mortality, 223; collecting lepers, 230 ff.; entertainments, 235 f.; occupations, 236 f.; government, 237; woman suffrage, 237; escapes, 237 f.; Sisters, 238 f.; cleanliness, 238; doctors, 239; segregation of sexes, 240 ff.; children, 242 ff.; funds for, 259 ff.

Cullen, Dr. Gilbert I., 157 ff.

Cumpston, Dr. J. H. L., 353, 354

Cushing, Dr. Harvey, 431

Damian, Peter, 443

Daniels, Josephus, 273

Darling Commission, 298 ff., 369; in Java, 465 f.

Darling, Dr. Samuel T., 270, 298

Davis, Dwight F., 432 f.

Dell, Mr., 161 f.

Denney, Dr. Oswald, 257

Dennison, Winfred T., 131 f., 171

Denver, Col., 190

Diabetes, 283 f.

Dickinson, Jacob M., 47

Dog eaters, 137 f.

Dubini, 268

Dürer, Albrecht, 216

Dyer, Dr. Isadore, 250

Dysentery, 127, 128 ff.

Earthquakes, 68 ff.

Edison, Thomas, 183

Egan, Martin, 246

Egypt, 29 f., 34 f., 302 f.

Ehrlich, Dr. Paul, 134

Eijkman, Professor C., 206

Eliot, Charles W., 276, 314

INDEX

Elkington, Dr. J. S. C., 352
Ellis, Dr. A. G., 500
Embrey, Miss Hartley, 236 f.
Emetine, 129 f.
Epul, 249
Ethiopian Leprosarium, 514

Fajardo, Dr. Jacobo, 149, 295
Faleroni, 448
Far Eastern Ass'n of Tropical Medicine, 207, 209, 291 f., 414, 499, 526
Father Caius, 342
Father Damien, 226
Father Valles, 230
Fau Mui Na, 377, 389, 392 f.
Ferrell, Dr. John A., 273
Fiji Islands, 367 ff.; hookworm in, 369 ff.; customs, 381 ff.; cannibalism, 383 ff.
Filariasis, 370 f., 377
Fleas, and plague, 83, 84 ff.
Flexner, Dr. Simon, 97, 267, 277, 278, 287, 413
Flies, and cholera, 115 f.
Folk migrations, and hookworm, 270
Forbes, W. Cameron, 50 ff., 131, 141 ff., 291, 387, 417 f.
Fraser, Henry W., 206 f.
Freer, Dr. Paul, 109, 164
Friar Lands Controversy, 48
Funston, General, 56

Galman, Captain, 144 f.
Gandhi, 338, 460
Gates, Rev. Frederick Taylor, 267
Germany, tuberculosis in, 200 f.
Gorgas, General William C., 34 f., 61, 276, 298
Gota de Leche, 195 f.
Goto, Viscount, 410
Grant, Dr. John B., 342, 401 ff.
Great Britain, tuberculosis in, 200
Greene, Jerome D., 276
Guiseppi, 27 f.
Gulfport, Miss., 256 f.

Hacker, Dr. H. P., 298
Hackett, Dr. L. W., 448

Haffkine, Professor W. M., 82 f.
Haile Selassie, 509, 512 ff., 517
Halsey Harbor, 228
Hamburg disaster, 116
Hanihara, Prime Minister, 399
Hansen, Gerhard A., 223
Harbord, General James G., 262, 434
Harding, President, 419
Harrison, Governor General Francis Burton, 53 ff., 74, 171 ff., 417, 420, 427, 433, 487
Harty, Archbishop, 102, 118 f.
Harvard University, 276
Hawaii, 292; leprosy in, 217, 218, 226 f.
Hazen, 124
Hell Roaring Jake Smith, 157
Hemp, Manila, 52
Herodian, 79
Herouy, Abyssinian Minister of Foreign Affairs, 507 f., 514
Hillgrove, Tom, 230
Hippocrates, 439
Holbein, Hans, 216
Holt, Dr. Emmett, 535
Hongkong, plague in, 81; beriberi in, 209
Hookworm, history of, 268 ff.; life cycle of, 270 f.; and Rockefeller Sanitary Commission control in South, 271 ff.; study on dogs, 285 ff.; and Darling Commission, 298 ff.; in Ceylon, 328 ff., 335 ff., 340; in India, 341 f.; in Australia, 352; in South Sea Islands, 365 ff.; in Fiji Islands, 369 ff.
Hoover, President, 279, 432, 535
Hospitals of the Holy God, 213
Hughes, Secretary of State, 399
Hughes, W. M., 353 ff.
Hydrick, Dr. John Lee, 476, 477 f.

Ibayat, 149 f.
Iberville Parish, 250, 257
Icterohemorrhagica, 288 ff.
Ide, Governor General Henry C., 48, 50, 61
Ifugaos, 90, 138 ff., 143 ff.
Igorots, 131 f., 134 ff., 142, 144 ff., 357
Ilocanos, 45
Iloilo, 181

INDEX

Ilongots, 140, 148
Immigration Law, 33 f.
Indenburg, Alexander W. Frederick, 465
India, plague in, 91; smallpox in, 176, 177, 183; leprosy in, 211, 217; malaria in, 458 ff.
Indian Camp Plantation, 257
Indian Medical Service, 338, 339, 341 f.
Indo-China, 294 f.
Insulin, 283 f.
International Cholera Convention, 18
International Congress on Medicine, Cairo, 34 f.
International Congress on Tuberculosis, 22
International Health Board, 272, 275, 285 ff., 291, 299, 447, 452
International Journal of Leprosy, 263
International Leprosy Ass'n, 263
Iraq, 520 f.
Iwahig, 53

Jacoby, Dr. Abraham, 77
Jacocks, Dr. W. P., 94 ff.
Jaffa, plague in, 94 ff.
Japan, 395 ff.; beriberi in, 205; leprosy in, 217; earthquake, 396 ff.; emigration, 398 ff.; Exclusion Bill, 399 ff.; medicine, 410 ff.; Health Institute, 414 ff.
Java, 461 ff.; beriberi in, 209; leprosy in, 218; public health education in, 475 ff.
Jefferson Medical College, 10
Jefferson, President Thomas, 179
Jenkins, Dr., 17
Jenner, Edward, 178 f.
Jesus, Dr. Vicente, 419
Johns Hopkins University, 276 f.
Johnston, Colonel Gordon, 418, 429, 430
Johnstown Flood, 3 ff.
Jones Act of 1916, 57
Judson, Harry Pratt, 276

Kalingas, 140 f.
Kanakas, 363 f.
Kandy, plague in, 93 f.
Katipunan, 45

Katzoff, Simon Louis, 190
King of Belgium, 286
King Edward VIII, 423 ff.
King Feisal, 323, 520
King Humbert, 22 f.
King Louis VIII, 213
King Maha Vajiravudh of Siam, 480 ff., 487, 490, 495, 498
King Philip IV of Spain, 219
King Prajadhipok of Siam, 498, 499, 500
King Victor Emmanuel III, 23
King, W. L. Mackenzie, 275
Kinyoun, Dr. J. J., 97
Kitasato, Shibasaburo, 81, 412 ff.
Kitasato Institute, 288
Koch, Robert, 103, 199, 298 f., 414
Kuala Lumpur, 206
Kuenen, 209
Kyne, Peter B., 261 f.

Lake Memphremagog, Vt., 32
Lake Mohonk Conference, 195
Lambert, Dr. Alexander, 168
Lambert, Dr. S. M., 363 f., 365 f., 370 f., 374, 376, 377, 378, 393
Landis, Judge K. M., 272
Lankenau Hospital, 10
Laurier, Sir Wilfred, 32
Laveran, 444
Lawshee, Auditor, 51
Lazy worm disease, 273
League of Nations, Commission on Leprosy, 263; Health Section, 441 f., 475
Leake, C. D., 254
Ledger, Charles, 441
de Legaspi, Miguel Lopez, 44
Leiper, Dr. Robert T., 278 f.
Leonard Wood Memorial for the Eradication of Leprosy, 262 ff.
Leprosy, 211; history of, 212 ff.; occurrence in Orient, 217 f., in Europe, 218, in America, 218, in Philippines, 218 ff.; types of, 220 ff.; in Hawaii, 226 f.; examination for, 232 f., *see* Culion; chaulmoogra oil treatment, 248 ff.; other remedies, 254; *see also* Carville

540

INDEX

Linnaeus, 440
Liston, W. Glenn, 82 f.
van Lonkhuyzen, Dr., 475 ff.
Looss, Professor, 271
Louisiana State Leprosarium, 257
Lukis, Sir Charles Pardey, 341 f.

MacArthur, General, 435
MacCallum, Dr. William G., 277, 309 f., 466
McCoy, Major-General Frank, 418, 419, 429
McKinley, President, 47 ff., 64, 433
McLaughlin, Dr. Allen J., 116
McRoberts, General Samuel, 262
Macaulay, 177 f.
Madras, Health Service, 340; hookworm campaign, 342 f.
Malaria, 437 ff.; history and description of, 437 ff.; and quinine, 440 ff.; transmission by mosquito, 443 ff.; survey of, 446 ff.; control in Philippines, 449 ff., in Palestine, 454 f., in Nicaragua, 455 f., in Malaya, 456 f., in Singapore, 457 f., in Ceylon, 458 f., in India, 458 ff., in Java, 464
Malaya, malaria control in, 456 f.
Manila, *see also* Philippines, 36 ff.; plague in, 86 ff.; cholera in, 100 ff., and quarantine and sanitation, 104 ff., and water, 121 ff.; and vaccination, 188
Manila *Bulletin*, 246
Manila Times, 246
Manson, Sir Patrick, 370, 371, 443 f.
Maoris, 357
Marine Hospital Service, 10, 12 ff., 265
Mariveles, Quarantine Station, 42 f., 59
Markham, Sir Clements, 441
Mason, Max, 532 ff.
Massachusetts, 188, 265
Mataafa, 377
Mather, Cotton, 179
Melanesians, 360, 365, 373
Menelik Hospital, 509
Mercado, Elidoro, 250
Mézeray, 213
Mhaskar, 342

Mikado, 410
Milk, in Philippines, 202 ff.
Miners' anemia, 269
Miracles, in Manila, 106 f., 122 f., 125
Molokai, 226
Monsoon, 66, 181, 182
Montagu, Lady Mary Wortley, 177
Morgan, Pierpont, 16
Moros, 45, 148, 149, 186 f., 249, 357, 373
Moses, 126 f., 212
Mosquitoes, and malaria, 443 ff.
Mountain tribesmen, 133 ff.
Muir, Dr. Ernest, 254
Mulholland, Professor John, 148 f.
Munson, Colonel E. L., 149
Murphy, Frank, 433
Murphy, Starr J., 276

Naples, 20 ff., 30 f.
National Research Council, 263
Necator americanus, 270
Negritos, 45, 146 ff.
New York, 15 ff., 99, 117, 194 f.
New Zealand, 355 ff.; Health Department, 377
Nicaragua, malaria control in, 455 f.
Noguchi, Hideyo, 287 f., 290
North Carolina, hookworm in, 269, 273 f.
Northern Luzon, 133 ff.

Oldrieve, Frank, 217
Opium, in Philippines, 167 ff.
Osler, Sir William, 210, 267
Osmeña, Sergio, 45, 54, 56, 429

Pack, Governor William F., 141, 145
Page, Walter Hines, 276
Palestine, plague in, 94 ff.; malaria control in, 154 f.
Papuans, 362 f., 364 ff., 390
Paré, Ambroise, 216
Paris green, 453 ff.
Paris, Mathew, 213, 214
Pasig River, 40, 105 ff.
Pasteur, 81
Pasteur Institute, in Siam, 489

INDEX

Patent medicines, 172 ff.

Pearson, Governor, 296

Peiping Union Medical College, 277, 282

Peninsular and Oriental, 312 ff.

Pepys, Samuel, 81

Pershing, General, 148

Peterson, Dr. Frederick, 535

Petrarch, 79 f.

Philippine General Hospital, 152

Philippines, *see also* Manila, 34 ff., 419 ff.; health and sanitation, 37 ff.; peoples, 44 ff.; government, 47 ff.; quarantine service, 59 ff.; Bureau of Health, 61 ff.; climate, 66 ff.; Taal volcano eruption, 69 ff.; Baguio resort, 72 ff.; heat, 74 ff.; cholera in, 100 ff.; quarantine and sanitation, 104 ff.; hygiene education, 117 ff.; Bureau of Health, 123 ff.; mountain tribes, 133 ff.; Bureau of Science, 152, 164 ff.; University, 152; Hospital, 152; nurses, 152 ff.; medical staff, 156 ff.; cemeteries, 160 ff.; *Journal of Science*, 165, 171 f.; legislation, 171 ff.; patent medicine bill, 172 ff.; smallpox vaccination in, 176, 179 ff.; tuberculosis in, 199 ff.; infant mortality and milk, 201 ff.; Health Service, 421 f.; Wood administration, 427 ff.; present government, 433 ff.; malaria control in, 449 ff.; *see also* Leprosy and Culion

Phipps, James, 178

Plague, 29 f.; history of, 79 ff.; discovery of bacillus pestis, 81; linked with rats, 81 ff., 83 ff.; and fleas, 83, 84 ff.; in Manila, 86 ff.; in Ceylon, 93 f.; in Palestine, 94 ff.; in California, 97 f.; endemic, 98; in Java, 470 f.

Plague Commission, First Indian, 82; Second Indian, 83

Polynesians, 357, 359, 360 f., 365, 372 ff.

Pope Leo XIII, 48

Powderly, Terence V., 33 f.

Prince Dhamrong of Siam, 496 f.

Prince Nagor Svarga of Siam, 498, 499, 501

Prince Rangsit of Siam, 487, 489, 491

Prince Sakol of Siam, 497, 498

Prince Songkla of Siam, 498, 500

Puerto Rico, hookworm in, 268, 269

Putnam, George Rockwell, 159

Queen Elizabeth of Hungary, 216

Queen Margharita, 23

Queen of Taytay, 122 f.

Queen Victoria, 485

Queensland Institute of Tropical Medicine, 352

Quezon, Manuel, 45, 54, 56, 421, 427, 429, 434 ff.

Quinine, 440 ff., 463

Raffles, Sir Stamford, 298

Raleigh News and Observer, 273

Rats, and plague, 81 ff.

Reggio, Duke of, 80 f.

Rennell Islanders, 361 f.

Rice, and beriberi, 206 ff.

Rinderpest, 203

Rio de Janeiro, 254, 263

de Rivera, Francesca, 440

Rivers, Colonel W. C., 69 ff.

Rizal, José, 45, 56

Rock, J. F., 252

Rockefeller Foundation, 93, 266, 275 ff., 281 ff., 292, 298, 301, 303, 306, 328, 329, 335, 339, 340, 342, 344 ff., 352, 354 f., 363, 365, 367, 373, 374, 380, 401, 413, 414, 421, 422, 432, 454, 458, 463, 464, 475, 483 ff., 490, 494, 500 f., 503, 532 ff.

Rockefeller General Education Board, 272

Rockefeller Institute, 267 ff., 287, 290

Rockefeller, John D., Jr., 281 f., 283, 401, 403, 534

Rockefeller, John D., Sr., 266 ff., 271, 275, 282 f., 340

Rockefeller Sanitary Commission, 272 ff.

Rockefeller War Relief Commission, 275

Rogers, Sir Leonard, 129 f., 251, 255

Roosevelt, President Theodore, 49, 101 f., 399, 419

Roosevelt, Theodore, Jr., 433, 435

INDEX

Rose, Wickliffe, 266, 272 f., 276, 279, 285, 298, 533
Rosebank, N. J., laboratory, 117
Rosenau, Dr. Milton J., 276
Ross, Major Ronald, 443 f.
Russell, Dr. Paul, 299
Russia, 196 ff., 304 ff.
Rutherford, Dr. G. J., 329 f., 335
Ryan, John, 314
Ryrie, Dr. Gordon, 254

St. Giles leprosarium, 213
St. Gothard Tunnel, 268 f.
St. Lazarus, 213
Samoa, 376 ff.
Samuel, Sir Herbert, 94
San Francisco, 192 ff.
San Juan de Dios Hospital, 104, 168
San Lazaro Hospital, Manila, 108, 156, 168, 219, 220
San Lazaro Hospital, Mexico, 218
Santo Tomas University, 152
Sawyer, Dr. Wilbur A., 320 ff., 491
Sayre, Francis, 489
Schapiro, Dr. Louis, 501
Schüffner, Dr. W., 303 f.
Shattuck, George, Dr., 159
Shidehara, Foreign Minister, 399 f.
Shiga, Dr. K., 288, 413
Ship Island, 257
Siam, 480 ff.
Silk hats, 55
Simond, P. L., 82
Singapore, beriberi hospital, 205; mutiny, 323 f.; malaria control in, 457 f.
Sinhalese, 328, 334
Sister Calixte, 238 f.
Sisters St. Paul de Chartres, 230, 238
Smallpox, description of, 176 f.; history of, 177 ff.; inoculation, 177 f.; vaccination, 178 ff.; vaccination in Philippines, 176, 179 ff.
Smillie, Dr. Wilson G., 342
Smith, James F., 50, 169 ff.
Smith, Dr. Theobald, 444
Snow, Dr. John, 102 f.
Soil pollution, 65, 127
South Fork Dam, 3

South Sea Islands, 359; Islanders, 359 ff.; witchcraft, 362 ff.; depopulation, 372 f.; medical education, 373 ff.; fishing, 389 ff.
Soya bean, 204 f.
Spain, and vaccination, 179; leprosy in, 213
Standard Oil, 272
Stansfield, Dr. H. S., 83
Stanton, A. T., 206 f.
Stiles, Dr. Chas. W., 268, 269 f.
Stimson, Henry L., 262, 432
Stokes, Dr. Adrian, 510
Stoll, Dr. Norman, 342
Stone, Senator William J., 56 f.
Straus, Mr. and Mrs. Nathan, 196
Strobel, Edward H., 489
Strong, Dr. Richard P., 134, 143, 144, 249
Sultan of Java, 471 f.
Sultan of Sulu, 148 f.
Summer Palace, China, 277
Sungei Buloh Leper Settlement, 254
Sunstroke, 75
Suva, Central Medical School, 374 f.
Syphilis, 134, 212, 221, 305, 377
Syria, 521 f.

Taal volcano, 69 ff.
Taft, Governor William H., 48 ff., 110 f., 160
Tagalogs, 44 f.
Tagbuanas, 227
Tagore, Rabindranath, 338 ff.
Tamils, 299, 328 ff., 333 f., 340, 368 f.
Tarbell, Ida, 272
Taytay, 122 f.
Tiedeman, Walter D., 452
Tiqui-tiqui, 208
Tokyo, 263
Torti, 438 f.
Towne treatment, 168
Tropics, white man in, 66
Tuberculosis, prevention, 199 ff.; in Philippines, 199 ff.
Turnipseed, Dr., 156
Typhoid fever, 127, 128
Typhoons, 67 ff.

543

INDEX

Ultra-violet ray, 75
Uncinariasis, *see* hookworm
Underwear, orange-red, 75 f.
Union Steamship Line, 311 f.
University of Chicago, 267
University of the Philippines, 152
U. S. Public Health Service, 265

Vaccination, smallpox, 178 ff.; in Spain, 179; in Philippines, 179 ff.; opposition to, 188, 189 ff.
Vedder, Captain Edward B., 129, 208
del Vego, Juan, 440
Vincent, Dr. George E., 284 f., 522
Virchow, Rudolf, 22
Visayans, 44
de Vogel, Dr. W. T., 465 f.

Wade, Mrs. Dorothy Paul, 261 f.
Wade, Dr. H. Windsor, 260 f., 263
Walker, Dr. E. L., 164
Walled City, Manila, 40 ff.
Walsh, Governor David I., 266 f.
Walter Reed Commission, 34
Washington, D. C., 10 f., 18 f.
Water, 39 ff., 65, 130 f.; and cholera, 102 f., 106 f., 111, 121 ff.

Waterhouse, Professor Benjamin, 179
Webster, Daniel, 189 f.
Welch, Dr. W. H., 276 ff., 285, 413
Whipple, Dr. George, 277
White ants, 42 f.
White, Major F. Norman, 341
William of Tyre, 222
Wilson, President Woodrow, 53 ff., 175
Wood, Cyrus, 399
Wood-Forbes Mission, 417 ff.
Wood, General Leonard, 34, 138, 148, 188, 189, 237, 239, 248, 260 ff., 387 f., 417 f., 419 ff., 427 ff., 451 f., 453
Worcester, Dean C., 48, 104 f., 124, 131, 140, 141, 144, 151, 152, 164, 227
Wright, Governor, 115
Wright, Frank Lloyd, 397
Wright, Luke E., 48, 49 f.
Wyman, Dr. Walter, 18

Yap, 186
Yaws, 133 ff., 212, 221, 357, 370, 377
Yellow-Dog Dingo, 256
Yellow fever, research, 287 ff.; in Abyssinia, 507, 510 f., 514
Yersin, Alexandre, 81
Young, Dr. Hugh, 434
Young, Owen D., 262